Philosophy of Time

As a growing area of research, the philosophy of time is increasingly relevant to different areas of philosophy and even other disciplines. This book describes and evaluates the most important debates in philosophy of time, under several subject areas: metaphysics, epistemology, physics, philosophy of language, philosophy of mind, cognitive science, rationality, and art.

Questions this book investigates include the following. Can we know what time really is? Is time possible, especially given modern physics? *Must* there be time because we cannot think without it? What do we experience of time? How might philosophy of time be relevant to understanding the mind–body relationship or evidence in cognitive science? Can the philosophy of time help us understand biases toward the future and the fear of death? How is time relevant to art—and is art relevant to philosophical debates about time? Finally, what exactly could time travel be? And could time travel satisfy emotions such as nostalgia and regret?

Through asking such questions, and showing how they might be best answered, the book demonstrates the importance philosophy of time has in contemporary thought. Each of the book's ten chapters begins with a helpful introduction and ends with study questions and an annotated list of further reading. This and a comprehensive bibliography at the end of the book prepare the reader to go further in their study of the philosophy of time.

Sean Enda Power is Postdoctoral Researcher in the Department of Philosophy at University College Cork, Ireland. He has authored, among other work, *The Philosophy of Time and Perceptual Experience* (Routledge, 2018) and has co-edited *The Illusions of Time* (2019). He is a previous Irish Research Council Postdoctoral Fellow and a previous Visiting Fellow at the Centre for Time, University of Sydney.

Routledge Contemporary Introductions to Philosophy
Series editor: Paul K. Moser, Loyola University of Chicago

This innovative, well-structured series is for students who have already done an introductory course in philosophy. Each book introduces a core general subject in contemporary philosophy and offers students an accessible but substantial transition from introductory to higher-level college work in that subject. The series is accessible to non-specialists and each book clearly motivates and expounds the problems and positions introduced. An orientating chapter briefly introduces its topic and reminds readers of any crucial material they need to have retained from a typical introductory course. Considerable attention is given to explaining the central philosophical problems of a subject and the main competing solutions and arguments for those solutions. The primary aim is to educate students in the main problems, positions and arguments of contemporary philosophy rather than to convince students of a single position.

Recently Published Volumes:

Philosophy of Western Music
Andrew Kania

Phenomenology
Walter Hopp

Philosophical Logic
John MacFarlane

Philosophy of Action
Sarah K. Paul

Animal Ethics
Bob Fischer

Philosophy of Time
Sean Enda Power

For a full list of published *Routledge Contemporary Introductions to Philosophy*, *please visit* www.routledge.com/Routledge-Contemporary-Introductions-to-Philosophy/book-series/SE0111

Philosophy of Time

A Contemporary Introduction

Sean Enda Power

Routledge
Taylor & Francis Group

NEW YORK AND LONDON

First published 2021
by Routledge
605 Third Avenue, New York, NY 10158

and by Routledge
2 Park Square, Milton Park, Abingdon, Oxon OX14 4RN

Routledge is an imprint of the Taylor & Francis Group, an informa business

Library of Congress Cataloging-in-Publication Data
A catalog record for this title has been requested

ISBN: 978-1-138-24048-3 (hbk)
ISBN: 978-1-138-24049-0 (pbk)
ISBN: 978-1-315-28361-6 (ebk)

Typeset in Times New Roman
by Newgen Publishing UK

Contents

Figures

Preface

If you ask anyone to point at *the time*, they will most likely gesture at a clock. When typically picked out as a distinct something, different from everything else, time is *clock* time. This is a useful social assumption about time. We need clock time to coordinate most social activities, whether getting to work, meeting a train, booking a restaurant, or following a recipe.

This idea of time—clock time—is a matter of convention. It is something socially determined. It can vary for the most convenient and practical reasons. For example, clock time can skip or repeat an hour for daylight savings time. The practice of dividing time into twelve months, seven-day weeks, twenty-four hours, sixty minutes, sixty seconds, milliseconds, and nanoseconds, is a matter of tradition, habit, convenience, or their combination. Other cultures have divided time differently. For example, pre-16th-century Japan divided time into six hours of night and six hours of day—the night hours varying in length relative to the day hours; and they did not have a seven-day week (Fernandez and Fernandez 1996).

Then there is the idea of *real* time. This is a feature of almost everything we encounter and are affected by. It is a feature of almost all that we can even think about. This real time is not read from mechanical clocks; it is there even if there are no such devices, for example, before the Earth formed and after the sun dies. Our ancestors thought about such time (Aveni 1989). And such time seems no more conventional than the turn of the tides, the growth of plants, or the spread of disease. Indeed, this time is a condition of tides, plant growth, and pandemics. Tides, crops, and pandemics change and persist—and take time to do so, even when there are no clocks.

We may need clock time to coordinate society. Real time is needed for anything to happen at all. Reading clock time is like reading a book. Reading real time is like reading the weather.

Yet, many philosophical problems have been raised against the possibility of such real time. This book is about these philosophical problems, and the theories of time that arise from them.

About This Book

This book is about the different competing philosophical theories of real time. It examines the philosophy of time under several headings—epistemology, metaphysics, philosophy of physics, philosophy of language, philosophy of mind, philosophy of cognitive science, rationality, and the philosophy of art. Finally, there is a chapter on the philosophy of time travel.

For some readers, they may be surprised by the philosophical study of time appearing under such a wide range of philosophical areas. In my very early graduate years studying time, one of my career advisers thought that the philosophy of time fell wholly under the philosophy of language. In recent analytic philosophy, a quick survey of courses in philosophy of time suggest they are typically found under metaphysics. Furthermore, papers on the philosophy of time appear more often in metaphysics than in other areas.

Indeed, some of the more challenging philosophical problems of time are found in metaphysics. For example, metaphysic papers discuss time's independence, time's limited or infinite nature, the conditions of real change, the uniqueness of the present, and the reality of the past and future. However, although these problems and answers to them may start in metaphysics, this book proposes not all of them stay there. They can arise in other philosophical areas as well. And, as this book also shows, how other philosophical areas approach time can impact proposed metaphysical answers to these problems.

Metaphysical or not, other readers may reject the idea that there is any need for a *philosophy* of time. We might, they state, look at the history of ideas about time. However, the philosophy of time is not a live topic of debate.

For example, in the early 20th century, a famous debate between Einstein and Bergson ended with Einstein stating that "the time of the philosophers does not exist, there remains only a psychological time that differs from the physicist's" (quoted in Canales 2016, 48). Some decades later, the philosopher Hilary Putnam analysed the concept of time in modern physics, which conceives of it as a dimension of four-dimensional space-time. He ends his paper by agreeing with Einstein. "I do not believe that there are any longer any philosophical problems about time" he writes, "there is only the physical problem of determining the exact physical geometry of the four-dimensional continuum that we inhabit" (Putnam 1967, 247).

This book is not about the physical geometry of space-time. Nor is it about the psychology or physics of time. Sections of it do discuss these subjects, but they focus on their philosophical aspects. As such, it cannot presume that Einstein and Putnam are correct. There are still philosophical problems of time, even when physics and psychology might also play a role.

For example, there are philosophical questions about the fundamental nature of physical time; how it relates to folk intuitions of time; how we experience time and encounter it in the everyday world of ordinary objects and events. Such questions may seem to be problems in physics, cognitive science, or both. However, they involve a great deal of philosophical work. They involve the *philosophy* of physics, the *philosophy* of cognitive science, or both.

There are also other philosophical problems of time. Here is a sampling from each chapter:

- *Epistemology* (Chapter 1): Can we know about time? There is a *folk* intuition of time. But can we know that this intuition represents something in the world? Or are there reasons for denying the folk view? That is, there are reasons to be sceptical of such intuitions.
- *Metaphysics I* (Chapter 2): What is needed for real time and change? Does it require a change in events' positions in time, what is called temporal passage? Does it require an unreal past and future?
- *Metaphysics II* (Chapter 3): What is needed for objects that change, or do not change, but persist? Can they change or persist, given our best theories of time?
- *Philosophy of Physics* (Chapter 4): What impact do physical concepts of time have on thinking about the nature of real time? Are we committed to such thinking, or are alternatives available?
- *Philosophy of Language* (Chapter 5): Might all philosophical problems about time be merely problems of language? How does language play into arguments for different positions in time? Is much of how we talk about time merely metaphorical, and what does this mean for metaphysical talk? And what role do specific tokens of language—such as saying something at a particular time and place—play in such analyses?
- *Philosophy of Mind* (Chapter 6): Could time be merely mind-dependent, or must it be mind-independent? How do we experience time? Which models of time-consciousness best describe the phenomenology of time? What impact do different philosophical theories of time have on the plausibility of these models?
- *Philosophy of Cognitive Science* (Chapter 7): How does the philosophy of time impact the relationship between the mind and the brain? Do they make a difference in interpretations of some temporal phenomena as illusory? For example, is it relevant to the timing of consciousness and the neural correlates of consciousness (NCCs), both in interpreting evidence and modelling their relationships?

- *Rationality* (Chapter 8): What is the most rational attitude to take toward time? Is it rational to prefer worse pains that are past over lesser future pains? Should we care only about present moments? Should we be temporally neutral—that is, indifferent to whatever time it is? Is it rational to fear death more than that other limit to life—birth?
- *Philosophy of Art* (Chapter 9): What defines an art of time, that is, a temporal artwork? What form is best for artistic research into time, for example, to expressing and exploring temporal ideas? Can temporal artwork play a role in philosophical debates about time?
- *Time Travel* (Chapter 10): Finally, what is time travel? Is it possible? Can we have otherwise ordinary entities, such as a book or a song, that exist in causal loops, without a clear moment in which they are created? Can we change the past? If we cannot change the past, can we make sense of compelling stories that seem to show we do?

These are all philosophical questions in one way or another. The intent here is to introduce discussions in the philosophy of time under multiple subject areas, but in a way that they can be often connected. You can read each chapter almost entirely on its own. "Almost" because you do need to know about some positions in the philosophy of time, especially those covered in the metaphysics chapter. But, in each chapter, there are sections that need no other chapters to be understood and, where other chapters are relevant, it is noted in the text.

Finally, this book does not cover every philosophical question, either in the history of philosophy or in current research. Space precludes the exhaustive survey required for that. Each chapter's subject can be a book in its own right (and, indeed, there are many books dedicated to these subjects). As such, I had to decide to omit topics that others might find important to the philosophy of time. For example, this book explains special relativity but not general relativity, quantum physics, or temporal anisotropy. Although there is some discussion of phenomenology, there is none on Heidegger's work. It does not cover branching time or a thorough discussion of Kant's concept of time. One omitted topic I suspect will yield fruitful work in future is that of ethics and time; for example, ethical questions about intergenerational justice, the open future, and free will. This is not say these topics are ignored entirely. Some of them are briefly discussed where they overlap other topics. For example, Kant's first antinomy is discussed in the *Epistemology* chapter; free will is discussed in the *Philosophy of Cognitive Science* chapter.

The topics here are intended as a sufficient introduction to the subject in several areas of philosophy. They enable readers to connect different discussions about time together, and place them in a broader philosophical landscape.

Acknowledgements

The material in this book comes from courses that I taught at University College Cork and Trinity College Dublin. There's also material from several academic and public talks. These talks were to audiences from a variety of backgrounds (including scientists, artists, and the public) and in many different countries. I am grateful to the students in my classes and audiences at the talks. Their questions and comments often showed me a surprising way of looking at the subject. One example that stays with me: in a public lecture in Dublin, I stated the common view that time is like space. An elderly audience member told me she did not think that time is like space; it is like weight. I had never come across this metaphor for time (perhaps I will understand it better as I get older).

I have also benefited from several conversations with other philosophers and academics over the years, whose expertise clarified many of the ideas of this book. And I am grateful to many who offered support while writing the book. In particular, Robin Le Poidevin and Lilian O'Brien's separate thoughts on the material, and frequent encouragement, were invaluable and irreplaceable. I also benefited hugely from conversations with Adrian Bardon, Valtteri Arstila, and Graeme A. Forbes. In addition, I gained important insight into non-philosophical researchers' ideas about time from many separate conversations with Virginie Van Wassenhove, Marc Wittmann, Mark Elliot, and Grace Weir.

Furthermore, at least as important: I am grateful to my friends and family – especially my parents, Nuala and Seán, who have been a solid support over the years; and, of course, my siblings Jane, Eveleen, Winifred, Dermot, Gerard, and David.

Lastly, Mona, who is the heart of my everyday life.

1   Epistemology of Time

Overview

Is there anything particularly challenging about our knowledge of time? In our everyday discourse, we commonly make claims about time: we say what time it is, or describe temporal properties of things, such as objects ceasing to exist, one thing happening after another, or processes taking a long time. Indeed, we need to know about such time, for time seems a central property to the objects and events of the everyday living world. In folk discourse about the world, time is as common and self-evident as other properties of things, such as shape and colour.

However, there are arguments against knowing about time itself. Aristotle argues that time independent of other things is not something we can be aware of or justify any knowledge of it. Kant argues that specific properties we attribute to such independent time—being infinite and having a beginning—are incompatible; yet, we have equally compelling reasons to hold time has both. This contradiction in our idea of time shows it cannot be something real, but only something in our mind.

Indeed, the sceptic Sextus Empiricus claims that, when we even consider temporal properties of things, we cannot claim to know what they are; we must be sceptical about them: they may, for example, belong to objects in the world (as we often describe them as); however, they may also not belong to such things. We cannot decide which it is, and so are forced to suspend such beliefs about time.

Furthermore, there is a particular challenge to how we can know about particular instances of temporal properties, the temporal order of events in the world. A common model of knowledge of particular things in the world is the causal truth-maker theory of knowledge (CTMP). This theory does not fit knowledge of temporal order. Le Poidevin proposes a modification of the theory to accommodate it.

These epistemological problems for time show it raises particular challenges. The way out of them is to go deeper into the philosophy of time, and to areas explored in other philosophical approaches (such as metaphysics).

Introduction

Every day, everyone uses and discusses time. We refer to what time it is and answer by looking at our clocks. We observe and discuss change, temporal order, and the length of time (that is, duration). We think about the past, present, and future. So, surely we know what time is? Otherwise, what are we all talking about? And, what is the time that we do not know about, if it is not this everyday thing?

Knowing about time is not like knowing about evolution, quarks, the Gnostic heresy, or Gödel's incompleteness theory. A typical person, untrained in science, religion, or mathematics probably knows little or nothing about these three topics. They might know something, such as how they are represented in fiction, popular science, or conspiracy theories; they might, as a result, be interested in them and have opinions about them. But the subject matter of these theories does not play any obvious role in how a typical person goes about their life. For ordinary, non-expert folk, these topics are not part of how we think about or act toward ourselves, each other, and the rest of the world.

Not so with time. Time is part of how everyone thinks about the world and relates to it. It is also part of how we understand and relate to each other. It is there in the most common human activities, such as boiling water or rushing to work; in the least interesting, such as sorting through email spam; in the most significant and profound, such as birth and grief.

As such, it might seem that knowing about time is important to everyone. Furthermore, since time is part of how everyone thinks about the world, everyone knows about time.

Yet, theorists—for example, philosophers and physicists—have often argued for counter-intuitive ideas of time. Some have argued that time is unreal (as we discuss in the first metaphysics chapter). Others argue that we cannot know about time itself. Yet others hold that our beliefs about time are contradictory. Others, again, argue that time—though it may exist—is really nothing like time as we think or encounter. There is time—but ordinary people do not know time.

Yet how can we not know about time? Again, it is not some rare or hidden thing. Time is obvious in everything we do. We are aware of it when boiling an egg or going to work. So, what can these theorists be talking about?

Perhaps they are talking about something else. In some subjects, theorists use a term common in everyday discourse and which refers to a familiar feature of the world. However, they mean something else entirely. For example, quantum chromodynamics is the study of fundamental particles; particle values or charges are labelled as "red", "green", and "blue". Yet, whatever these "colours" might be, they are nothing like the colours we see. The "colours" have a more technical meaning, one which a non-expert (such as this author) can only struggle to understand.

Some physicists might dispute the claims of chromodynamicists. For example, they might argue that quarks in fact do not have colours (I have no idea if that makes sense). This is no problem for our everyday knowledge of colour through seeing things. If a physicist claims that folk cannot know about quarks' colours, it does not mean we do not know about colours as we understand them. We are each talking about a different thing.

Theoretical Time Is Not Folk Time

So, perhaps it is the same with theories about time. We do not know about the philosopher or physicist's concept of time because it is not *time* as we use it every day. "Time" in physics or metaphysics does not, for example, include the period of time—the *duration*—it takes for an egg to boil; the theorist's time does not include the change in a ripening apple. The *temporal order* of events in physical time is not the same temporal order found between an apple hanging from a branch, the apple falling, and it rolling to the side of a stream.

It is something else entirely. Just as there is no connection between a red quark and a red fire engine, there is no connection between temporal order in physical time and temporal order in everyday life.

This is how Bergson responds to theorists who make such puzzling claims about time. Bergson argued against the modern physical concept of time, in particular *relative simultaneity*. He added:

> What ought you to do? [...] if you felt sorry for the poor philosopher condemned to tete-a-tete with reality, acquainted with it alone (rather than physical theory)? You would give another name to learned simultaneity, at least when you talk philosophy.
>
> (Bergson 1999, 46)

Bergson pushes back as a philosopher against physicists' counter-intuitive claims about time. However, as evident from his more general attack on the physicists' concept of time (discussed in Chapter 4), his claim is on behalf of how time is lived. It is based on how we experience time and use it in everyday life.

We examine Bergson's arguments in more detail in other chapters. For now, this approach cannot work for theorists about time. What they discuss is also purported to include time as we encounter it. As we see in other chapters, no theoretical discussions on time first define what is meant by "time" as something that is not actually time. An example of the temporal order in physical theory is the order found in an apple falling from a tree. The duration in metaphysics includes that of the boiling egg. This is why Bergson's statement is an objection to physicists' views on time. They intend to talk about time—but, he says, they ought not to.

So, it appears that we know something about the time discussed in physics and philosophy in everyday life. They are not different things, not like quark red is different to fire engine red.

Yet, again, some theorists do argue that we cannot know about time. Given how we think about time, it is not possible to know there is such time. Another argument is more technical, but also illustrates why even the most basic of temporal features that we take for granted can be problematic.

When they make this argument, they do not mean something else and merely refer to it as time. So, we have a puzzle. We seem to know about time but, given how we think about time, we cannot know about it.

Perhaps it is this: the folk just are significantly mistaken about time. In response to Bergson, Einstein stated that there is no time as understood by philosophers (Bergson 1999; for discussion, Canales 2016). Given what Bergson purported to be defending, Bergson and those who agree with him would take Einstein to be stating that there is no time as ordinarily understood.

There is a precedent for such an approach. Time might be like how some colour theorists think about colour. This is not the colour of quantum physics but that of everyday life. Anti-realists or non-physicalists about colour think the folk view of colour is mistaken. From seeing objects, folks think that colour is a property of physical objects. It is possessed by things in the external world separate from us. However, many colour theorists argue that colour is not possessed by external things at all. It is a result of processes within the observer (for discussion, Arstila 2005).

Similarly, the nature of time, how time is *really* or in fact, could be significantly different to how we normally think it to be. For example, we might think that time is part of the external world; however, we might find on further investigation that time is not.

A World Without Time Is Not a World We Understand

This analogy may be correct. One may be as anti-realist about time as one is about colour. However, moving time into the mind and removing it from the external world, or denying its existence entirely, raises much deeper problems than doing the same for colour. This is discussed in more detail in other chapters (Chapters 4 and 6), but a brief note here is enough to illustrate what is at stake.

If time is not in the world, then the world lacks almost all the entities encountered or described in everyday and scientific discourse. Dog training, the evolution of organisms, the formation of continents, the microscopic bubbles in cooking bread: all of these in one way or another require time to be in the world independent of the mere appearance to us or thinking about time.

In addition, time plays a role in our explanations of how things happen in the world. Our explanations of the world include appeals to *causation*. In explaining, say, how a bird can fly or bread bakes, we include descriptions of cause and effect: the bird beats its wings, causing it to lift into the air; the oven's heat causes the dough to rise.

Causation of the kind in bird flight and bread-baking involves temporal order. Such causation happens *over* time. Any knowledge we have of causal processes involves knowledge about time. According to Hume, our beliefs about causation come from our regular observations of temporally ordered sets of events. If we regularly observe A *followed by* B, then we form the habitual belief that that A *causes* B.

For example, if I often observe the sun become warm before a block of ice melts, then I form the habitual belief that the sun's becoming warm *causes* blocks of ice to melt (Hume 1776/1993, 16–19).

Because causation is a factor in common explanation, and involves temporal order, temporal order is a factor in such explanation. As such, if we doubt that there is temporal order, we must doubt such causation as well, and all the explanations we offer based on it.[1]

Removing time as folk understand it from the world raises problems close to the problems of radical scepticism. Radical scepticism is an argument against knowledge of the external world. For reasons concerning how we form beliefs about the external world, such beliefs can never be sufficiently justified to count as knowledge (Pritchard 2017). If radical scepticism is accepted, then one cannot claim to know about the external world. Similarly, if one accepts that the folk understanding of time does not point at anything in the world, one cannot claim to know about much of what is familiar in the world, for example, change and persistence of everything we encounter.

Yet, maybe that is how it is: there is nothing that matches the *folk* understanding of time, just as there may be nothing that matches the folk understanding of an external world. Yet, as with radical sceptical arguments against the external world, any arguments to the conclusion that there is no such time must be strong indeed. For if we cannot know about such time, then we are radically mistaken about the world itself.

Folk Time

We all seem to know about time. Still, it is worth making explicit what exactly it is we all seem to know about.

Yet, perhaps we cannot make what we know explicit, we cannot say what we know about time. Amongst philosophers of time, St Augustine is famous for asking: "What, then, is time? I know well enough what it is, provided no-one asks me; but if I am asked what it is and I try to explain, I am baffled" (Augustine 1961, 264, 11.14). Although we know what time is, and how to use it in ordinary life, we cannot explain why we know it or what it is we know.

Yet, again, it seems that I can very well talk about time. At least, we can talk as well about time as we can talk about most other things. Furthermore, the beliefs we express by such talk seem as justified as beliefs about most other things. There seems to be nothing especially problematic about time at all.

For example, say that I see a red apple on a branch and then watch it fall from the branch to some green grass near a stream. In seeing this, I can pick out the following:

a)   The apple is on the grass beside the stream.
b)   The apple is red, and the grass is green.
c)   The apple is on the branch and then the apple is on the grass.

a) is an instance of spatial relations: the apple is *on* the grass and *beside* the stream. "on" and "beside" are spatial relationships between things that I can pick out. And my ability to pick these out justifies my belief about those spatial properties. I pick them out because I perceive them as distinct from other properties and relations, and the things that have them. My belief in the spatial properties of the apple, grass, and stream, and the spatial relations between them, is justified because I *perceive* these things and their spatial properties and relations. If that is right, and it is also true that the apple is in the grass by the stream, I have a justified true belief—I know the apple is on the grass by the stream.

b) is an instance of colour difference: the apple is red, and the grass is not red. Again, my ability to pick out the differences in colour properties justifies my belief about those colour properties. If it is also true that the apple and grass are those distinct colours, then I can say that I know the apple is a distinct colour to the grass.

Finally, c) is an instance of temporal order: the apple is on the branch *before* it is on the grass. Once again, my picking out the temporal order of the events justifies my belief about those temporal properties of the apple on the branch and the apple and grass. If it is also true that the apple is on the grass after being on the branch, then it seems that I know the apple is on the grass after being on the branch.

What differences are there between the spatial and colour cases, on the one hand, and the temporal cases, on the other hand? Initially, it seems nothing relevant to questions about our knowledge of these properties.

Objects and Events

Here is one difference between them:

- The spatial relations belong to *objects*. They belong to the apple, grass, and the stream. For example, the apple has the colour property of being red; the grass has the colour property of being red; the grass and stream have the relation of being beside each other.
- The temporal relations belong to *events*. Events are something that *happens*, for example, to objects. In this case, they belong to the apple being on the grass, and to the apple being on the branch. The event of the apple being on the grass is *later* than the apple being on the branch.

As conceived in this book, events are common and uninteresting. An event is simply *something* that *happens* or *occurs*. In this sense, a drop of water falling into a puddle is an event; the slow wearing away of a mountain into sand is an event. (Another concept of event is not important here: Davidson discusses events as special kinds of happenings, often particular to their participants, e.g., Davidson gives an example of *Jones buttering bread at midnight* is an event (Davidson 2001).)

But does this difference matter to our knowledge of time? The very concept of events includes time because events have temporal properties and relations:

1. An event happens *at a time*. Nothing happens that does not happen in or at a time. Water falls into a puddle at some moment; a mountain wears away in time.
2. Most events are *temporary*. There is a moment after a drop of water falls, a time after the mountain has become sand.

Similarly, the apple lies by the stream at some time. It also does not lie by the stream forever. There is a time when the apple is in the tree and there is a time when the apple is no longer by the stream—it has rotted clean away or been carried off by a bird.

If these descriptions of events are correct, then it seems that we pick out time, just as we pick out space or colour. We pick out time by picking out it out as the temporal properties and relations of events. We seem to see apples falling from trees and then lying by streams as obviously or directly as we see the stream they lie by or the colour green.

With these considerations in mind, we can ask: what is it that we pick out when we distinguish time from everything else? What sort of entity is time?

Here are some possibilities:

- Time is like a normal, everyday object (a concrete particular)? For example, time is a thing like an apple is a thing.

- Time is a property of objects? For example, things have time like they have shape or colour (if we are not anti-realists about colour, at least).
- Time is a relation? One entity is temporally related to another, as one is *bigger than* or *far from* another.

It seems in common discourse that time is often referred to in all these ways. We talk about time flying (like a thrown apple); we talk about the time of events (such as how long it takes for the apple to fly through the air); we talk about the order of events in time (such as my throwing the apple coming before it lands in a stream).

So, which is the correct folk understanding of time? Do people think time is an object, property, or relation?

Temporal Properties and Relations

Here are two ways we typically think of time as it is found in things in the world:

- *Change*: we think of time in the changing seasons, daylight cycles, and ticking clocks; processes of any kind, for example, a bubbling pot of water and a developing polaroid.
- *Persistence*: we think of time in waiting for the dentist; in unchanging things, such as a mountain on the horizon that stays the same no matter the weather; in states, such as a humming computer or words fixed on a page.

We can pick out several distinct aspects of time—different temporal features—from change and persistence:

- *Duration:* we are aware of time through how long things last, for example, how long it takes the season to change or how long the computer's humming persists.
- *Temporal order:* we are aware of temporal order in change, from autumn following summer, to a polaroid picture following a blank sheet.

In these examples, and others like them, we can have a set of *folk* beliefs about time—beliefs about time that most people share. As such, we seem to have a simple answer to what we know about time, and how we can know about it. We know that time is the duration and temporal order of things we meet in the world. We know about time because we encounter such things.

However, are temporal properties and relations really all there is to how folk understand time?

In everyday discourse, we also talk and think about time flying, as speeding up and slowing down. This also carries into how physicists and science fiction authors talk. Physicists will talk about time being bent by the mass of black holes. Science fiction stories refer to travel *through* time, like it is a corridor or other kind of space. The physics and science fiction claims may seem strange or fanciful—but it is still the case that, even in ordinary discourse, we talk sometimes as if time is an object or container, as something with its own properties and relations independent of anything else. It is not the events that slow down, or the objects that fly, when time does these things. Time itself does.

So, can we know about time conceived in this way, as something independent of other things? This concept of time is as time as a *substance*.

Independent Time

According to Newton, time is *independent* or *absolute*:

> Absolute, true, and mathematical time, in and of itself and of its own nature, without reference to anything external, flows uniformly and by another name is called duration
>
> (Newton 1972)

The "external" here includes such mundane objects as apples and streams. An apple is obviously not this something that flows independent of other things. It is *one* of the other things. Changes in things, such as the apple's fall, are not independent of other things. Furthermore, they are not necessarily uniform, involve a flow, or have their own nature. Instead, changes in things:

- Require things (something external), for example, the fall or rotting of the apple requires the apple. In the absence of apples, what can a fall in an apple be? If there are no apples, what can it mean for there to be a change in an apple's position?
- Are not necessarily uniform: A change in an apple is not in step with the change in the water of a stream or a dripping tap.
- Are not necessarily flows: Some changes in things can be brittle, staccato, abrupt; there need be no flow about it: ice cracks, a rock bounces down a hill, a twig snaps.

If Newton is right, then there is a time that does not fit the above list. It is not merely temporal properties, relations, or anything dependent on objects or events. It is something independent. It is a *substance*.

Substantivalism

The position that time is independent of objects and events is a conception of time as a *substance*. As such, this position is known as *substantivalism* (e.g., Forbes 1991, Thomas 2019).

"Substance" here is a metaphysical term. It stands for a concept that is often disputed in metaphysics; some of its problems concern what role substances play in the description of objects—or, as they are often called, concrete particulars.[2]

Here, we need only know the following about a substance: it is like an object in that it exists or is real independent of anything else. It is neither derived nor determined by anything else. It is in some way fundamental and cannot be reduced to other things. For example, in the philosophy of mind, *substance dualism* is the view that there are two substances in human beings: the mind is one substance and matter (such as the brain or body) is another substance. For substance dualists, they both exist or are real independent of each other. Both are in some way fundamental (at least, relative to each other); there can be mind without matter, and matter without mind. There is a possible world in which there is only a mind; there is a possible world in which there is only matter.

In opposition to this position, there are physicalists and idealists. These alternatives at least deny that either the mind or matter is a substance: physicalists deny that the mind is a substance; idealists deny that matter is a substance.

Similarly, substantivalism about time conceives of time as something that can exist independent of anything else: there can be time without other things. Under this conception of time, there is a possible world in which there is time and nothing else. This is a world with no objects—no apples, streams, forests, planets, or fundamental particles. There are no changes in anything. There is also no space—not even a spatial void with nothing else in it. In this possible world, there is only a series of moments, each one following the next.

Relationalism

In opposition to substantivalism, there is *relationalism* about time. Relationalism is the view that time is dependent on other things in some way. Time is just a property of or a set of particular relations between other things. For example, it is just the order between the apple in the tree and the apple by the stream; or the duration of the change that is an apple rolling to rest. There is nothing more to time at all: take those away and there is no time. There are no possible worlds in which there is time but no objects, no changes, or no space.[3]

Epistemologically, there are reasons to prefer relationalism over substantivalism. If relationalism is true, then all there is to time is the set of temporal properties, relations, and changes of things. If we know what this set of properties, relations, and changes in things is, then we know what time is. Such changes are all there is to time. "[I]f the universe were not Newtonian we would surely still have knowledge of time, for instance, about how much time elapses between events" (Forbes 1991, 83).

Furthermore, according to Aristotle, by definition, time *requires* something else. It requires change. For Aristotle, time is "the measure of motion with respect to the before and after" (Aristotle, *Physics* 219/b1–2). Motion is a kind of change. If time is a measure of motion, then it is a measure of a kind of change. If there is no change, then there is no measure of change, i.e., there is no time. If we are unaware of change, then we are unaware of its measure, i.e., we are unaware of time. As such, to know about time, we need only know something about time (its measure).

Note that relationalism does not alone require that there be no time at all. There can be time just as there is colour and shape. It is only that, when there is nothing else, there is also no time—just as, when there is nothing else, there is no colour or shape. Time in relationalism can still be distinct from other properties and relations.

However, if relationalism is true, then time cannot be an object. It cannot simply fly, slow down, or speed up. It cannot, in physics, bend. It is not a container in which things happen, in which objects exist. Instead, all there is to time is the properties of and relations between things that happen.

So, can we know that time is a substance?

Objection: A Frozen World Is Possible

In the 1980's *Twilight Zone* episode "A Little Peace and Quiet", a woman with the power to freeze time freezes it at the moment a nuclear missile is about to hit her town. Everything stops moving or changing. Balls hang in mid-air, children running hang balanced on one leg, spilled milk on a table hangs over the table-edge like a glistening tablecloth. And the nuclear missile hangs a few feet above the ground, milliseconds from exploding. She spends the rest of time wandering the streets, unable to unfreeze time, unable to condemn anyone, and unable to save them.

This fantastical scenario is an example of a world without change yet also in which there is time. We might then think that, at least for this cursed woman, she knows that there is time without other things. After all, nothing else moves or changes.

However, Aristotle's other argument offers a response to this. If time were more than a mere measure of change, we could not know about it. We might *imagine* a world like this—as in the *Twilight Zone* episode—but we could not know if the world were this way—not even for a little while. We cannot be aware of anything without change. Whatever we experience or think, we must be aware of one of the following: change in the world, change in *ourselves* (e.g., in our changing thoughts), or both.

In the *Twilight Zone* story, the woman is not aware of change in the frozen world around her. But she is aware of the change in her own thoughts. To be aware of such a frozen world, she must herself undergo change. She must be aware of something like the following a sequence of thoughts:

1. I am about to freeze the world to stop its destruction.
2. I have just frozen the world.
3. I froze the world some time ago.

4. Some time remains—perhaps eternity—without change.
5. Some time remains until I unfreeze the world.
6. Soon I will unfreeze time (and join everyone in oblivion).
7. Now, I am unfreezing—

All these thoughts are awareness of change in herself—at least her own thoughts—in relation to the rest of the world.

Could she be aware of time without such change in her own thoughts? If so, she would have only the first thought:

1. I am about to freeze the world to stop its destruction.

… And nothing more.

If this thinking is right, then it is not possible to know about time without change while it is going on. Furthermore, it is not possible to remember having gone through it.

As such, if knowledge of substantival time depends on awareness of time without change while it is going on, then it is not possible to know of substantival time.

Objection: We Can Have Indirect Knowledge of Substantival Time

This argument only shows that it is not possible to know about substantival time during the period of time without change, that is, directly, or in unreflective awareness afterwards. However, although we cannot directly observe time without change, perhaps we can know about such a period indirectly through what we do observe.

There are many things we cannot observe but are justified in claiming that we know about. Cases of such knowledge range across common everyday events to the most complex physical, chemical, or psychological theories. For example, after some days away during a storm, I walk into my house and find my windows smashed and glass everywhere. I infer that something unobservable caused it—the storm outside my house. Similarly, I observe particular trails of moisture in a cloud chamber and infer certain particles passing through that space.

So, can we similarly infer independent substantial time through observing other things?

Frozen Worlds

Shoemaker (1969) argues that there are possible scenarios where we can have just that. As such, we need not directly observe a period of time without change. We can *infer* that there is a period of time without change.

Imagine a possible world divided in three regions, A, B, and C. We live in region C. This possible world has a property that distinguishes it from the actual world: for each region, at regular intervals, there is a *freeze*: all change in that region stops. Birds stop flying, the air stops moving, light stops propagating, people stop thinking or seeing, corpses stop decaying. If a nuclear missile is about to hit a town in one of those regions, it stays in the state of being about to hit a town. Everything stops.

In addition, observers in each region can observe the freezes in other regions. From C, I can observe the freeze in A and B. However, for obvious reasons, they cannot observe the freezes in their own regions. Along with everything else, they freeze, even their own thoughts and perceptions. So, from C, I cannot observe the freeze in C.

Shoemaker argues that observers can infer the freeze in their own region. While they can directly observe the freeze in other regions, they notice sometimes that everything in the other regions abruptly changes. The abrupt changes are evidence that some period of time has been missed. From C, I see a bird in B flying through the air, then suddenly settled on a distant branch. Someone running through the park is suddenly asleep in bed. A corpse is now buried or a bag of bones. A nuclear missile winging its way to a town is replaced by scenes of devastation.

This inference to our own region's freeze is not itself direct evidence of time without change. It is evidence of change that we could not observe. It is the same kind of evidence that we get if we sleep and wake up, noticing changes overnight.

How we are entitled to indirectly judge time without change in our freeze is that we know such freezes happen in other regions. And, talking to others in those regions, we know that they experience their own freezes just the same: they observe sudden changes in the other regions, including ours.

This set us up for the position of being able to infer time without change for the entire world.

During the years when the observer is frozen, they can tell from other regions that a year of change has occurred there in an instant for the observer. Furthermore, the observer can infer that there is a regularity in these freezes. They can even predict when each region next freezes. Say they discover the following:

- A freezes every three years.
- B freezes every four years.
- C freezes every five years.

This regularity leads to the following prediction: Every few years, the freezing of each region happens together. In those cases, we have a period of time without change. Furthermore, we are justified in inferring from observing other freezes that there is such a period.

Say that each region's freeze is a year long, and the regularity of each region's freeze is as follows:

1. Region A: every three years
2. Region B: every four years
3. Region C: every five years

This leads to the following observations by occupants of region C:

Year Three.	Freeze in A. Change in B and C.
Year Four.	Freeze in B. Change in A and C.
Year Five.	Nothing—observer in region C is frozen.
Year Six.	Freeze in A. Change in B and C.
Year Seven.	Change in all regions.
Year Eight.	Freeze in B. Change in A and C.
Year Nine.	Freeze in A. Change in B and C.
Year Ten.	Nothing—observer in region C is frozen.
Year Eleven.	Change in all regions.

... and so on, until:

Year Fifty-seven.	Freeze in A. Change in B and C.
Year Fifty-eight.	Change in all regions.
Year Fifty-nine.	Change in all regions.
Year Sixty.	Nothing—observer in region C is frozen.
Year Sixty-one.	Change in all regions.

Year sixty is the year of a *global freeze*: all three regions freeze for one year. This gives us reason to hold that there is time without change. Assuming as we do that all three regions comprise the whole possible world:

1. If there is no change in any of the regions A, B, or C, then there is no change.
2. When there is a global freeze, then there is a year with no change in any of the regions A, B, or C.
3. A year is a time.
4. (1 and 2) When there is a global freeze, then there is a year with no change.
5. (3 and 4) When there is a global freeze, then there is a time with no change.

As such, in this world, observers in region C—and observers in A and B—can infer from a global freeze that there is a time with no change. Thus, given this argument, there can be reason to hold that there is time without change.

Objection 1: We Do Not Know There Is a Global Freeze (Other Explanations Available)

Is this inference necessary or the best of a range of possible inferences? It does not seem necessary. There are other possible patterns here than a global freeze, and so time without change. For example, one could have a more complex *skipping* pattern: the regions usually freeze at regular intervals. However, when all three coincide, the freeze is *skipped*.

As such, if we infer that there is a global freeze for a year, we are mistaken. Indeed, the mistake leads to a further mistake about how many years have passed, for example, because we assume that year sixty is a global freeze, we think year sixty-one is the year after a global freeze. However, because there is no frozen year, year sixty-one is, in fact, year sixty.

Response: Inference to the Simplest Explanation

Shoemaker responds that, if there is no reason to choose between such an alternative and a global freeze, we should choose the global freeze. It is a simpler explanation than the alternatives (Shoemaker 1969, 72). To introduce extra rules (such as skipping, in our example) for no other reason than to avoid global freezes makes such explanations more complex.

Yet, when it comes to being justified in believing something, the simplest claim is preferable to the more complex one. In this case, the simplest claim is that there is a global freeze. If we can claim to know anything about what happens, the best answer is that.

A philosopher may yet stress that this preference for simplicity does not mean that we know *without doubt* that there are global freezes. It is only that it is the *better* explanation. However, in everyday life, this is a common epistemological situation to find ourselves in. Many ordinary everyday situations require only the best explanation to count as acceptable knowledge. Maybe the glass broke in my house because of something entirely different to the storm. Yet, in the absence of reasons to think otherwise (e.g., I do not see muddy footprints on the windowsill beneath the broken window), the best explanation is the simplest. If we are preserving our folk view of time—which includes it as an object—then this is enough.

Objection 2: Time in an Unchanging World Still Needs the World

Even in the frozen world scenario, we do not know that time is a substance. The time we are aware of needs other things. When discussing things in time, we often do discuss change—for example, the changing location of apples. Yet, we can also have periods of time in which things do not change, but instead merely persist.[4] They only exist from one moment to another, with no change in their properties or relations to other things. For example, the apple may sit on a table, unchanging: not rolling about, not rotting, and persisting in its colour. In that case, the object persists through a period of *time without change*.

This persistence of things does not show the kind of independent substantial time. Nor does it give a reason for holding that time is more than a property of other things.

However, Shoemaker argues that the presence of an unchanging period of time cannot be explained by anything that is frozen in that period. The period, no matter how long it lasts, does not start because it is prompted by some physical or mental process. Nor does it end—and change begin again—because some physical or mental process prompts it to end. Whatever processes the other things in that world are in when a freeze occurs, those processes continue when the freeze ends.

This also means we cannot explain the freezes merely through the temporal properties and relations of other things. The freezes have their own rules and regularities which are imposed externally on everything else and continue without regard to the non-temporal rules governing those other things.

As such, to explain the start and stop of global freezes, we can only appeal to something about time itself. Whatever it is we appeal to, we are appealing to time independent of other things—and so, we are appealing to time as a substance.

Objection 3: Shoemaker-Style Arguments Do Not Suit Lived Experience

Shoemaker-style arguments do not suit actual lived experience. In some possible world, we might justifiably infer substantial time from the way the world freezes in separate places. Yet, this is not what we do in the actual world. There are no frozen parts of the actual world, or at least we do not know if there are any.

In the actual world, how could we know about time without change? A natural response to this objection is that is not the point of Shoemaker's argument. The argument is to show that, given the right circumstances, we *would* be justified in believing that there is time without change. As such, we would be justified in believing substantivalism is true.

Yet, the questions are still there about time as we actually live in it. There may be a possible world in which its inhabitants are justified in believing time is a substance. But this does not justify any beliefs we may have that time is a substance here.

For example, when I talk about the time it takes for an apple to go from ripe to rotten, I do not mean some independent time, such as asserted by Newton. I mean by time a number of changes in the world, for example, the ticks in a clock on my phone, or the changes in months, days, or seasons, or even changes in the colour and shape of the apple.

That is, we talk sometimes as if time is a substance. But Shoemaker's argument only shows that we *could* be justified in believing it to be true. It does not justify the belief that it *is* true.

Scepticism about Time

Even if time is only the number of changes, there are some arguments against knowing about it. Some are metaphysical; we cannot know about time because there is no time as we must conceive it to be. The most impactful for modern philosophy of time is McTaggart's paradox.[5]

Other arguments are epistemological. First, there is Kant's first antimony, which is an argument that we cannot know about time as it transcends the empirical world. Second, the sceptic Sextus Empiricus claims that we cannot even know about time in events, that is, the kind of time acceptable to relationalists.

Kant's Antinomies

Consider for a moment your sense of events in time. Include everything you can think of. Think about these on a cosmic scale. For me, that includes possible cosmic events such as the Big Bang, the formation of the solar system, the tectonic formation of continents, the burning out of midrange stars like the sun, and the Heat Death of the universe.

Neither you nor I (I expect) have experience of time on this scale. Any idea we have of what happens in it comes from what we learn, for example, from astronomy. However, part of this idea of time is that no matter what we learn about what happens, there is a time in which it can happen. One might disagree with the beliefs that motivate this view of the time, but not from the view that the time is too long. Before the Big Bang, there may be nothing we can describe, but there can still be time before it. After the universe's Heat Death, there can be a continuation of time, despite all physical change having ceased. Time can extend to any cosmic events astronomers might imagine or propose.

Indeed, time can extend beyond modern astronomer's work. In Hindu mythology, the universe is already trillions of years old, that is, at least hundreds of times greater than the time since the Big Bang (Kragh 2007, 13). We can imagine time extending infinitely further than that. No matter how inexplicable or unchanging the world is at these far reaches of time, there is time there. There seems to be no end of time, either in the past or in the future. Even if there is nothing else, there is time.

At least, it is an *idea* that time has no end, either in the future or the past. However, Kant argues that we cannot know that time is like this. We cannot know that there is time independent of other things in the world. More: we cannot even know that there is time independent of our *sense* of time, other things aside. Such independent or *noumenal* time is transcendent time. It is time that is not found in the empirical world, a time beyond the objects or events that we might observe or infer from observation.

Kant's arguments against the transcendent reality of time (and space) is found in his first *antinomy*. The first antinomy is an indirect argument for the position that our concept of time as something independent of us is inherently contradictory. Such time, if were to exist, would be part of what Kant refers to as the *noumenal* world, the world of "things-in-themselves". But, argues Kant, we can never know about the noumenal world. One reason is that we can never know about transcendent, independent, and substantival time.

The first antinomy (as with the other antinomies) is not a straightforward argument against the reality of noumenal time. Instead, it is a pair of arguments, each *for* a different feature of noumenal time. The first antinomy has a thesis "[t]he world has a beginning in time" and an antithesis "[t]he world has no beginning [but] is infinite as regards" time (Kant 1787/1996, A426–434/B454–462, 458–463).

Thesis: Time Has a Beginning

If time did not have a beginning, then, up to any arbitrary moment in time (such as the moment you read this), an infinite series of moments have elapsed and passed away. Yet, no infinite series can elapse and pass away like this. Say you worked in a call centre in hell. You have an infinity of calls waiting in your queue. You could never clear your queue, no moment how many calls you took or how much time you had. Similarly, an infinite series of moments never completes and so can never have wholly elapsed.

Therefore, instead, a finite series of moments has elapsed. The beginning of this finite series is the beginning of time. (Kant 1787/1996, A428/B456.)

Antithesis: Time Has No Beginning

A beginning of anything is an "existence preceded by a time in which the thing is not". In the same call centre, there is the moment when work begins. In the moment before work begins, there is no work; if there was work, then work would not begin at that time. Similarly, if time has a beginning, then it is preceded by a time in which there is no time. However, because it is preceded by a time, there is time.

Therefore, time has no beginning. There is an infinite series of earlier and earlier times. (Kant 1787/1996, A429/B457.)

The conclusions of the arguments for each of these theses conflict with each other. And each of the arguments is equally compelling. This antinomy "declaimed that either aspect of it was as capable of being proved as the other, i.e., that the world could have had and could not have had a beginning in time and an end in space" (Holmes 1955, 241).

If both arguments are equally compelling, then we cannot believe that either is true of time; each contradicts the other. Yet, if anything exists, it must either have a beginning or not have a beginning. For example, a call centre queue must have a beginning or have no beginning. However, Kant's first antinomy purports to show that how we conceive of time means it cannot be either finite or infinite. As such, unable to be either, time cannot be anything real.

Elapsing Time and Temporal Passage

However, there is a concept in Kant's arguments that is debated in the philosophy of time.[6] Kant's thesis includes the idea that time *elapses* into the past. Times (or better, as we discuss in Chapter 2, events) elapse by *becoming past*. For example, the time of your sixth birthday elapses by being present and then becoming past. This is a change in an event's position in what philosophers of time call the *A-series* or *tense* series. It is commonly called *temporal passage*. Not every philosopher of time agrees that the A-series and temporal passage are fundamental to time. Not every philosopher agrees with Kant's claim that there is a genuine elapsing of time. As such, at least as conceived of times *becoming past*, there is no genuine problem with elapsing infinite times.

Independent of such considerations, Kant's argument against the reality of transcendent time is not a denial of the reality of time itself (Paton 1936). It is only an argument against time transcending the empirical world. It denies there is time beyond the world of observable things or what we can infer from them. Time is real in the empirical observable world, i.e., in other things that exist.

Indeed, for Kant, time (along with space) is an *a priori* form of our sensible intuition. In Kant's terms, time is a condition of the empirically observable world; to say that time is "empirically real is to say that [time is] objectively valid so far as all sensuous experience is concerned" (Paton 1936, 143). More, Kant is taken to argue for transcendental *idealism* about time. That is, independent time is a product of our ideas. We have a concept of how time is beyond the empirical world. However, that is all it is—a concept. There is no such real time.

Idealism or Scepticism?

Yet, are we entitled to hold this position of idealism? For those familiar with sceptical moves in arguments about knowledge, an argument from equally compelling positions is not an argument to idealism but an argument to *scepticism*. That is, the argument is not for the view that time depends on the mind; it is an argument that we cannot know what time is independent of the mind. If the antinomy holds, then time as we conceive of it cannot be mind-independent. However, this does not mean it is mind-dependent (this makes it unlike Augustine's argument for time's mind-dependence, which we discuss in Chapter 6).

Instead, what we are left with is that, whatever it is we conceive of as time, there can be no such thing. Kant's main work on time concerns "the impossibility of knowing space and time". For Kant, "time and space could not be resolved into experience alone, neither could their *a priori* character allow that they be thought of in absolute independence of experience" (Holmes 1955, 241).

Given the target of Kant's antinomies is transcendent time, for our ordinary knowledge of time, we might find this result unproblematic. So, we cannot know about time in its entirety, as a limited or unlimited thing. This transcendent aspect of time seems far removed from the time in everyday life. Time in everyday life includes neither an edge of time nor an infinity of time.

However, there is another sceptical challenge to knowing about time. Sextus Empiricus argues that there are equally compelling but contradictory positions on time in everyday life.

Sextus Empiricus

Sextus Empiricus belonged an ancient group of sceptics known as the *Pyrrhonists*. A Pyrrhonist claims to have no beliefs, or at least no beliefs that she *chooses* to believe. "The [Pyrrhonist] sceptic does not assent to [that is, does not believe in] anything he is not forced to assent to" (Sextus Empiricus 2000, 1.7). Furthermore, the only beliefs a Pyrrhonist is forced to assent to are appearances or beliefs that are necessarily true. For example, a Pyrrhonist might agree that "honey *appears* sweet" (appearances) or "honey is honey" (a necessary truth) (Sextus Empiricus 1.10). However, they do not believe contingent truths or matters of contingent fact, such "there is honey" or that "honey *is* sweet".

Like many other philosophers of the time, Pyrrhonists considered the ultimate purpose of philosophical enquiry to be tranquillity (or *eudemonia*). What distinguished them from other philosophers at the time is they held that the best way to achieve tranquillity was to suspend beliefs (*epoché*) (Sextus Empiricus 1.7). Suspension comes through *equipollence* about some proposition; it comes from a state in which, for every proposition that one has some reason to believe to be true, one has an equally compelling reason to believe it is false. This does not compel one to believe the reverse is true (and so believe an opposing proposition); instead, one is compelled to suspend any belief about the proposition; one neither believes it is true nor believes it is false.

We can see in this approach similarities to Kant's antinomies. If his arguments are true, then the claim "there is a beginning to time" has both compelling reasons to accept it and compelling reasons to deny it.

Sextus Empiricus also attacks our idea of time through this sceptical method. In Sextus' book 3 on scepticism, *Against the Physicists*, he presents a number of arguments denying that one can have beliefs about time. He presents what he thinks are equally compelling reasons for both believing that there are certain aspects of time and for believing there are not. If he is right, then we must suspend our beliefs about these aspects of time (which, given Pyrrhonists are correct, is fine, for we achieve tranquillity).

However, Sextus Empiricus is not attacking the transcendent concept of time that Kant does. These are features found in our everyday thinking about time. The main targets of his attacks are:

- Change
- The divisibility of time
- The past, present, and future

Scepticism about Change

Sextus argues that we can neither believe that there is change nor believe that there is no change. This is one way into scepticism about time. If we cannot know that there is change (or that there is not time), and time is dependent on change, then we cannot know there is time (or that there is not time).

Here is the most relevant passage from Sextus. It is worth quoting in full:

> [106] What changes must change in some time. But nothing changes either in the past or the future or yet in the present... Therefore, nothing changes. Nothing changes in past or future time; for neither of these is present, and it is impossible for anything to act or be acted upon in a time which is not existent and present. [107] Nor yet in the present. Present time is [...] partless. But it is impossible to think that in a partless time iron, say, changes from hard to soft or that any other change occurs; for changes appear to need duration. Thus, if nothing changes either in past time or in the future or in the present, it must be said that nothing changes at all.
>
> (Sextus Empiricus 3.106–107)

We can extract the following argument:

1. *If A changes, A must change in time.*
   If there is no time, then A does not change. This does not deny that there is time without change. It denies there is *change without time.*
2. *If A is past or future, then it is impossible for A to change.* We can extract the following argument:
   1. If A is past or future, then A is not present.
   2. If A is not present, then it is impossible for A to act or A to be acted upon.
   3. If A does not act or A is not acted upon, then it is impossible for A to change.
   4. Thus, if A is past or future, then it is impossible for A to change.
3. *If A is present, then it is impossible for A to change.*
   1. If A changes, then A changes in a period of time, that is, in a duration.
   2. The present does not have a duration in it.
   3. When A is in the present, A is not in a period of time, that is, in a duration.
   4. Thus, when A is present, A does not change.
4. **Conclusion:** If A is present, past, or future, then A does not change.

Objection: This Argument Is Against the Reality of Change

This is an argument against the reality of change. It not an argument for *scepticism* about change and time. If the argument is valid, then we should not be sceptical, but believe there is no change. We should not *suspend* belief about change but deny that there is change. We might then say that we do, in fact, know something about change—we know that *there is no change*.

However, given Sextus' approach, this is an erroneous conclusion. According to Warren 2003, this argument is one side of an overall sceptical position on time. He only focuses on the argument that there is no change or time because he wants to induce "suspension of opinion in everyone, not just merely the philosophically interested or committed". Sextus does not "linger in offering arguments for a common or universally held belief" (Warren 2003, 314).

The omitted part in Sextus' argument is the common view amongst non-philosophers (and many philosophers) that there is change and time. This is driven by appearances. Although Sextus accepts the appearances, he does not accept that the appearances give us reason to believe that what is apparent is, indeed, the case. For Sextus, such appearances can be treated as one side of an argument toward suspension of belief. Then, we also have arguments that oppose any conclusions about time we may draw from appearances. These arguments are as compelling as appearances. Thus, we have equally strong reasons to believe in change (we experience it in many ways) and to deny it (arguments that lead to the conclusion that change is absurd). This leads to suspension of belief.

In Chapter 2, we return to a similar argument that runs counter to the common view or the appearances of change. For now, we can note the following: if time depends on change, then, if we must suspend belief in change, we must also suspend belief in time.

However, as discussed, we can conceive of time without change. In that case, we might easily reject the argument against beliefs about change from Sextus. Perhaps we cannot have beliefs about change. But what does that matter for time? We can have beliefs about time that is *independent* of change.

But Sextus also gives reasons to suspend beliefs about time. He notes that "so far as the appearances go, there seems to be such a thing as time; but so far as what is said about it goes, it appears to be non-subsistent" (3.136). Let us consider the arguments most relevant to the philosopher of time.

Against Time's Divisibility or Indivisibility

First, he argues that time cannot be either divisible or indivisible. Yet, if there is time, then it is either divisible or indivisible (Sextus Empiricus 3.143]. As such, given it cannot be either of these things, there cannot be time.

Time is not indivisible because it is divided into the past, present, and future. It is also not divisible (and so is indivisible) because "everything divisible is measured by one of its parts". For example, we measure a foot by its inches. In all such cases, the measuring quantity, such as an inch, is set against the measured quantity, such as the foot, and is part of the measured quantity.

Similarly, if time is divisible, it is measured by something part of it and during its period. However, time cannot be measured by any of its parts. If the present measures the past, the present is "set against the past and for that reason is in the past". But then the present will be part of the past, which is absurd. Similarly, if the present measures the future, the present is in the future; this again is absurd. The same reasoning applies to using the future or past to measure time: if the future measures the past or present, then the future is, respectively, in the past or present. If the past measures the future or present, then the past is, respectively, in the future or present.

In all such cases, the measuring quantity is part of what is measured, and so must be within the time that is being measured. But then it cannot be the present, past, or future, because none of those can be in any of the others. The past, present, and future are distinct.

This may initially strike one as odd. When we measure a string with a metre stick, the stick is not part of the string. However, it is easier to understand if we consider that we are using a length of space on the stick to measure the same length on the string. If we do something similar for the divisions of time in the past, present, or future, then we metaphorically use a "length" of one of these parts of time to measure the same length of the others. For example, we use a "length of future" to measure the same length of past or present.

To measure these other times by the future, we must put the future into those times.

Thus, time is neither divisible nor indivisible. However, everything that exists must be either divisible or indivisible. If time is neither of these, then it cannot be anything that exists.

The Argument Against Time as Past, Present, and Future

The next argument is against the parts of time themselves. Time is tripartite—it is divided into past, present, and future (Sextus Empiricus 3.144). Even if time is divided into past, present, and future, time cannot exist.

The past and future do not exist, states Sextus, because "if they did exist they would be present". But even if they could be present, they would not exist. This is because the present cannot exist either.

If the present exists, then it is either divisible or indivisible. However, it is neither divisible nor indivisible.

The present is not indivisible because "things which change are said to change in the present, and nothing changes in a partless time—e.g., iron becoming soft, and all the rest". However, it also not divisible because it cannot be divided into present parts; the present time "is said to pass with inconceivable speed into past time"; furthermore, only one of the parts can be present. If it has parts, then all its parts are either earlier or later than all the others. If one of those parts is present, then the others are either earlier or later. The parts later than the present part cannot be present because they are future; the parts earlier than the present part cannot be present because they are past. (This reasoning is a key part of St Augustine's argument toward the view that time is mind-dependent. We discuss that in Chapter 6.)

However, the present cannot also be divided into past and future parts; otherwise, "it will be unreal—one part of it no longer existing and the other not yet existing". Thus, the part of time that is past or future cannot exist and the part that is present cannot exist.

For anyone trying to know about time, scepticism is not an ideal outcome. Scepticism about time is *not* knowing about time. It is doubting time can be known. If you know something, then a variety of things are the case: for example, you understand that thing's conditions, the limits of its possibility, its difference from other entities, and the relationship between it and those other entities (such as their possible and necessary interdependencies). None of this is possible if, for every reason you must believe something about it, you have equal reason to believe the opposite.

Sextus' arguments, if they work, undermine just such an understanding or knowledge of time and change. Say that you have compelling reasons to believe that time is composed of a single real moment that is the present, an unreal past, and an unreal future. Say that you also have compelling reasons to believe time is measurable and is so by being divisible. Given Sextus' claims, you hold a contradictory set of beliefs: you believe time is divisible but also believe that, because the only thing real about time is the moment of the present, then there is nothing about time to divide.

If you find conflicting beliefs equally compelling, then you are in equipollence. You cannot justifiably believe that either claim is true of time; you have as much justification to believe the opposite of the claim.

Similarly, Kant's antinomies, if they work, undermine knowledge of time—at least, knowledge of time independent of our own experience.

Objection 1: We Cannot Suspend Beliefs about Time

One response here is to say that it does not matter. We *must* hold these beliefs about time, contradictory or not. We are helpless to believe in time, however contradictory it is. We are forced to assent to our beliefs about time, much as we are forced to accept the appearances of things.

However, such a response misses the point. Even if we accept that we have such beliefs, and cannot help having them, we also know that they contradict each other. We can certainly say things such as "I believe X is the case and X is not the case". If sceptical arguments work, however, we cannot say that we know what we are describing. We believe in a real duration that is unreal (because it is past); a temporal extent that has a beginning (because the past cannot be an infinite series of elapsed times) and no beginning (because all beginnings are preceded by a time). Even if what we say is true, we cannot justify it. Any justification we have for part of such a contradictory belief is also justification for denying the whole belief—because it denies the contradicting part of the belief.

Objection 2: Scepticism Depends on One's Metaphysics of Time

Historically, Kant and Sextus' arguments reveal something about how time was considered in their time. But must we suspend belief about time and change? Can we know anything about time and change or must we deny such a possibility? If we wish to follow sceptics, we may wish to suspend belief; if we follow Kant, it seems we pull back to only having beliefs about the observable world. However, many philosophers of time have not stopped at either suspending belief or constraining it to the empirical world. Instead, they argue for some of these features of time and deny others.

That is, instead of accepting that there equally compelling reasons to hold opposing views, they seek reasons to hold one and deny the other.

Some of the features that philosophers deny of time are central to Sextus' arguments. Sextus' arguments rest on two assumptions: first, that time *must* be divided into past, present, and future and, second, that only the present is real. As Warren writes, Sextus' arguments

> trade on the non-existence of the past and future in comparison with existence of the present, and the existence of time as a whole will stand or fall with the status of the present. *If any time exists, the present exists. If the present does not exist, no time exists.*
>
> (Warren 2003, 318)

The position that only the present time is real is called *presentism*. One kind of response is to take the opposite position: the past and future are as real as the present—what is known as *eternalism*. As such, one response to scepticism is that Sextus' arguments rest on taking a particular metaphysical position on time. We discuss other positions in more depth in Chapter 2.

Knowledge of Time through Perception

There is another argument against knowledge of time that seems to be immune to metaphysical positions on time. There is a remaining epistemological puzzle about time. Given a common theory of perceptual knowledge, it seems we cannot know about a central feature of time—temporal order.

As discussed earlier in the chapter, one reason to defend folk beliefs about time is that temporal order has a role in how we explain everything in the world. According to Le Poidevin, there are problems with explaining our knowledge of temporal order. An important way that we know about the world is through perception. However, there is a problem with explaining how we could know about temporal order that way.

The Causal Truth-Maker Principle

The *causal truth-maker principle* (or CTMP) concerns a question of how we gain knowledge about the actual world:

> The causal truth-maker principle: Perceptual beliefs that qualify for the title 'knowledge" are caused by their truth-makers.
>
> (Le Poidevin 2004, 113)

For most such beliefs, we gain this knowledge through perception. But how does perception give us this knowledge? According to Le Poidevin, for beliefs based on perception, CTMP provides most of the answer.

What is a truth-maker? For our purposes, a truth-maker is whatever makes a particular belief true. For example, if my belief that there is a cat on the roof outside is made true by the fact that *there is a cat on the roof outside*, then the truth-maker is *there is a cat on the roof outside.*

However, there is a further constraint from CTMP. Truth-makers cannot merely be anything at all. I may be sitting in the dark, windows and curtains closed, and form the conviction that there is a cat outside. There may indeed be a cat outside but that does not mean my conviction is knowledge. For the resulting belief to be knowledge, the truth-maker—the cat—must justify my belief about it. Where it comes to something like the cat, the truth-maker causes the perception that leads to my belief. If I know that *there is a cat on the roof outside* because I perceive the cat out there, then the fact *there is a cat on the roof outside* must cause that perception.

According to Le Poidevin, CTMP raises a problem for beliefs about temporal order and duration. The standard relevant conception of causes for CTMP is that causes are events. The cat being on the roof outside is an event, and through my perception of it, it causes my belief in it.

Temporal Order Cannot Cause Belief

The problem for beliefs about temporal order and duration is that they cannot cause our beliefs in them (although see Bowen 2013). As such, Le Poidevin proposes an expanded principle for perceptual belief, what he calls the *explanatory truth-maker principle* (ETMP). Instead of requiring truth-makers always be causes of our perceptual belief, we should allow other roles for them. We do so when what we know about cannot be causes—for example, time as temporal order and duration.

Le Poidevin's proposal shows something important about deliberating about our attitudes toward time. Questions about time are not merely about abstract aspects of the world, with little relationship to ordinary life. They concern basic components of ordinary life. They concern our awareness and deliberation about events in the world, and their relationship to us. Furthermore, in some cases, to solve epistemological problems of time, we cannot assume that it is enough to copy solutions for knowledge about other things.

As we discuss in Chapter 5, time may even be like *logic*. It may be in our thinking about anything at all. If right, then any argument about time must not be about what we can know of time. It must presuppose a knowledge of time that is also obvious to us. There is nothing missing or hidden from our knowledge of time.

Perhaps nothing is missing or hidden. However, as Sextus Empiricus' arguments show, our knowledge of time sometimes seems to be knowledge of contradictory elements. We seem to know that time is A and time is not-A. We might think that, because time is comparably as important as logical operators, then we must know it. However, if our claimed knowledge includes cases that conflict with one another, then it is an open question whether we do know it.

That is, time plays a role in our acquisition of knowledge, our deliberation, and our basic thinking about our relationship to anything else. As we see in other chapters, changes in our thinking about time can, in important ways, change how we think about other things. Thinking about time does not only change how we explain justified beliefs about the actual world. It can change how we think about many other things, including change itself, the physical world, the interpretation of evidence, and the relationship between the mind and the physical world. This may be no surprise: if time is important in everyday life, it can be important in theory as well.

Study Questions

1. This chapter refers to some ideas of time as everyday, folk, intuitive ideas of time. Do you agree that they are? Are any ideas missing from them? How might clock time relate to these ideas of time?
2. How would you describe a world without any time at all? You can have anything else in it that you like (e.g., space, objects). Is the correct description of it as a *frozen* world?
3. Can you imagine a first moment in time? Again, not of something *in* time—but time itself.
4. Sextus Empiricus claims his conflicting propositions about time and change are equally compelling. Do you agree? If not, which are more compelling and which are less compelling?
5. It is natural to think that we see a distant flash of lightning because the emitted light causes our perception of the lightning; thus, we have knowledge of distant lightning. We also hear thunder after seeing a flash of lightning; thus, we believe there is thunder after lightning. Can anything *cause* this belief that the thunder follows the lightning?

Notes

1 Hume doubts there is causation in the world—or at least that we are aware of such causation; the causation we are aware of is a product of our minds. Yet, in his argument, he still assumes that there is temporal order. Or, at least, his account of how we form beliefs about causation depend in a temporal order of impressions—if not impressions of temporal order (Hume 1776).
2 See Chapter 3.
3 Another view that is not discussed here is *super-substantivalism*: the only substances are time and (perhaps) space; other things are merely properties or relations of these substances (see Schaffer 2009).

4 See Chapter 3.
5 See Chapter 2.
6 See Chapter 2.

Suggested Readings

Shoemaker 1969 is the classic paper on global freezes and the substantivalism debate (also reprinted in Le Poidevin and McBeath 1991).

Kant's antinomies own work is worth reading, from his *Critique of Pure Reason* (*CPR*). Paton is also a clear early 20th-century commentator on Kant's work. For Sextus Empiricus' own text, see the 2000 Cambridge text, with editors Annas and Barnes. Le Poidevin's 2004 paper develops and proposes a solution to the problem of CTMP and temporal order knowledge.

Finally, Turetzky 1998 is an excellent general survey of the philosophy of time from the pre-Socratics to the 20th century. It includes discussions on Aristotle, Newton, Kant, and Sextus Empiricus.

2 Metaphysics of Time I

Time and Change

Overview

We have common, shared intuitions of time. One is that there is a single time series in which events occur. Unlike space, there are not two dimensions of time. However, we often describe events in time in two different ways. We describe events as being earlier, later, and simultaneous with each other. We describe events as lying in the past, present, and future.

How do these two ways of describing time relate to how we think of real or fundamental time? The way into such an approach is to look at another challenge to time. In this case, the focus is not on scepticism about our conception of time. It is on the metaphysics: McTaggart's paradox is an argument against the reality of time.

The responses to this argument come from different contemporary metaphysical positions on the nature of time. First, there are the tense theorists, who hold that time is fundamentally divided into the past, present, and future—forming a series known as the A-series. There is a unique present; there is also temporal passage, the change of events in the A-series. Second, there are tenseless theorists, who hold that time is fundamentally divided into moments ordered by the relations of simultaneity and succession (before and after)—forming a series known as the B-series.

Each theory and its sub-variants make different claims about the nature of time, of change, and what exists in time. The tense theories of presentism, moving spotlight, and growing block theory make different claims about what is real in the A-series; presentism holds that only the present is real; for the moving spotlight all times are real; for the growing block, the past and present are real and the future is unreal. The tenseless theories of B-theory and, more recently, R-theory are less divisive. Both hold that all times are real; it is only that the distinction of past, present, and future is not fundamental to time.

As we will see, these theories go further than the metaphysics. They extend to other areas of the philosophy of time.

Introduction

Metaphysics is "the most general investigation possible into the nature of reality". It uncovers "what is ultimately real, frequently offering answers in sharp contrast to our everyday experience of the world" (Craig 1998).

Metaphysics is not science. Science is empirical; it involves observation of the actual world, of experimentation, of empirical evidence. If questions are scientific, they require empirical confirmation or disconfirmation. Metaphysics is not subject to such empirical constraints (Hawley 2006). Metaphysical questions neither require confirmation nor disconfirmation. They can be investigated through reason and analysis alone.

So, the *metaphysics of time* is the most general investigation possible into the nature of real time. The main question it asks is if there are principles applying to everything real about time, all that there is to time. The metaphysics of time uncovers what is ultimately real about time, frequently offering answers in sharp contrast to our everyday experience of time. Metaphysicians of time do not investigate time through scientific experimentation, but through analysis of time alone.

Such analysis might seem simple. As discussed in Chapter 1, we have an everyday encounter of time. Time does not appear to be a rare element, discovered on some distant mountain or produced in a high-energy laboratory. It permeates every event and process in our lives. Perhaps we need only reflect on the time we encounter to grasp its most general and fundamental nature.

Yet, of its fundamental nature, our assumptions about time may be wrong on one or both counts. There may be more to time than the events and processes in our lives. Alternatively, these events and processes may fail to capture anything fundamental about time at all. Indeed, the temporal aspects of our lives may be different to how time fundamentally or really is. Time independent of our ideas of it, and in terms of its necessary and sufficient properties and relations—this real time may have nothing to do with our everyday life.

As also discussed in Chapter 1, there are issues with such a view. There are problems with knowing about time independent of our encounter with it; it is either undetectable or leads to contradictory views of time.

However, we can also metaphysically investigate time in events. This is the time we seem to encounter in everyday life, in our experience and ideas of events. We can investigate how such time is structured, what entities time requires and contains, what time is made of, and what things in the world there must be for there to be time. This is a metaphysical investigation into whether time is possible.

One influential 20th-century argument is that time is impossible; time is unreal.

McTaggart's Paradox

What does it mean for something to be real? Perhaps something is real because it is independent of anyone's attitude toward it; it is what is sometimes called *mind-independent*. It is not merely the content of an *idea*. It is more than the meaning or reference of a thought or some other attitude, such as a belief, experience, desire, or fear. Unicorns are not real; dragons are not real. Dragons and unicorns are not thoughts; thoughts do not breath fire or whinny. And beyond our thoughts of them, there are no dragons or unicorns.

However, horses and lizards are real. Horses whinny and lizards bask— thoughts do neither. But unlike dragons and unicorns, they whinny and bask beyond our thoughts of them. Unlike a dragon, a lizard is not merely the content of a thought.

This definition is complicated by *idealism*. According to idealism about the observable world, most of the normal everyday objects are complexes of ideas; they are dependent on what someone thinks about them; they are *mind-dependent*. For example, horses and lizards are complexes of different ideas— some of them human ideas about horses and lizards; perhaps some are lizard ideas or horse ideas as well; for the noted idealist Berkeley, many important ideas are God's ideas.

In this conception of ordinary things, we cannot distinguish unicorns from horses, dragons from lizards, by saying some are real and others are not. They are all mind-dependent in one way or another. But, for the purposes of this debate, I ignore idealism. I assume that there are lots of things that are real, things that exist even if there are no thoughts or beliefs at all. This might include horses (if or when horses do not think); it excludes unicorns. It also includes thoughtless things such as stars and magma beneath the earth.

Similarly, if time is real, then, like any real things, it is not merely the *content* of our attitudes about it. It is something more that is independent of our minds. There is time even if no one thinks about it or has any other attitude toward it at all.

However, McTaggart argues that there cannot be such a real time. Time must be merely apparent, something mind-dependent. This is because a real time is impossible.

The Two Main Concepts of Events in Time

An event is something that happens. More precisely, an event is something that *happens at a time*. Events can be something explicit, involving things, for example, events such as *your* birthday, your *exams*, the *death of the sun*.

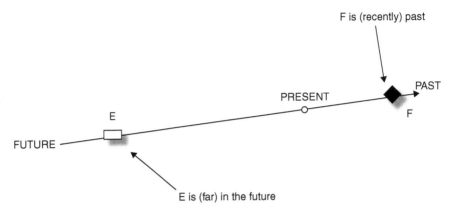

Figure 2.1 The A-Series

In this conception of events, time defines events. Events do not define time. McTaggart argues that events are defined by time in an important way. Events occupy positions in a *time series*. We typically conceive of events in one of two time series. McTaggart calls these the *A-series* and the *B-series*.

A-series

Figure 2.1 depicts events in the A-series. E is in the *far future* and F is in the *recent past*. There is also a single moment in which neither event lies, the *present*.

The A-series is the series of times that run from the past, through the present, to the future. It includes more specific positions such *the near future, the far future, the recent past*, and *the distant past*. It also includes more specific times such as *a million years ago, last week, this year*, and *next Tuesday*.

The main feature of the A-series is that events in it are either positioned in the past, present, or future, or are some determinate of those temporal positions. For example, an event can happen *a million years ago* or *yesterday* (determinates of the determinable *past*); an event can be *past* or *future* (determinates of *time*).

B-series

The B-series is the time series of events in which events are earlier, later, or simultaneous with each other. For example, in Figure 2.2, G is later than E, E_1 is simultaneous with E, and F is earlier than E.

We can also derive A-series positions from their relative positions in the B-series. For example, G is later than E_1. As such, we can derive an A-series position for G and F relative to E_1; relative to E_1, G is in the future; relative to F, G is in the past.

However, some philosophers object that such a derived A-series is not enough for any real A-series position. A real A-series position is special; it is not merely

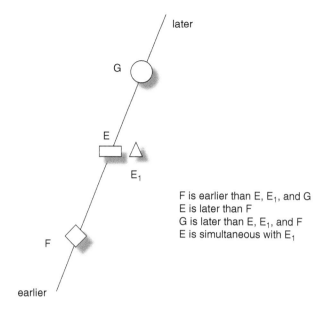

F is earlier than E, E₁, and G
E is later than F
G is later than E, E₁, and F
E is simultaneous with E₁

Figure 2.2 The B-Series

derived from any B-series; it is fundamental in a way that past, present, and future positions defined relative to B-series positions are not. The B-series is derived from the real A-series, not the other way around.

In contrast, other philosophers argue that all A-series positions are derived from B-series positions (or something similar). They argue that, if the A-series is fundamental, then it is impossible to escape what is known as *McTaggart's Paradox*. If this paradox holds, then there can be no real change, time, and so no real A-series at all.

McTaggart's Argument

Here is one way of describing McTaggart's Paradox (this is somewhat similar to Mellor's 1998 account; it only uses events and change):

1. If time is real, then change is real.
2. If change is real, then events change.
3. If events change, then events have more than one position in the A-series. They change by being future, being present, and being past.
4. No event has more than one position in the A-series.
   For example, event E cannot have the following combinations of properties: E is both past and present; E is both past and future; E is both present and future; E is recently past and in the far past.[1]

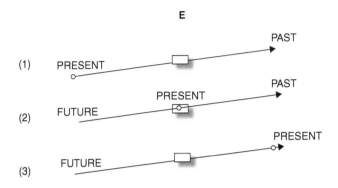

E is either (1) only past, (2) only present, or (3) only future
but NOT (1, 2, and 3) past, present, and future

Figure 2.3 No Event is Past, Present, and Future

   E can *only* be past (and not present or future), or present (and not past or future), or future (and not present or past).
5. (3 and 4) Events do not change.
6. (2 and 5) Change is not real.
7. (1 and 6) Time is not real.

This argument strikes many theorists as obviously wrong (e.g., Prior 1967). There seems to be an obvious and easy answer: premise 3 is misleading. No event is present, past, and future *simpliciter*. This is not a full description. There is more to the account.[2] An event is one of the following:

- An event is past to some events.
- An event is future to other events.
- An event is present to yet other events.

For example, E is past to G, future to F, and present to itself and E_1.
   However, this answer raises two questions:

(1) How do we assign the A-positions to the further events, that is, those events by which the original event's positions are defined—for example, F and G?

Each of the events (and times) to which the original event's positions are defined is also past, present, and future, and must only be past, present, or future.

(2) Why is an event past, present, or future to these other events? For example, why is E past to G, and future to F?

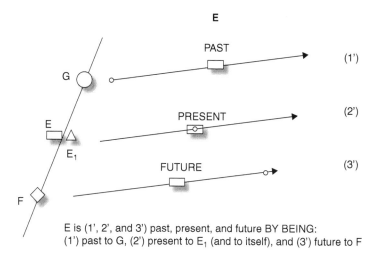

E is (1', 2', and 3') past, present, and future BY BEING:
(1') past to G, (2') present to E_1 (and to itself), and (3') future to F

Figure 2.4 Every Event is Past, Present, and Future

Take (1) first. The events from which the original event gets its position must themselves be in time. They cannot *lack* a position in time. Otherwise, the original event's position cannot be defined in relation to them. So, what position do they have?

Whatever position we give, it has the same problem as the original event's position; it has some position in the A-series, and this must be explained by its own relationship to some other event's position in time.

For example, we have the same problem for F and G as we do E. F and G also have the incompatible properties of being past, present, and future. We might solve this by holding that every event has A-positions the way the original event has these positions: they are past, present, and future to *yet other events*. However, although this solves it for those events as much as it does for the original, it does so by moving the question of how those positions are attributed to further events. Those yet further events are also events in time, with A-series positions, requiring the same kind of account.

That is:

1. If we try to explain some event α's position in the A-series by appealing to another event β in the A-series, then for consistency we must explain β's position in the A-series. β's position is no less a problem than α's; they are both just events in time.
2. Yet, if we use the method we used to explain α's position to explain β's position, then we are forced to appeal to a yet further event and its position in time, an event which requires the same explanation.

There seems to be no end to this explanation. Whatever further event (or time) we introduce to explain β's position, we must give the same explanation for that further event (or time). We must continue explaining the positions of each event by appealing to others, those others requiring the same explanation. This is an explanation with infinite steps: each step attempts to solve the problem by appealing to another event; yet, that further event has the same problem, requiring appeal to a still further event ... and so on.

This is a *vicious infinite regress*. It is vicious because the solution contains the very problem that needs to be solved; all that varies from problem to solution is which event is involved. It is infinite because the act of solving can never end.

Almost all philosophers of time reject McTaggart's paradox as a reason to deny the reality of time. Yet, despite what Prior has called "the outrageousness of his conclusion, and the fallaciousness of the reasoning which leads up to it", the argument is important. Almost all philosophers agree it can be solved, but many disagree about how to solve it. The disagreements spur important thinking in the philosophy of time.

Here are two solutions about which philosophers disagree:

- Solution 1: Any event's A-series positions are derived from B-series positions. Real time is best described in B-series positions.
- Solution 2: Only one A-series is fundamental to time. The fundamental A-series positions are real and unique A-series positions. The B-series positions and any other A-series positions are derived from this real A-series.

Solution 1: A-Series Positions Are Determined by B-Series Positions

There seems to be a simple solution to the paradox. It is also an answer to question (2) above. This answer is part of an important theory in the philosophy of time. It is this:

- Events are really in the B-series.
- The B-relations of temporal order, *earlier* or *later*, and *simultaneity* explain how events have their A-series positions.

Indexicals

In this answer, A-series positions of past, present, and future are *indexical* times. Indexicals are "elements of context", such as "who the speaker is, who his audience is, the time and place of the utterance, the objects referred to by words like "that", "this" (Lakoff and Johnson 1980, 198).

In this solution, all A-series positions are instances of such indexicals. As Diekemper puts it, an A-series position such as the " 'present' does not pick out any objective feature of reality, it merely functions as an indexical (like 'here' or 'I')" (Diekemper 2014, 1087).

Compare these A-series positions to indexical spatial positions—for example, "here", "in this place", "there", or "yonder". These indexical positions are determined by points in space; these spatial points are not themselves fundamentally "here" or "there". They are defined in some other way, for example, by a location (a train station, for example) or what is at the location (a person or a train at the station).

Spatial location or object can have incompatible spatial indexes without there being any spatial paradox. Say it is true both that, on a train, a person is sitting *here*, and, on a station platform, no one is sitting *here*. This is no paradox. The train's *here* is indexed to the train and the platform's *here* to the platform. Both *here*s are indexed differently. Furthermore, being at separate places, the train's *here* can be the platform's *there*, and vice versa; a person is sitting *there* on the platform, where "there" refers to the train.

Similarly, indexical A-theory positions can include "present", "past", "future", "now", and "then". They are like "here" and "there", defined by something else. For spatial indexes, "here" and "there" are defined by such things as trains and platforms. In time, the positions are defined by *B-series* positions, or what are sometimes called "dates" (Smart 1963; Mellor 1998).

For example, event E is simultaneous with another event E_1, earlier than event G, and later than event F. As such, it has the following indexical A-series positions:

- E is *present* to E_1 (and to itself) because E *is simultaneous with* E_1 and itself.
- E_1 is *past* to G because E *is earlier than* G.
- E_1 is *future* to F because E *is later than* F.

This avoids McTaggart's paradox. There is no infinite sequence of steps. The sequence is stopped short because events' A-series positions are not explained by events in *other* A-series positions; it explains them by events in B-series positions. There are the events in the B-series, each related by the B-relations of simultaneity or succession (being earlier or being later). Being so related, they are past, present, or future in relation to each other.

Importantly, in this answer, all there is to an event being past, present, or future is its being earlier, simultaneous with, or later than some other event. A-series positions are derived from B-series positions, and that is all there is to A-series positions.

This explanation of A-series positions is that of the *B-theory* or *tenseless theory*: B-theory because time is conceived as fundamentally the B-series; tenseless theory because the A-series positions (e.g., past, present, future) are also known as *tenses*; this theory holds that time is not fundamentally the A-series, and so is not fundamentally tensed.

We return to this theory further in this chapter. For now, we must consider a common objection to this theory. It concerns real change.

Objection: The B-Series Is Not Enough for Change

McTaggart was not satisfied with the B-theory or tenseless theory approach. Many philosophers since McTaggart agree. The problem they see is that it prioritizes the B-series over the A-series. A-series positions are derived from their B-series positions. However, so these objectors claim, this approach has two problems:

(1) The B-series does not define real A-series.
(2) The B-series has no change in it, and real time needs change.

Objection 1: The B-Series Does Not Provide Real A-Series Positions

The B-theory solutions suits any A-series positions that are derived from the B-series. However, such A-series positions are not *real* A-series positions. These are derivative, indexed A-series positions. *Real* A-series positions are fundamental. If time is real, then events in it must have real A-series positions. And such real A-series positions are not derived from another series.

Indeed, B-theory does not have a means of picking out a single real A-series from all the others. In B-theory, all A-series positions are equal. They are all derived and not fundamental: they are indexed to different positions in the B-series. Just as no single real "here" or "there" can be picked out by indexing "here" and "there" to different things or points in space, so no "present" and "past" can be picked out by indexing "present" and "past" to different events or B-series positions.

Yet why is this a problem? Why should an A-series be fundamental? Why not have all A-series be indexical, derived from the B-series?

Objection 2: The B-Series Does Not Capture Real Change

The problem, according to McTaggart, is real change. McTaggart's contemporary Bertrand Russell gave a tenseless theory-like account of change: change is just objects having one property (such as being hot) at one time and lacking that property at a later time.

McTaggart responded:

> Mr Russell looks for change, not in the events in the time series, but in the entity to which these events happen … [I]f my poker, for example, is hot on a particular Monday, and never before or since, the event of the poker being hot does not change. But the poker changes, because there is a time when this event is happening to it, and a time when it is not happening to it. [...]
>
> But this makes no change in the qualities of the poker. It is always a quality of that poker that it is hot on that particular Monday... [and always a quality that it] is not hot at any other time … The fact that it is hot at one point in a series and cold at other points cannot give change, if neither

of these facts change—and neither of them does. Nor does any other fact
about the poker change unless its presentness, pastness, or futurity changes.
(McTaggart 1927/1991, 28)

According to McTaggart, the B-series cannot describe real time because events
in the B-series do not change. Real change requires change in positions in time.
Events do not change positions in the B-series. They do change positions in the
A-series.

Here is an example of the thinking. It is a fact that the sun's death is later
than your death. Relative to your death, the sun is a future event. Relative to the
sun's death, your death is a past event. These are all facts that do not change.
The sun's death never changes from being later than (or a future event relative
to) your death; your death never changes from being earlier than (or a past event
relative to) the sun's death.

What does change is this: both your death and the death of the sun change
A-series positions. They change positions in the A-series in the following order:

1.   Your death is future. The sun's death is much further future.
2.   Your death is present. The sun's death is future.
3.   Your death is past. The sun's death is present.
4.   Your death is long past. The sun's death is past...

For McTaggart, the differences 1–4 capture real change. (Well, except that he
denies such change is possible—this is central to his paradox.) Tenseless theorists
can account for some kinds of A-series positions by the B-theory. For example,
the sun's death is in the *future* of your present. But they cannot account for the
real change described above.

Motion and A-Series Change

There are accounts of change that seem only to involve B-theory relations. One is
Russell's description of the poker being hot and cold on different days. Another
example is a common description of motion: this is the difference in some thing's
location from one moment to a later moment.

Le Poidevin describes a kind of motion as follows (this account is what he
calls *static motion* (Le Poidevin 2003, 150–163).

Motion: an entity O *moves* from spatial location S_1 to S_2 if:

1.   At time t_1, O is in S_1 and is not in S_2.
2.   At another time t_2, O is in S_2 and is not in S_1.

The object O must be in different spatial locations from one time to another. It
cannot merely be at different spatial locations at *the same time*. For example, O
does not move if, at t_1, it is at both S_1 and S_2. That is merely occupying or filling
multiple locations. A car occupies more than one place merely by having one

wheel on the path, another on the tarmac. It is not moving by doing this. To move, the object must be at one location at one time and another location at a later time. For example, the whole of the car is on the path at one time and then on the tarmac at a later time.

Indexical A-Series Change

Can we adapt this kind of motion to get McTaggart's real, A-series change out of the B-series?

A first step is to adapt the above account to an indexical account. We can describe the above motion in terms of spatial indexicals. We need only ensure the same context for any indexed terms we use. That is, we ensure the same non-indexical spatial location is used when referring to *here* and to *there*.

Indexed motion: an entity O *moves* from *here* to *there* if:

1. At time t_1, O is *here* and is not *there*.
2. At another time t_2, O is *there* and is not *here*.

Next, adapt it to an indexical A-series account of change in time. Replace *moving* and *at spatial indexicals* with *changing* and *at A-series positions*. For example, replace *here* with *present* and *there* with *past*. Then we define *A-series change*:

A-series change: an event E changes from *present* to *past* if:

1. At time t_1, E is *present* and is not *past*.
2. At another time t_2, E is *past* and is not *present*.

How do we account for the times at which E is at its A-series positions? One answer is we use B-series positions. For example, if t_1 is earlier than t_2, then E is present *before* it past.

Objection: This Is Not Real Change

Such B-series-derived A-positions are the case for an event whether the event is past, present, or future. Even if E is in the future, E is also, at some later time than E, past. It does not get the unique and real A-series in which events undergo real change. Instead, it is only past, present, or future within *different* indexed A-series. It is not change in the *same* A-series—and certainly not in the same fundamental A-series.

This is shown in Figure 2.5.

In the example, E's pastness is in one indexed A-series (the A_1-series), E's presentness is in another indexed A-series (the A_2-series), and its futurity is in yet another A-series (the A_3-series). We must then describe the change in A-series positions as follows.

A-series change (2): an event E changes from *present* to *past* if:

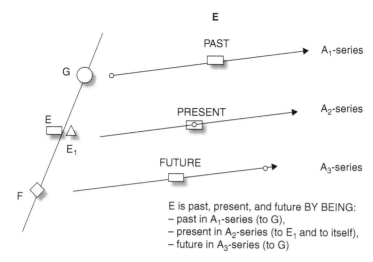

Figure 2.5 Multiple A-Series Derived from the B-Series

1. At time t_1, E is *past* in the A_1-series and is *not present* in the A_1-series.
2. At another time t_2, E is *present* in the A_2-series and is *not past* in the A_2-series.

Both 1 and 2 may be true. However, again, they ignore that real change (according to McTaggart) is through a *single* A-series. The past, the present, and the future through which events have different A-series positions are not part of the same A-series. For McTaggart's real change, we need a change in *one and the same* A-series.

Analogy between a Fundamental A-Series and Absolute Space

Another spatial analogy may help us grasp this. At some points in history, theorists believed that there was a difference between relative motion and rest, and absolute motion and rest:

1. Relative motion and rest are defined in relation to other things. For example, standing at a station, I am moving relative to occupants of a train passing through the station.
2. Absolute motion and rest are defined in relation to absolute space. For example, on the train, I may appear to move in relation to the rest of the world. However, it happens that I and the train are at rest relative to absolute space. The station (and the landscape around it) is what is really in motion.

For those who hold to absolute motion and rest, the motion of 2 is the real, fundamental motion and rest. If I move in relation to absolute space, I am actually or really in motion. Any other kind of motion or rest is derivative, merely in relation to other things. For example, if I am moving in relation to absolute space, but am at rest relative to the Earth, then I am only derivatively at rest.

Similarly, for those who hold that real change is change in real A-series positions, those A-series positions are not derived from B-series positions. Indeed, B-series positions are derived from A-series positions. For example, E is earlier than F because E is really past and not present, and F is really present and not past. If real change is change in A-series, it needs to be something other than A-series change derived from the B-series.

The underlying point of this objection—that there is a fundamental A-series—is asserted by philosophers of time who subscribe to *A-theory* or *tense theory*.

Tense Theory

A-theory or tense theory is the position that time and change are fundamentally tensed or composed of A-series positions. Tense theory differs from McTaggart in also holding that such fundamentally tensed time is real. There are two common components of such tense theories:

- Temporal passage
- A unique and real present

Temporal Passage

Temporal passage, also called time's passage or the passage of time, is a common term for change in real A-series positions. According to tense theorists, such passage is necessary for real time. Without temporal passage, there is no change or time. With temporal passage, there is change and time.

Temporal passage is a change in events. However, it is not just anything we might call "change in events". We might describe an event as changing by having different properties over the time it occurs. For example, my tenth birthday party is an event that might start as fun, then become upsetting; a lecture by a famous thinker might begin as incomprehensible, then become dull. These are changes in events—of a party and of a lecture, respectively.

Temporal passage is change in the *times* of events. More specifically, it is the change in the times that are *A-series positions*, or what are sometimes also called tenses. Temporal passage is *events* changing from being far future, to being near future, to being present, to being recently past, to being far past.

That is, temporal passage is the real change demanded by McTaggart.

As such, temporal passage cannot be reduced to indexed change. It belongs to one A-series—the present, past, and future in which events change belong to one A-series. As such, this passage is exactly the change that a B-theorist or tenseless theorist cannot accept.

The Unique and Real Present

According to tense theory, there is only one real present. That there is one such present arises naturally out of the conception of a single real A-series. In any A-series, derivative or otherwise, there is only one present, a present that is singular and unique in that series. If tense theory is correct, and there is a real A-series, then there is only one, unique present, the present of the real A-series.

Like all positions in this A-series, this real present is not derivative but fundamental to time. But why it is a single or unique present is particular to the more general concept of being present.

Say that there are multiple presents in the real A-series. For there to be multiple presents in a series, they must be at different positions in the series to one another. Since all of the multiple presents are real presents, in this hypothesis, all of these presents belong to the real, fundamental A-series. If one of the presents is derived or in relation to something, then it is part of a different, derived A-series. As such, these presents are not derived or only present in relation to something, such as some event in the past, or some position in the B-series.

Yet, if one of these real presents lies in the A-series, then any other of the presents is either past or future to it. If the other is past, then this other is both present and past. If the other is future, then it is both present and future. This is a contradictory description: no present can also be past (or future). In addition, it is the kind of contradiction that tense theorists try to resolve with a real A-series.

Again, such a contradiction cannot be dissolved by holding that one of the presents is indexed and derived. Each present is supposed to be real and fundamental. As such, in the real A-series, there are not multiple presents, but one unique and real present.

Real Present and Temporal Passage

Tense theorists frequently use the unique present to explain many of the features tense theorists consider fundamental to time. For example, it provides a point from which events are described as how they really are in time. If some event or time is past relative to the real present, then it is really past; if some event or time is future to the real present, then it is really future.

This can then give us temporal passage. Real change can be distinguished from merely indexed change by being change in tenses—A-series positions—that are relative to the real present. If, relative to the real present, an event is first future, then present (i.e., it is in the real present), and finally past, then the event need not have any of these positions derivatively. This is unlike similar positions in an A-series derived from the B-series. Relative to the fundamental present, events have real tenses (or really have these tenses). If they change these tenses, then this is a real change—it is a change in the specific tenses of this A-series. It is not different relations to tenses in different A-series.

Such an explanation of how real change is possible also dissolves McTaggart's claim that such events also have other tenses, tenses that are incompatible with the changing tenses (that are relative to the real present). Given a unique present, and a unique real A-series, these other incompatible tenses—these other A-series positions—are not an event's real positions; they are derivative.

For example, an event E is past relative to the *real* present and is also present relative to itself. However, E's being present to itself is not E really or fundamentally being present; E is derivatively present. Because it is past to the unique present, it is really past.

Real Present and the Real A-Series

The tense theorist denies that the B-series is fundamental to time; as such, anything derived from or indexed to it is also not fundamental (again, such as an indexed A-series).

In contrast, one way of understanding the real A-series is that it is defined in relation to a unique present. Defining an A-series by *the* present is not reducing it to a mere derivation from a non-fundamental B-series; it is explaining it by a fundamental feature of time.[3]

In addition, a fundamental present that grounds all other aspects of time has an advantage for tense theorists: a unique present reduces the question of accounting for a real and fundamental series, such as an A- or B-series, to merely accounting for a real and fundamental present. The whole of the real A-series is in relation to this present. So, if we can have the real and unique present, then we can have a real A-series.

As such, some tense theorists try to offer some explanation of why there is a real present, and through it temporal passage and a fundamental A-series.

Time Defined by Events and a Static A-Series

Here is an explanation of the unique present that cannot work. The unique present is defined by an event. Events can define positions in an A-series. Call such an A-series an *event-defined A-series*. For some event E, in an event-defined A-series:

- E is present.
- Any event earlier than E is past.
- Any event later than E is future.

We may say that only one A-series is the real A-series, with a real present and real temporal passage. However, if we define A-series *only* by events, this real A-series leads to counter-intuitive results. Whatever event we choose, change as conceived by tense theorists is impossible. It requires events be frozen in what we might call a *static* A-series.

Here is how. There are multiple event-defined A-series, each defined by different events. For example, the death of the sun is present to itself, past to some later event, and future to your reading this. Your reading this is present to itself, your preparing to read it is past to your reading this, and the death of the sun is future to reading it.

We might say that one event defines the real A-series. However, if we do pick out some such event, then this prevents the possibility of temporal passage. Each event is supposed to change its positions in the A-series, while also being in the past and future of other events. If any of these events *define* the real A-series, then that event must be present, and only present, in the A-series that they define.

Say that your reading this is the event that defines the real A-series. In that case, your reading this does not change its A-series position. As the event that defines this A-series, it can only be present. Yet, also, all other events that are present with your reading this must remain present; any events that are future to it remain future and any past to it are forever past; indeed, they were never present or future.

As such, no event can change their position in the A-series time. If your reading this defines the real A-series, the death of the sun is in the (real) far future and must stay there. It cannot undergo passage to be in the (real) present.

We might call such a conception of tensed time a *static conception of tensed time*. It is static because the things to which it refers never change. It is tensed because the things that never change are the tenses of events.

Again, this is the case only if some events in time define the real A-series. No one holds to this static conception of tense time (although another important theory is often called static, as discussed below). That no one holds it means tense theorists hold that features such as a real present, A-series, and passage are defined by something other than events. What, then, picks out the real present and A-series?

Kinds of Tense Theory

The three main explanations for the real present and A-series are presentism, the "moving spotlight" theory, and the growing block theory.

Presentism

The core tenet of presentism is that the present of the real, fundamental A-series is all that there is. The present encapsulates all of reality. Reality is wholly confined to that single time. If some X is real, then X is in the real present. In contrast, any X that is past or future is unreal. Like unicorns or dragons, past dinosaurs are not real and future humans are not real.

There is history to this concept of time. As discussed in Chapter 1, elements of presentism are found in Sextus Empiricus' scepticism. The unreality of the past and future drive his arguments from contradictory concepts of time to suspending belief in time. Similarly, as discussed in Chapter 6, for Augustine, presentism is central to his puzzle about what we measure when we measure duration.

Presentism is opposed by another position about time—*eternalism*. For an eternalist, all times are equally real. It is irrelevant which of these moments is present. What is at separate times can belong to or be part of something that exists or is real.

One way to grasp this difference is to consider which logical operator, according to presentism and eternalism, connects existential statements about entities occurring or existing at separate times.

Say that an apple is green on Tuesday and red on Wednesday, but neither green nor red on any other days. Then, since the apple is red at one time and green at another time:

- According to presentism, either only (i) the apple is red and is not green (it is presently Wednesday) or (ii) the apple is green and is not red (it is presently Tuesday).
- According to eternalism, both the apple is red and the apple is green, irrespective of which time it is, Tuesday or Wednesday. It is enough that the apple is green on Tuesday and red on Wednesday.

Some philosophers have expressed scepticism about whether there is a real debate here (e.g., Dolev 2007 and Dorato 2006). Are presentism's assertions about reality merely a qualified form of eternalism? Eternalists refer to reality or existence at multiple times; presentists only ever refer to reality or existence at one time. Given they only refer to what is at one time, *of course* things only at other times are not at that time. And so, neither are they real or existing at those times.

For example, take dinosaurs. According to presentists, dinosaurs are not real; they do not exist. However, all that is meant by this is they are not real or do not exist in the present. But no one thinks dinosaurs exist in the present.

However, presentists argue that there is a difference. The difference is shown by two important reasons to hold presentism over eternalism:

- Presentism is intuitive, unlike eternalism.
- Presentism dissolves McTaggart's paradox, unlike eternalism.

Presentism Is Intuitive

Many presentists hold that presentism is intuitive. Indeed, it understates their position to say that it is intuitive. For some presentists, presentism is a basic component of how everyone thinks about time. Here is Bigelow:

> I am a presentist: nothing exists which is not present. I say that this was believed by everyone, both the philosophers and the folk, until at least the nineteenth century; [...] Presentism was assumed by everyone everywhere, until a new conception of time began to trickle out of the high Newtonianism of the nineteenth century.

(Bigelow 1996, 35)

In support of this view, Bigelow notes that denying presentism was open to ancient scholars to solve some of their philosophical problems. However, they never took denying presentism as a solution to that problem. Indeed, we see this with Sextus Empiricus. According to Warren, Sextus Empiricus' argument against the unreality of time fails given eternalism. It rests on the idea that the past and future do not exist; yet, for eternalism, the past and future do exist (Warren 2003, 318). Similarly, as discussed in Chapter 6, Augustine's arguments against mind-independent duration fail if we ignore presentism.

Yet, despite their otherwise reflective and questioning stance, these scholars never considered denying presentism and accepting eternalism.

In response, one might argue that this is only an argument from *traditionalism* about time. That is, we are asked to believe presentism because everyone believed it for thousands of years. However, advocates of presentism hold that it is more than that. It is not just that the folk historically believe it. It is that it is the view that everyone, even self-proclaimed deniers of presentism, in fact, believe.

For example, Crisp argues that presentism is *Moorean*: the belief in it is part of the common-sense views that, according to McTaggart's contemporary Moore, everyone, even philosophers, believes. Moore argued against Hume's radical scepticism, that is, Hume's argument against certainly about the external world's existence. Moore responded that we are more certain that an external world exists than we are of Hume's argument (Moore 1953, 137).

Similarly, just as—to use an example from Moore—I believe that my hands are in front of me, so do I believe that only what is present is real. We are more certain that only the present is real than any arguments against presentism (Crisp 2005).

Presentism Solves McTaggart's Paradox

A second reason for holding presentism is that it picks out a fundamental A-series, allowing us to dissolve McTaggart's paradox.

For tense theory, the real A-series is real because it is the A-series defined or relative to the real present. It is also fundamental because all other time series are derived from this real A-series, for example, the B-series or an A-series defined by events.

The main challenge for tense theory is to account for why one A-series is real, and no other A-series is real. The presentist answer is that, in reality, no event has an A-series position given by non-present times or events. These events are not real. Unreal events cannot define anything real, including real positions for events. For example, my writing this may be future to some past events involving dinosaurs; however, it is not *really* future; the past events are not real and so do not give events their real A-positions. My writing this is, however, present because it is present to other present events, for example, it is present to my neighbour's music downstairs.

There is another consequence that supports tense theory: the B-series must also be derived from the A-series. In the B-series, all but one of B-related events must be non-present, for example, if E is present, then all other B-related events are at some other time; if any other events are present, then E is not present. As such, B-relations constitute the B-series; for any of these B-relations, at least one unreal event is a relatum. It is a series constituted by unreal entities (be they times or events).

As such, presentism must deny that time fundamentally has a B-series or multiple A-series. It is not just an incidental feature of this theory of time, or one that requires further explanation. It is a necessary feature of it.

By requiring only one fundamental or real A-series, McTaggart's paradox is dissolved. The paradox requires that events have all their A-positions. Yet, because A-positions are incompatible, this requirement leads to contradiction. Presentism dissolves the requirement of this paradox: events do not have all their A-positions: events only have A-positions given by present things. This eliminates the incompatibility.

However, there are several objections to presentism. Some are unpacked in later chapters, where other areas of philosophy are relevant (and thus showing that such a theory need not merely be a *metaphysical* theory). It suffices to mention a few here before moving on.

Objection 1: No Real A-Series

As discussed in Chapter 1, Sextus Empiricus argued that time is not real because the past and future are unreal. Similarly, as discussed in the Chapter 6, duration and thus time are mind-dependent because, again, the past and future are unreal.

These challenges to the reality and mind-independence of time arise directly out of assuming presentism. If presentism is true, it is susceptible to these sceptical challenges. It cannot hold that time is real if only the present is real; time is primarily constituted by the past and future. Furthermore, many features of tense theory, such as temporal passage, are problematic given there is only present change, and no real past or future (Leininger 2015).

How can a presentist answer them? They can agree there is no time where time is something constituted by a past and future. However, this does not matter. Present features of the world explain why we can still talk about such times and something like a "duration". We explore what such features might be in Chapters 5 and 6.

Objection 2: Presentism Lacks Truth-Makers for Truths about the Past

Presentism holds that the past is unreal. This is similar to merely possible or imaginary worlds (at least, given intuitive views of such worlds). Yet, we often make claims about the past that seem true. For example, it seems right that there were dinosaurs. If the past is unreal, then what makes statements about the past true?

An initial response is the dinosaurs in the past make it true. However, such truth-makers are not real, given presentism. Unlike, say, horses, there are no dinosaurs to make true our statements about them.

We might, instead, answer that *signs* or *traces* of dinosaurs make statements about them true—for example, fossils (e.g., Mellor 1981; Bigelow 1996). However, that only shifts the truth-maker to something specific in present things—the trace or sign—that point at the past. But what is it about the present truth-maker—such as the fossil—that makes true that there are dinosaurs? If the answer is simply that the fossil is a *trace of dinosaurs*, then the truth-maker once more contains past things (the dinosaurs that of which it is a trace).

According to Sider, these answers turn on *cross-time* relations, and presentism cannot work with such relations (Sider 1999, 327–331). Cross-time relations are relations that hold between my present belief in dinosaurs and past dinosaurs, or a present fossil and past dinosaurs. There are other kinds of cross-time relations involving truth-makers as well. For example, there are causal relations between a truth-maker that causes my perceptual belief in it (see Chapter 1).

One answer is that there is a past fact about dinosaurs. This *tensed* fact makes true beliefs about the past, much as perceptual beliefs are made true by truth-makers in the world. Just as the event of a distant thunderstorm can be a truth-maker for my perceptual belief that there is a thunderstorm, so the event of Jurassic dinosaurs roaming the Earth makes true my belief that there were Jurassic dinosaurs.

However, again, presentism denies the reality of the past; it denies the reality of dinosaurs. There cannot be real truth-makers with dinosaurs in them (such as their roaming around in the Jurassic period). Presentism cannot work with them because, no matter which time is considered present, the other time is unreal.

Some presentists do try to answer this by appealing to metaphysical entities. For example, Bigelow proposes necessary facts that, although not themselves past, are *about* the past, for example, there is present fact that *there were dinosaurs*. This is not a fossil or a perceptual belief. It is a fact of the universe itself (Bigelow 1996). However, the use of "about" here seems to have all the cross-time problems of traces and truth-makers. A present entity that must include the past in some way still needs to explain how it can do so without the past being real.

Others, "nefarious presentists", argue that presentists should give up trying to sincerely answer this challenge. We can talk as if there are truth-makers, but we need not commit to their existence. Here's Tallant and Ingram (2015):

> [W]e advise presentists to be nefarious and to endorse both of the following two principles:
>
> (1) Truths about the past are expressed using primitive (and unanalysable) tense operators;
> (2) The primitive (and unanalysable) tense operators do not pick out some distinctive ontological category, or aspect of reality.

In addition, one may answer these questions by answering them non-metaphysically—and instead, turn to the grammar of statements about the past.

This is to treat past talk, and talk of tensed facts, as primitively true or false; we discuss it further in Chapter 5.

Objection 3: Presentism and Physics

Presentism has problems with current physical concepts of time. Briefly, the distinction between the past, present, and future in current physics is relative to arbitrary and conventional frames of reference. Such frames are defined by one's velocity. As such, tense distinctions are also defined merely by one's frame of reference and velocity.

Given presentism, this means what is real or not is defined by one's velocity, which is far from intuitive.

We discuss the consequences of relativistic physics in Chapter 4.

Eternalism

Some philosophers of time advance non-presentist theories about time. Most of these are *eternalist* theories about time. Eternalism just is the position that not only present things are real. Things at other times, both earlier and later than the present, are also real.

The "Moving Spotlight"

The "moving spotlight" theory holds the real present, and change in relation to it, is explained by there being a singular moment—the present—that changes in relation to everything else. Events do not change; instead, the present changes. It changes by being first at one set of events, then being at another set of events, and then yet another set of events … and so on.

The moving spotlight gets its name from an analogy by Broad: it is as if the present changes its position in relation to events as a spotlight might change in relation to different houses on a street. First, the spotlight is on one house and then it is at another house; similarly, the present is at one event and then at another event (Broad 1923).

The order in which the present is at one event and then another event determines the events' locations in the A-series. When the real present is at an event, the event is really present; when it was at an event, the event is really past; when it will be at an event, the event is really future. The point is that the events do not change, the present changes. The change provides real temporal passage and the real A-series.

The advantage of the moving spotlight is that it folds both temporal passage and the real present into one metaphysical entity that has a simple-seeming metaphysical feature: it is a unique present that changes (it "moves"). This explains the unity of events undergoing temporal passage. These events do not really change. Instead, what changes is the present. Events only "change" in relation to the present.

The events are like a person who never changes height; yet, because her younger brother grows up, goes from being tall to being short (relative to her brother). The events never change positions in time; yet, because the present is no longer at those events, they go from being present to being past.

Objection: Events Must Change

The moving spotlight fixes the existential or ontological status of events. The events do not change no matter how they are placed in time. However, events must change their ontological status. They must change when they *become present*. They must undergo what Broad calls *pure becoming* (Broad 1923), that is, an event *becoming real*. This is a fundamental change in events that is their coming into existence. As such, since no longer being future means an event becomes real, the event must be unreal when it is future.

The concept of future events as unreal is a concept of an *open* or *unreal* future. But an unreal future is not available to the moving spotlight theory: in the moving spotlight, all that changes is the present's relation to events in the world. Events in the future do become present and past. However, all that means is that, when the present "moves" to these events, events that are future become present. These events otherwise do not change their status, ontologically or otherwise. They do not become real or come to exist; they do not undergo pure becoming.

With respect to advocating an open future in this way, presentism has an advantage over the spotlight view. According to presentism, the future is not real. As such, when events become present, they come into existence. However, as discussed, presentism has the problem that, for the very reasons it allows an open future, it also has problems with what might be called an open *past*. It must explain why the unreality of the future allows an open future while the unreality of the past does not. (For extended discussion of the "moving spotlight", see Cameron 2015.)

The Growing Block Theory

The growing block theory holds that the present and past are real (as well as what is in those times), but the future is not real (and neither is what is at those times). Central to the idea of the growing block theory is that real change is an increase in what is real: the number of past events constantly increases while the events that are present constantly change.

The present is the boundary between both future and past: it is the latest real time; it has no real time after it—only the unreal future times. The theory "accepts the reality of the present and the past, but holds that the future is simply nothing at all" (Broad 1923, 66).

This theory holds to a tensed concept of change because this change involves a change in events from their being future and non-existent to being present and existent. Furthermore, this change in A-series positions is a *fundamental* change. It is neither derived from nor merely one amongst other events we may call "change", such as apples ripening. "To 'become present', in fact, is 'just to become' …; i.e. to 'come to pass' … or, most simply, to 'happen'. Such 'absolute becoming' is presupposed in all change, and therefore cannot be treated as a case of it; probably, indeed, it cannot be analysed at all" (Prior 1967, 8).An advantage of the growing block is that it captures some people's intuitions, while avoiding the pitfalls of both presentism and the moving spotlight. It avoids the spotlight's fixed future and avoids presentism's open past. According to Briggs and Forbes 2017, the growing block theory is committed to *asymmetric ontology*:

> ASYMMETRIC ONTOLOGY is based on the intuition that the future is "open" while the past is "fixed". An asymmetry between past and future seems important in our deliberation, planning, intervention in, and memory of events. [It] gives a simple explanation for this asymmetry—it is a question of existence. The past is fixed because it exists, and the future is open because it does not exist.
>
> (Briggs and Forbes 2017, 927)[4]

One disadvantage of the growing block is that it is more complex than both presentism and the moving spotlight. The growing block theory has more things in it than presentism; the growing block has a real past and present; presentism only requires a real present. The change under the growing block theory is more complex than under the moving spotlight theory; in the growing block theory, pure becoming is a change in recent past events and the present, rather than just a change in the present; in the moving spotlight theory, all that changes is the present.

However, the growing block theory can be simpler than the moving spotlight in how it conceives of the present. The present just is the latest in real events. There is nothing more that is unique about it. This is not to say that it cannot add there is something unique about the present, other than this status of being the latest real time; it is only that it does not require there be anything unique (Broad 1923, 66).

So far, we only consider tense theories in detail. However, as we have already seen, they are not the only approach to McTaggart's challenge. Tense theories agree with McTaggart's view of real, fundamental time and change. Tenseless theories do not.

Tenseless Theory

Tenseless theory is the theory that the A-series is not fundamental to time or change. As such, neither is a unique present or temporal passage. Events do not need to change A-series positions for there to be real change.

The most common version of tenseless theory (as already mentioned) is *B-theory*, the position that the B-series is sufficient for time. For A-theorists and tense theorists, the real or fundamental time series is the A-series or tense series. For B-theorists and tenseless theorists, the real time series is the B-series or tenseless series.

How does tenseless theory solve McTaggart's paradox? We already discussed it—they make A-series positions derivative and then define real change differently to tense theorists. That is, they consider the paradox's regress to halt at A-series positions' relativization to B-series positions. If the present is defined as when an event occurs, then the past is any time earlier than the event and the future is any time later than the event.

However, given McTaggart's objections, the questions of real change still remain. How does tenseless theory account for real change? For the tenseless theorist, real change is not temporal passage. It is just what Russell thought of it, and what is captured in descriptions of motion.

It is any variation in anything's properties between different times. Change only requires that something possess at least one property at one time and not possess it at another time. For example, if an apple is green on Monday and not red on Tuesday, then there is change. Similarly, an event can change by having different properties at different times. If my birthday is fun in the morning and miserable in the afternoon, then my birthday changes.

This conception of change rejects temporal passage. There is no real change in event's positions in an A-series. Such "change" is a by-product of how A-series positions are derived. If an event E is earlier than event F, and G is later than event F, then we can say the following of F:

- At event E: F is future.
- At the later event F: F is present.
- At the much later event G: F is past.

This is all there is to passage: events have "passage" because they have different tenses relative to different events at different times. If we occupy each of these times, then, at each of these times, F "changes" in relation to us.

As discussed, this is not temporal passage. There is no single A-series in which E changes position. As we occupy one moment and a later moment, some event varies in its A-series positions. But this is not because of some changes in the events, or in some moving spot-lit present, or even in some increasing reality. It is because we evaluate tense positions from the different B-series positions that we occupy. That is all.

For tenseless theorists, then, temporal passage is not real change. What is real change is the change in non-temporal properties of objects and events. It is the variation over time in an apple's colour or a lecture's dullness.

Change, Static and Dynamic

Tense theories are often claimed to be descriptions of the universe as *dynamic*. For example, the growing block has a universe that *grows*. The moving spotlight theory has the present *move*. For these theories, reality is dynamic because it changes in one of the following ways:

- In growing block theory, reality increases.
- In the moving spotlight theory, the present changes.
- In presentism, what is real changes.

In contrast, the tenseless theory's conception of the universe in time is sometimes described as a *static block*—a frozen unchanging whole containing all things (e.g., Loizou 1986; Peterson 2016; Golosz 2018; for discussion, see Prosser 2013, 71–72). "Whatever properties an event possesses, and whatever relations it bears to other events, it does so in a tenseless manner", Weingard writes. "In this sense, the whole history of the world is static, there being no property like 'being present' with respect to which portions of it are continually changing" (Weingard 1977, 120). The tenseless conception of time does not include a change in reality in the way the tense theory does: what is future is just as real as what is present or past. Reality does not grow (or shrink, for that matter); it does not lose what is past and gain what is future. Thus, in this conception, tenseless theory holds reality to be static.

We might take this description to mean that the tenseless theory has a disadvantage against tense theory. Being static, it omits change, an important aspect to any theory of time. As Oaklander writes:

> On typical interpretations, the ontology of B-time is construed as antirealist because it denies that temporal passage is an objective, mind-independent feature of reality. [...] B-relations [that] constitute the foundation of the B-theory of time, are "nontransient" and static in that what appears to be the flow and flux of events in time—time's dynamism—is an illusion [...]
>
> (Oaklander 2020, online)

However, as Oaklander goes on to say, this interpretation is too quick.

It is true that tenseless theorists hold that time is fundamentally the B-series, that one event is earlier than another event. Such relations have held, hold, and will always hold between events. If it is the case that my singing on some Tuesday causes the neighbourhood dogs to howl, then it was, is, and always will be the case that my singing on some Tuesday causes the neighbourhood dogs to howl.

In that sense, something does not change—is not dynamic, is *static*. However, the missing "something" that makes this static is the change in events' locations in the A-series. For example, what is missing is that the moment of my singing changes from being present to being past (to present canine relief). Or, one might say, the present moves away from the moment of my singing to a later time (such as next morning, when I am not singing).

What is left out in this "static" tenseless account of time is the tense theory's conception of change, temporal passage.

However, this is not a "static" rooted in a neutral conception of change. The tenseless theorist does not agree that passage is either fundamental or actual. Under tenseless theory, change is only things and events undergoing changes in their properties. For example, on Tuesday, I sing and the dogs howl; on Wednesday, we both stop. Such changes are only in something non-temporal— location, colour, taste, pain. They do not involve a change in temporal properties, such as A-theory positions.

R-Theory

Yet, this does not mean that there is no real change. There is just not change in something *temporal*, such as positions in time.

Oaklander responds to McTaggart's insistence that real change be tensed passage that it is based on a mistake. The mistake is this: McTaggart thinks that Russell's analysis of change cannot be change because the B-relations between the different stages of the change cannot themselves change. For example, that the event on Tuesday is earlier than the event on Wednesday cannot change.

However, for Oaklander (a tenseless theorist), changing temporal properties or relations is not needed for change or time. All that is needed is the variation in non-temporal properties *over* times, for example, variation in things from one B-theory position to another.

When a tenseless theorist refers to something as *dynamic* or *changing*, they mean variation in something's properties over a tenseless series, such as the B-series. In that way, tenseless theory is not a static conception of the world at all. It contains change in it.

Oaklander calls the tenseless theory that makes this understanding of tenseless change explicit *R-theory*. The "R" stands for *Russell*, in that it is developed from Russell's thinking about time and change (Oaklander 2012, 2015, 2020). However, part of any tenseless theory position that time is real should be that *change* and *dynamic* are understood in B-relation terms. Again, no B-theorist thinks real change is temporal passage. Removing the condition that real change is temporal passage also removes the distinction between a static tenseless theory and a dynamic tense theory.

Without temporal passage, such as a tenseless theory of time, there is no such distinction. As such, a tenseless theorist ought not to accept their view of time is as a static block.

Of course, tense theorists disagree with this analysis of change, and so disagree with this understanding of *dynamic* and *static*. Yet, as tenseless theorists are not tense theorists, that is to be expected. It does not mean tenseless theorists must hold their own position to be a static conception of time.

Study Questions

1. McTaggart and other philosophers agree that time can be described in terms of either the A-series or the B-series. Do these two series exhaust time's descriptions as a series?
2. Real change, says the tense theorist, is passage or changes in tense, e.g., the sun's death from future, to present, to past. Is this the correct description of change?
3. What would the world be like without temporal passage? What would it be like without change? Is that what tenseless theorists claim is true of time?
4. If you find presentism convincing—many have and many do—what about the world most convinces you that it is true? If you do not find it convincing, then what is the best argument for it as a *metaphysical* position?
5. Do we live in a static block universe? How is that different from the frozen universe discussed in the epistemology chapter?

Notes

1 Of course, if it lasts long enough, an event could have these positions. For example, the process of the Indian Ocean's evaporation could have started in the recent past, be ongoing in the present, and cease in a million years. As such, it is recently past, present, and far future. However, the whole of the event—from start to finish—does not simply have these A-series positions. Stages of it are past, stages of it are present, and stages of it are future. And, if we mean any of its stages, such as the ocean's heating today, then these stages are only either past, present, or future.
2 McTaggart at this point talks about times. However, as Mellor notes, we need not talk about times, and can talk about events (Mellor 1998, 8).
3 For the tense theorist, the B-series is also derived from this fundamental present. In that case, the B-series could be a second-order derivation. If the A-series in its entirety is derived from the present, then the B-series is further derived from the A-series.
4 Lately, Forbes thinking about the growing block theory has changed. Briggs and Forbes 2017 allowed "an ontology of regions of space-time, and the volume of spacetime is growing. The present is the limiting case of that." But he now thinks of an ontology that is "irreducibly dynamic", with enduring entities and processes that always change, "rather than simply regions of space-time" (Forbes 2020, personal correspondence).

Suggested Readings

As said in the preface, philosophy of is frequently taught under metaphysics. As such, there are many texts on metaphysics of time. For different sides on the general debate, see Lowe 2003 for a tense approach and Le Poidevin 2003 for a tenseless approach. Both are helpful and accessible surveys of the issues, including

McTaggart's paradox. For historically informed philosophy, Ingthorsson 2016 is a thorough introduction to McTaggart's paradox from a presentist perspective. Bourne's 2006 *A Future for Presentism* is a thoughtful defence of presentism.

Oaklander's 2020 is a similarly thorough text, but on Broad's philosophy of time, and from a tenseless theorist perspective. Oaklander's work is also the source of the tenseless alternative to B-theory, the *R*-theory (e.g., his 2020, but also his 2015). For defences of the growing block theory, see Broad 1923, Tooley 1997, Forbes 2016; Briggs and Forbes 2017; for discussion of the growing block theory, see Dainton 2001, Sider 2001, and Thomas 2019.

Dolev 2007 is an interesting attack on the very idea that there is a serious debate here between the different sides. Similarly, Dorato 2006 has an argument that the eternalist/present debate is irrelevant to physical theory (perhaps read Chapter 4 before looking at this paper).

There are also many metaphysical anthologies that either focus on or have sections dedicated to the philosophy of time. Nearly all anthologies of recent years are excellent sources of papers for the introductory reader. Most collections have a balance of views from all sides of the debates. Here is a sampling: Le Poidevin and MacBeath 1991; Bardon 2012. Callender 2013; the section on time in Van Inwagen and Zimmerman 1998; for something somewhat more challenging, section II in Jokic and Smith 2003.

3 Metaphysics of Time II

Change and Persistence in Objects

Overview

Does time matter to objects, or objects matter to time? Many theorists think so. They think our theories of time affect our understanding of the nature of objects; our intuitions about objects affect the plausibility of our theories of time. This is because everyday things—objects or concrete particulars—change and persist in time. When we think about such change and persistence under different theories of time, various intuitions about objects are strained and undermined. Notably, intrinsic change in objects raises the *problem of temporary intrinsics*. How objects can have temporary intrinsics has different problems under different theories of time.

The theories of persistence and change discussed here are *endurantism*, *perdurantism*, and *exdurantism*. Endurantists hold that objects persist by enduring through time: at each time that they exist, they must be the same numerically identical thing as they are at every other time; they are wholly present at each time.

However, other theorists hold that such a theory cannot account for change in persisting objects. Instead, according to perdurantists, objects persist by *perduring* through time: at each time that they exist, they have different *temporal parts*; what exists at each time is numerically different to what exists at other times.

Yet, other theorists disagree again. Such a perduring object does not resemble what we take to be everyday things, objects, or concrete particulars. Instead, these theorists argue that objects persist by *exduring* through time: like perdurantists, at each time that they exist, they are something numerically different to what is there at other times. Yet, what is at each time is not a temporal part of an everyday object; it is the very object itself. Each object exists only at a time, standing in a special relationship to other objects. This relationship explains persistence. However, counterintuitively, the everyday objects only exist at each time.

Indeed, theories of object persistence suggest that, no matter which theory of time we have, there is some conflict with our intuitions about such objects. Intuitions about time, however important, can never be fully satisfied.

Introduction

In Chapter 2, we discuss the various theories about time, change, and events. Time is tensed or tenseless, eternalist, presentist, or a growing block; it is like space; the present is like a bright light moving over events in time. The future and past are unreal; they are real. The difference between the past, present, and future is like, and as significant as, the difference between *here* and *there* in space.

Events are what happens at a time. What happens includes variation in properties, stages in processes, and the beginning and endings of things. Some events are changes—variations over time in something, such as the rotting of an apple. For some philosophers, change *happens* to events; change is temporal passage and, for some, this passage is a change in events' positions in time.[1]

However, we have not yet discussed *objects* in time. We have not discussed the implications of the objects themselves for theories of time, or the implications of theories of time for such objects.

Are there such implications? Some philosophers think so. To see why, we begin with what is meant by an everyday or ordinary object. Such an object is, at the very least, a *concrete particular.*

Concrete Particulars

Korman writes that ordinary experiences "present us with a wide array of objects: dogs and cats, tables and chairs, trees, and their branches, and so forth. These sorts of ordinary objects may seem fairly unproblematic in comparison to entities like numbers, propositions, tropes, holes, points of space, and moments of time" (Korman 2020).

In metaphysics, such ordinary objects are commonly referred to as *concrete particulars.* Although challenging to provide a generalized definition of concrete particulars, it is easy to provide examples of them. They are what "the nonphilosopher thinks of as 'things'—individual persons, animals, plants, and inanimate material objects" (Loux 2002, 97). If your hand, the moon, or plantains exist, then they are all concrete particulars. Concrete particulars also include simple objects—fundamental particles such as electrons, quarks, or neutrinos.

We can also say what concrete particulars are not. They are not other kinds of entities or things that metaphysical theorists dispute or defend. Here are the main types of such metaphysical entities. Not all are compatible with each other, and no metaphysician accepts all of them:

- *Universals:* for example, properties such as the colour *red* or the shape *cube*; kinds such as *plantain* and *neutrino;* relations, such as plantains *being larger than* neutrinos, neutrinos *being faster* than plantains.
- *Tropes* or *abstract particulars*: for example, the particular red that is the colour of *this* particular plantain; the particular difference in size between this particular plantain and this other particular red cube.
- *Substances* or *bare particulars:* depending on one's theory, these bear (possess, exemplify, or have) universals or tropes. For example, there is a bare particular that has the properties of neutrinos (e.g., charge, mass); there is another bare particular that has the properties of plantains.
- *Propositions*: for example, the propositions "plantain herbs move faster than oak trees" and "the square root of two is irrational".
- *Events*: for example, the plantain herb is very slowly moving away from where you planted it.

One metaphysical dispute is how these other metaphysical entities relate to and explain concrete particulars. Concrete particulars are not undifferentiated, structureless "blobs" (to use a term from Armstrong, cited in Van Inwagen 2011). They have colours, shapes, sizes, relations to each other, and seem also to group in different ways. These motivate arguments for the existence of such things as properties, kinds, relations. However, not every metaphysician or philosopher accepts these arguments; they are not universally accepted.

Yet, unlike these other metaphysical entities, almost every metaphysician or philosopher *does* accept that there are some kinds of concrete particulars. What they debate is how to explain them and how to understand the way we think about them. Furthermore, accepting there are some concrete particulars does not mean that everyone accepts all things that most people would consider objects and philosophers would call concrete particulars. Some metaphysicians argue that normal, ordinary, uncontroversial objects in the world do not, in fact, exist. We only tend to think of them as existing.

For example, Van Inwagen argues that only living things and fundamental particles exist. Everything else, such as chairs and mountains, does not. These are only chair-like and mountain-like arrangements of fundamental particles. Rosen and Dorr (2002) argue for fictionalism about composition or *mereological nihilism*: there are only simple things; there are no complex things. Complex concrete particulars do not exist. Nothing constitutes anything else. If this is right, then it denies the existence of almost everything from the list above—the moon (it has made of dust and rocks), your hand (at least parts of it are fingers), or plantains (its skin, its flesh).

Yet, even these metaphysicians accept that there are some concrete particulars. They only disagree about which concrete particulars there are. For example, neutrinos and quarks are some of the fundamental particles of the universe. If neutrinos or quarks are simple, and nothing constitutes them, neither Van Inwagen nor Rosen and Dorr deny their existence.

Most importantly here, concrete particulars have the following properties:

- Concrete particulars exist in time.
- All concrete particulars exist at a time. They are in time.
- *Physical* concrete particulars also exist in space. Physical concrete particulars are at a location. They are surrounded by space.

From now on, I refer to concrete particulars by the more common term *objects*. All the examples of this chapter are either everyday objects, such as the moon or plantains, or fundamental particles, such as neutrinos (and a particle is a kind of object).

A way to describe these objects as existing in space or at a location is that they have *spatial properties*. Similarly, a way to describe these objects as existing in time or at a moment is that they have *temporal properties*. However, if we do characterize them as having temporal properties, we run into a problem. There are challenges to how we can describe their persistence and change, while preserving our everyday intuitions about them.

An Object Exists in Space

Consider an object existing in space. Say that, in existing in space, it is in some way related to space. For example, the object is *in* space or *at a* spatial point or location (see Figure 3.1).

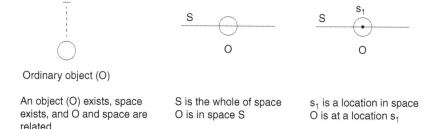

Space	S ◯ O	S s₁ ◉ O
Ordinary object (O)		
An object (O) exists, space exists, and O and space are related	S is the whole of space O is in space S	s₁ is a location in space O is at a location s₁

Figure 3.1 An Object in Space

As Figure 3.1 shows, if ordinary objects exist (i.e., mereological nihilists are wrong), they exist at some location in space. However, they also fill a region of space—a volume or a surface. They extend through an area of space. They occupy multiple locations in space. For example, your hand is resting on your desk. It is located in the space of the room you are sitting in, and at the location of the surface of your desk. But it also fills a volume of space above the desk, extending over the surface of the desk. It occupies multiple locations: all the different points in space occupied by different parts of your hand.

Spatial Parts

An intuitive view of how objects extend through space or occupy multiple spatial points is that they have multiple *spatial parts*. Each part is at a different point in space. So, your hand extends through a space or occupies multiple points of a space by doing the following. Different parts of your hand occupy each of those points. Your fingertips, knuckles, and palm each occupy some spatial point. Your fingertips, knuckles, and palm are parts of your hand. Through these hand-parts occupying these spatial points, your hand also occupies these spatial points.

This explanation requires some further clarification about the intuitions behind it:

- These parts are *proper parts*: each part is different to the whole, e.g., your palm is not identical to your hand. (An *improper part* of a hand is the hand itself.)
- These parts are different to each other, e.g., each of your fingers is different to the other fingers; your palm is different to each finger and to all the fingers together.

Thus, by this account, an object extends through a region of space composed of multiple spatial points: it does so by having parts at each point in that region. These parts are not identical to the whole object, nor are any of them identical to any other part.

An Object Exists in Time

Consider now an object occupying time. We often describe objects as if they have some kind of relation to time. We also commonly refer to them as being *in time* and being *at a time* (see Figure 3.2). For example, the moon, along with being at a place, also exists now; along with filling a region of space, it exists between the solar system's formation and the sun's death.

Again, however, we not only talk about ordinary objects as being at a time or in time. They are also at *multiple* times. The objects *persist*.

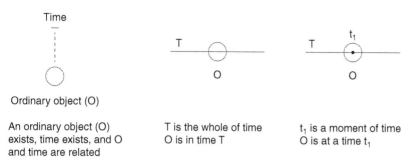

Figure 3.2 An Object in Time

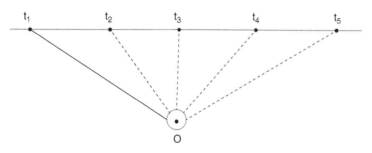

Figure 3.3 An Object Persists

An Object Persists

Objects are not just commonly thought to exist in or at a time. They are thought also to exist *through* time. Objects are thought to be what some philosophers call *continuants:* things that continue to exist through change (e.g. Le Poidevin 1998). Others dispute this, as we will see. But most agree that, at least, ordinary objects *seem* to occupy multiple times (see Figure 3.3). They are not ordinarily thought to exist for a single instant—to come in and out of existence in a moment—but to exist for several moments. That is, ordinary objects are thought to *persist*.

For example, the moon has not simply popped into existence for an instant, to pop out of existence in the next. The moon exists from the moment it is created, through the time of the dinosaurs, to the moon landing in the 20th century, until, perhaps, the death of the sun. Its moment of creation is a different time to that of the dinosaurs; both are different times to the moon landing; all three are different times to the death of the sun. So, the moon persists throughout the time encompassing all these times.

Endurantism: An Object Is at Each Time it Persists

Although ordinary everyday objects are thought to persist over multiple times, ordinary objects are also thought to exist at each one of these times. It sounds

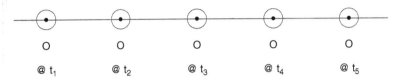

Figure 3.4 An Object Exists at Each Time in its Persistence

counter-intuitive to state that they persist over several moments and yet are not at those moments. If the moon persists *through* the asteroid impact that killed the dinosaurs to the moon landing, it also exists *at* the asteroid impact and exists *at* the moon landing.

This, it seems, is what it is for objects to persist. They are *at* multiple times, exist through or over the period of those multiple times, and do so by existing at each of those times (see Figure 3.4).

Being Wholly Present

Along with their persistence, amongst the intuitions about ordinary objects in time, is that they are also *wholly present* at each of the times through which they persist. The *whole* of the moon is at each time during its existence—the entire moon is there when the dinosaurs die and also when humans land on it. The whole of an object is what it is at a time.

This intuition of objects even holds when objects change. Many millions of years ago, the moon is still glowing hot after first forming. Later, the moon spins freely on its own axis around the Earth, such that different sides face the Earth at different times. Now, the moon spins with only one face ever facing the Earth (the moon is what is known as *tidally locked*). And the moon is cold.

Yet, this intuition goes, through all these changes, it is still the whole of the moon at each time. The whole moon is glowing, free, locked, or cold.

This intuitive position on an object's persistence is known as *endurantism*. It is the view that a persisting object exists wholly at each time in its existence, and even through any changes it might undergo. Skow writes that endurantism is "the thesis that a persisting thing is wholly located at each time at which it exists" (Skow 2011, 382).

Another way of defining endurantism is that it is the position that (a) an object is located at each of the times through which it persists and (b) the object at each of those times is numerically identical to the object at each of the other times: "the heart of the endurantist's ontology is expressed by claims like '[object] O at [one time] is identical with [object] O at [another time]' " (Merricks 1994, 182).

For example, in Figure 3.5 the ordinary object is O and O_1, O_2, O_3, O_4, and O_5. Each of these objects (O, O_1, O_2, O_3, O_4, and O_5) is identical to all the others:

- $O = O_1 = O_2 = O_3 = O_4 = O_5$

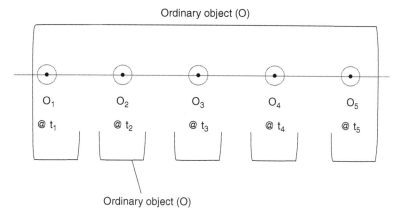

Ordinary object (O)

O_1 @ t_1 O_2 @ t_2 O_3 @ t_3 O_4 @ t_4 O_5 @ t_5

Ordinary object (O)

Figure 3.5 The Ordinary Object Is Both the Object that Persists and Exists at Each Time

Objection: Endurantism Has No Spatial Analogue

The endurantist intuition is unlike our intuitions about objects extended through space. We do not consider objects to be wholly present at each of the spatial locations they occupy. And, although we do accept that an object spread out over several places is identical to itself at other places, what is at each of those places is not strictly identical to what is at the other places. My body occupies the space filled by my hand. But my body is not wholly present in that space filled by my hand. Only part of my body—the hand part—is wholly present in that space. Furthermore, my hand is not identical to parts of my body at other locations, for example, my foot or head.

However, this does not mean it is counter-intuitive for objects to exist in time by being wholly at a place. Not everything true or intuitive about space must be true or intuitive about what is analogous in time. In fact, some philosophers claim that such a spatial view of existence over multiple times is counter-intuitive.

We can see this with responses to a further challenge to theories of persistence. This is persistence through change.

The Persistence of Objects through Change

Intuitively, most ordinary objects can change their properties. Living things grow, vehicles change location, the sun loses fuel, and humans solve problems. As intuitively, these objects survive these changes. They persist through the changes; they are continuants. The fox persists from being a cub to being an adult; the car that picked you up at home is the same car that drops you off at work; the swollen red sun is the same as the fiery blue sun millions of years before; the human with a problem is the same human as the one who has worked through the problem.

Ordinary objects do not persist through all changes, of course. Some changes may destroy an object, and so they do not survive them. However, that objects do survive many changes is enough to raise challenges to theories of persistence.

Hinchliff's Four Conditions of Change

Hinchliff describes a candle changing its shape, with two shape-properties: *being straight* and *being bent*. According to Hinchliff, there are four intuitive conditions for an object changing like this:

1. An object persists through a change. "[The candle] existed when it was straight, and it exists now when it is bent. The change in shape alters the candle but does not destroy it."
2. An object can change properties that are not relations. "A single thing cannot be *taller than* [...] but a single thing can be straight because *being straight* is not a relation but a property.
3. The object itself has the properties. "Not just a part but the candle itself was straight, and not just a part but the candle itself is bent. If the candle itself were not bent or had not been straight, the candle would not have changed its shape."
4. The properties are incompatible. "If the shapes were compatible, there need not have been a change. Change requires incompatible properties." (Hinchliff 1996, 119)

These conditions have spatial analogues. Consider a ball that is both red and white.

1. *The object extends over variation in properties in space:* Analogous to condition 1, the ball extends over the point it is red and the point it is white. It exists at those locations by having different parts. For example, if the red and white covers only its surface, then parts of the ball are where the ball is red and parts of the ball are where the ball is white.
2. *Objects in space can have properties and not just relations:* Analogous to condition 2, objects in space can have properties and not just relations. The ball can have the property of *being spherical*, which (intuitively) is not a relation to anything. (As discussed further on, it is also considered something more, an *intrinsic* property of the ball.)
3. *Objects in space have the properties themselves:* Analogous to condition 3, the ball itself has the shape of *being spherical*. Nothing else is spherical through which ball has this shape. It is not like saying *I was traveling at 50mph* when what I mean is that I was in my car and the car was traveling at 50mph. It is also not like saying that the ball is red. The ball is a mixture of colours—red and white. The ball is not red—part of the ball is red. The ball is red through that part, but is not itself red.

4.   *Objects can have incompatible properties over space:* Analogous to condition 4, just as change requires incompatible properties over time, an object can have incompatible properties over space. White and red are incompatible properties. Nothing can be wholly one colour or the other. However, the ball can have both properties by having some spatial parts that are red and other spatial parts that are white.

Objection: There Is No Analogy for Specific Properties

However, when it comes to any specific property, the analogy breaks down between the conditions of an object's persistence and its occupancy and extension in space. It is sufficient to show this by considering only two conditions: condition 1, that an object extends over variation in its properties, and condition 3, that an object has the properties itself.

Take *shape*. Given Hinchliff's conditions, an object can change its shape—Hinchliff's example has a candle doing just that. Yet, for a specific instance of the shape property, not all the conditions for change can be met by spatial analogies.

The ball is spherical. Say also that there are two parts of the ball—say, on its surface, a red patch and a white patch. Each also has a shape. The red patch shape is six-sided and only a little curved. For convenience, ignore the curve and call the red patch's shape *hexagonal*. The white patch is four-sided. Call the white patch *rectangular.*

We then have three things with two different shapes:

- The ball is spherical.
- Part of the ball, the red patch, is hexagonal.
- Part of the ball, the white patch, is square.

Consider these objects and properties under spatial analogies with Hinchliff's four conditions.

Take *being hexagonal* or *being square*. The red patch has the hexagonal property itself—thus, it meets condition 3. However, it does not extend over variation of that shape, such as hexagonal and rectangular. Thus, it fails to meet condition 1. The patch is just hexagonal and no other shape. We might say that it has some other shape. For example, part of the hexagonal area might be *triangular*. However, that is because part of it has that shape. The red patch is not itself triangular.

In contrast, the ball does extend over variation between being hexagonal and rectangular. In one place, the red patch, it is hexagonal and, in another place, the white patch, it is square. Yet, as with the example of the red patch being triangular in parts, the ball has neither being hexagonal nor being rectangular itself. Only part of it—either the red patch or white patch, depending—is one of those shapes. It only has those shapes because its parts do.

Of course, the ball does itself have a shape—it is spherical. However, just like the red patch with the hexagonal shape, the ball does not extend over variation in this shape. It is just spherical and no other shape. As described above, it does extend over variation in some shapes. However, those are the shapes of its parts, and not the ball itself.

A solution to this for space would be to have the ball wholly present at each location in space that it occupies. That is, where the red patch is, the whole of the ball is; and where the white patch is, the whole of the ball is. In that case, the ball itself could be both hexagonal and rectangular, extending over variation in these shapes that it has itself.

Yet, this is not how we conceive of objects extending through space. Objects have different and incompatible properties at different spatial locations by having different parts at those locations, each part of which has one of these incompatible properties. That the whole object is at each point in space, and thus has each property at that point itself—this is a counter-intuitive account of objects and properties in space.

Yet, as said, it is not a counter-intuitive account of objects and properties in time. That the whole object is at each point in time, and thus has each property at that point itself—this is an intuitive account of objects and properties in time. Space and time, in this case, are not analogous.

Yet, even given these intuitive conditions, there are problems with describing persistence. There is a problem with holding that an object persisting over multiple times is identical to an object that is wholly present at one of those times. Or, to use the other characterization of endurantism, there is a problem with holding that an object at one time is identical to an object at another time.

Leibniz' Law

Leibniz developed the concept of identity to a point where it is possible to formulate laws about it. Fittingly enough, such a law became known as *Leibniz' law*. The law has two parts: the *identity of indiscernibles* and the *indiscernibility of identity*.

- *Identity of Indiscernibles*
  If A has no property that B does not have, and B has no property that A does not have, then A is identical to B.

  For example, say that an object (A) has the following properties: it is a white sphere at specific spatial location s_1 and persists between two specific points in time, t_1 and t_2. In that case, if there is an object (B) that is white, a sphere, located at the same specific location (s_1) and between the same times (t_1 and t_2), then B *just is* A. B is identical to A.
- *Indiscernibility of Identity*
  If A is identical to B, then any property A has is a property B has, and any property B has is a property A has.

For example, say that object A is identical to object B. A has the following properties: it is a white sphere at specific spatial location s_1 and persists between two specific points in time, t_1 and t_2. In that case, because B is identical to A, B is white, a sphere, located at the same specific location (s_1), and between the same times (t_1 and t_2).

Numerical Identity

A note on "identity" in these definitions: the identity is sometimes further specified as *numerical identity*. The "numerical" is to strengthen the point that the identity here that holds is between one and only one thing and itself. If A and B are numerically identical, then, when it comes to counting how many things there are, we only count A and B as being one thing. Say that a room has the following objects: A, B, and C. A is numerically identical to B. C is not numerically identical to A or B. Then, counting the number of objects, we get two: A (also called B) and C.

Moving on to the laws, the first part of the law is considered problematic in metaphysics. Although asserted by some metaphysicians, notably bundle theorists, it is denied by many substance theorists (for discussion, see Loux 2002). In contrast, the second part of the law—the indiscernibility of identity—plays a significant role in debates around persistence.

The issue for persistence is this: given Leibniz' law, if an object O has a property, and some X is identical to O, then X also has that property. If an object O lacks a property, then X lacks that property. Again, this is because they are *numerically identical*—they are the same thing. Strictly, there is no "they" in O and X. There is just one object referred to as both O and X.

Here is the problem for endurantism: we have an object persisting by being wholly present at different times. All of the object is at one time and all of the object is at another time. Alternatively, the object at one time is identical to the object at another time.

This "wholly" and "identical" either do useful work or they do not. They can either be adjusted to suit whatever one needs or they are strictly meant: strictly, the *whole* of the object is at each time; the object at each time is strictly *identical* to the object at every other time. This "object at each object" refers to the object with all its components, parts, and properties at each time.

However, a changing or persisting object at a time cannot have all its properties at each time.

For example, at a particular time, the object cannot have *being at another time*; that is, it cannot be at another time. When an object is *being at t_1*, it is not *being at t_2*. When an object is *being at t_2*, it is not *being at t_1*.

So:

1. If O is wholly present at t_1, O has all its properties at t_1.
2. If O is wholly present at t_2, O has all its properties at t_2.

3. Leibniz' law: If A is identical to B, then A has all of B's properties, and B has all of A's properties.
4. If O is at t_1, then O has the property of *being at t_1*.
5. At t_1, O has *being at t_1* and O does not have *being at t_2*.
6. At t_2, O has *being at t_2* and O does not have *being at t_1*.
7. At t_1, O does not have all of O's properties at t_2.
8. Leibniz' law: At t_1, O is not identical to O at t_2. At t_2, O is not identical to O at t_1.

If endurantism is true, then O at each time is identical to O at every other time. If that is right, then something must be wrong with the above argument. So, what is wrong with it?

To defeat this argument, other than showing the argument as invalid, we must offer reasons to reject the premises. Here are some options:

a. Deny premises 1 and 2: give reasons for why an object is not wholly present at the times it exists in.
b. Deny premise 3: give good reasons why Leibniz' law is false.
c. Deny premise 4: when O is at t_1, O does *not* have a property of being at t_1.
d. Deny premises 5 and 6: at t_1, O *does* have the property of being at t_2.

As will be discussed, a is not available to endurantists. It is a competing theory of persistence that uses *temporal parts*. We discuss this in the next section.

We may work on b. However, denying the second part of Leibniz' law involves a great deal more counter-intuitive claims than denying the whole presence of objects. It allows one thing to have incompatible properties *in general*.

For example, one might hold that an object is wholly red and wholly green at the exact same point in space, and in no way a mixture of both. If Leibniz' law no longer holds, what is to stop such a view? Alternatively, if the law only does not hold for properties in time, one assumes a theory of persistence denying the law can explain why such properties are exceptions. Otherwise, the theory is simply asserting it is false specifically for time, for no reason at all why this specific violation is acceptable.

This leaves c and d. Let us see how we might use them.

Relations-to-Times: Temporal Location Is Not a Property

One concept of time is *substantivalism*: time is independent of other things.[2] Time is separate to the objects that exist in it, having its own independent nature. Whether substantivalism is true or not is a matter of a separate debate. However, if it is true, then it offers a way of answering the challenge to endurantism from Leibniz' law.

Given substantivalism, time is not a property of objects. It is something separate. If an object is at time t_1, this is not an object with a particular property of *being at t₁*. The relationship between objects and time does not require different objects, each with a different temporal property, e.g., O$_1$ is *being at t$_1$*, O$_2$ is *being at t$_2$*. Time is not a property of objects at all. And so, Leibniz' law does not apply to the time–object relationship.

Instead, there are times and there is the object. The object stands in a *relation* to the times. There are different relations the object can have to these times. It can be *at* those times. Or, the object is *present* at the times. This situation has a spatial analogue. An object stands in a relation to space; there are different relations the object can have to space. It can be *at* those places. The object can be present at those places.

We can of course talk *as if* time is a property of objects. For example, a tyrannosaur lives in a prehistoric period. We might say that the dinosaur has the temporal property of *being prehistoric*. But the tyrannosaur does not have such a property. Based on how we express ourselves, we conceal a relation between the dinosaur and a time. It is the relation of *being at*. The dinosaur is *being at* a prehistoric time. Metaphysically, objects do not have time as a property. Objects have a relation to time.[3]

This solution has some challenges. Again, as it has been described, it requires particular ontological commitments. For there to be relations, there need to be *relata*. In this solution, for each relation, one relatum is an object and another relatum is a time. The solution requires a commitment to *moments of time*.

In this case, we are committed to one of two things: either substantivalism is true of time, i.e., these moments are part a substantial time, separate to objects, or else relationalism is true, i.e., time is derived from objects and their properties. This solution means that, to have objects persist through times, we must commit to substantivalism or commit to objects' persistence being dependent on relations to something derived from other objects and properties (for more on this, see Sider 2001).

Adverbialism

Another way of characterizing the relationship between objects and time is to take something from language. *Adverbialism* is the position that times are modifiers of the object's existence in time. It gets its name because the modifier is like adverbial modifiers of verbs. We may run *slowly* or *quickly*. The running—the verb—is modified by the adverbs "slowly" and "quickly". This changes the meaning of what we describe. According to Haslanger:

> The idea is that having a property—understanding "having" as some sort of "non-relational tie"—is something that can be temporary, and this temporary "attachment" should be understood by analogy with other adverbial modifiers.
>
> (Haslanger 2003, 342)

For example, it can be the case that a candle is actually straight and possibly bent. Similarly, if a table persists from Tuesday to Thursday, its existence is modified as follows:

- The table Tuesday-ly exists
- The table Wednesday-ly exists
- The table Thursday-ly exists

The solution offered by this analysis is that the time is a difference that is not in the properties of the object nor does it require a separate entity—a substantival time—for the object to be related to. Instead, the object's existence is modified by the time.

The relevance of this is clearer when we bring in different ways of thinking about events in time.[4] Instead of times like "Tuesday" or "Wednesday", we use past, present, and future. In that case, we get a table that exists from the past, through the present, into the future as:

- The table past-ly exists
- The table present-ly exists
- The table future-ly exists

The main objection to this solution is that these adverb-like modifiers seem to describe either properties or relations, yet they are explicitly introduced to deny both. What is the difference between (a) an object *existing in the future* or *being in the future*, a temporal property, and (b) an object *future-ly existing*? If Leibniz' law prevents an object being in the future and being in the past, then how does it allow an object future-ly *existing* and past-ly *existing*?

It is unclear what these modifiers are supposed to be if they are not properties of the object or relations between the object and something else. Perhaps these modifiers arise from objects' positions in the A-series. We return to that answer when we talk about temporary intrinsics.

Perhaps these solutions do solve an object's temporal characteristics, such as their *being on Tuesday* or *being past*. This may allow an endurantist account of persisting. Yet, objects do not only persist. They persist through *changes* in their properties—including what are called *temporary intrinsic properties*. We can run similar analyses on temporary intrinsic properties. Let us see if relations-to-times or adverbialism can also resolve temporary intrinsics. We will see any alternative to both draws on the analogy with space: objects persist by having *parts*.

The Problem of Temporary Intrinsics

The problem of temporary intrinsics is a problem of persisting through changes in intrinsic properties.

I see an apple fall from the tree. Then I see it rot on the dark soil by a stream. I see the apple become a hard, red object on a tree branch and then a soft black object on the soil. I see the apple *change*. There are two kinds of change I see the apple go through:

- *Change in relation to other things:* the apple changes its spatial relations relative to the tree and the stream. It is near the tree and far from the stream; then falling, it is far from the tree and near to the stream.
- *Change independent of other things:* the apple changes colour, from red to black. The apple changes texture and shape, from hard and spherical to soft and indefinite.

These two kinds of changes can be conceived of as changes in two kinds of properties: *extrinsic* properties and *intrinsic* properties. Extrinsic properties are properties that are dependent in some way on things other than the object. Intrinsic properties are not dependent this way.

Intrinsic Properties

The apple's colour and shape may resemble other objects' colours and shapes. However, the particular instance of that colour and shape is possessed by that apple alone. It is not possessed along with other things; the apple does not have them dependent on other things. Furthermore, any change in its colour or shape seems to be a change in something in the apple; even if the change is caused by other things, the change is only in the apple—e.g., a bird pecks a piece out of the apple, changing its shape, but not changing the shape of anything else.

These properties are *intrinsic* properties. According to Langton and Lewis, a thing's possession of an intrinsic property "is independent of accompaniment or loneliness":

- *Accompaniment:* a thing has accompaniment (or is accompanied) if and only if it coexists "with some contingent object wholly from itself".
- *Loneliness:* A thing is lonely if and only if it does not coexist "with any contingent object wholly distinct from itself".

So, an intrinsic property is a property that something can have whether the thing is either accompanied or lonely. The property is "compatible with both; it implies neither" (Langton and Lewis 1999, 117).

What examples are there of intrinsic properties? Common examples are shape or colour: objects can have them if they are alone or accompanied. As such, if these properties are intrinsic, changes in shape or colour are changes in *intrinsic* properties.

We might wonder however: *are* such properties intrinsic? Lewis seems to take it for granted they are. When we sit down, that we are "sitting down"-shaped is a property of us that we have even if we are alone, unrelated to other things, or related to other things. It may be possible to argue against this. For example, maybe objects cannot have their shapes on their own but only in relation to other things. Like being large or small, an object is only "sitting down"-shaped in the absence of other things; or an object is only the colour red in the presence of other things, i.e., when it is accompanied.

We may object to such reasoning. This is not enough to hold these properties are intrinsic. And, given other examples, we may argue that those examples are also not intrinsic properties. However, if we insist that ordinary objects have no intrinsic properties, then we are insisting that they have their properties only in relation to other things or only in the absence of other things. This means the following: take an ordinary, everyday object; take any property of that object; no matter what that property is—shape, colour, weight, sound, smell—it is the same as the object *being small* or *being far away* or *being loud* or *being alone*. The object only has it in relation to something else, or in the absence of something else.

Another objection to the idea that ordinary objects have intrinsic properties is that intrinsic properties cannot *change*. Intrinsic properties must belong to the object throughout the object's existence. If the object persists, then the object's intrinsic properties persist. For example, an intrinsic property of the object might be its *morphology*: the general shape of an object independent of how it twists or bends, such as the general body plans of mammals. An object may have this morphology throughout its existence, only ceasing to have it at the object's destruction.

However, along with morphology, objects also have temporary shapes. Their morphology may persist through twisting and bending, but their *shape* changes through twisting and bending. Either their shape is not intrinsic, and depends on other things, or it is intrinsic. If the shape is intrinsic, then, since the shape changes, it is an intrinsic property that changes.

Temporary Intrinsic Properties

A common theoretical way of understanding changing intrinsics is that one temporary intrinsic replaces another temporary intrinsic. For example, an object changes its (intrinsic) property of shape when one temporary shape replaces another temporary shape.

As such, we might ask: how does the same object replace one intrinsic property with another? We have already discussed attempts at explaining how persisting objects have the property *being at a time*. Being at a time that is not the entire duration in which an object exists is, if a property at all, a temporary property. So, let us consider similar attempts to explain intrinsic change.

Endurantism

For endurantism, ordinary everyday objects persist over multiple times and exist at each of those times. The theory solves the problem of temporary intrinsics by

O itself having each of the temporary intrinsics. The object that possesses one temporary intrinsic is numerically identical to the object that possesses another temporary intrinsic.

However, a temporary intrinsic property cannot be as easily solved as being at a time. Say that, for an object O to change some class of intrinsic properties P_c, the following is the case:

- Ordinary object O changes intrinsic properties P_c if and only if O has an intrinsic property P_m [member of P_c] for a temporal period t_1. After t_1, O does not have P_m and has another intrinsic property P_n.

According to Leibniz' law, an object cannot both have a property and not have a property. Yet, O seems to have just that: O has P_m (at t_1) and, later, O does not have P_m (at t_2). Since O at each time is numerically identical to O at the other time, it both has this property and does not have it. More needs to be said to explain this.

Relations-to-Times and Adverbialism

Relations-to-times fails for temporary intrinsics. Time may not be a property of objects, but temporary intrinsics must be. An object's colour or shape is not something belonging to time; nor is it some kind of relation to time (Lowe 2003). It belongs to the object.

So, we turn to adverbialism. *Adverbialism* offers the following solution: the object's possession of the intrinsic properties is modified by the time at which it has them (e.g., Merricks 1994). For example, an apple changing intrinsic colour from green to red to black over the future, present, and past:

- The apple is past-ly green.
- The apple is present-ly red.
- The apple is future-ly black.

One objection to adverbialism is that it is a concealed version of relations-to-times (e.g., Hinchliff 1996; Lewis 1998; Sider 2001; Hawley 2004). This is the case given tenseless theory. The reality behind past, present, and future is relations to different events or different times. If it is events, then the above adverbial answer becomes:

- The apple is "earlier than some event"-ly green.
- The apple is "simultaneous with some event"-ly red.
- The apple is "later than some event"-ly black.

What are these events? Are they something that happens to the object itself? Or are they something that happens to some other object? If it is to another object, then the property is no longer intrinsic. It is had only if the original object is accompanied by those other objects. Yet, if it is to times, then this is a version of relations-to-times.

One might respond that this only reduces adverbialism to relations-to-times if tenseless theory is true. Tense theory does better. For tense theory, the past, present, and future are positions in the fundamental A-series. So, the apple is green in the past, red in the present, and black in the future. It does not always have these properties at these positions. Given the nature of A-theory, the apple has each of these intrinsic properties at each of these A-series positions.

Yet, this does not separate adverbialism from relations-to-times. Relations-to-times can give the same answer. The times are A-series positions. The intrinsic properties are related to the past, present, and future. The main difference is that, for relations-to-times, the intrinsic properties are had by one object because they are, in some way, related to a time (be it a tenseless position or a tensed A-series position). The time does something to the object such that it has this property.

For adverbialism, the intrinsic properties are had by one object because they are, in some way, *modified* by times. The difference, taken not as a grammatical difference but a metaphysical difference, is unclear. More explanatory work is needed to distinguish a temporal modifier from a relation.

Temporal Parts: A Different Object is at Each Time an Object Persists

In this solution, an object persists over multiple times. However, not all of the persisting object exists at any one time. At each time, instead, there is a part of the persisting object at that time.

This part is known as a *temporal part* (see Figure 3.6).

The temporal parts are O_1, O_2, O_3, O_4, and O_5. Each of these objects (O, O_1, O_2, O_3, O_4, and O_5) is different to all the others. The theory that advances temporal parts as the solution is sometimes called *four-dimensionalism*. Balashov writes that "Four-dimensionalism is the view that concrete objects have temporal parts, or stages, at all moments at which they exist" (Balashov 2007, 143; see also Sider 2001).

How do temporal parts solve the problem of temporary intrinsics? Each temporal part has a temporary intrinsic. The persisting concrete object has one part with one temporary intrinsic and another part with another temporary intrinsic.

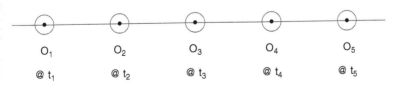

O_1 O_2 O_3 O_4 O_5

@ t_1 @ t_2 @ t_3 @ t_4 @ t_5

Figure 3.6 An Object Persists through Change by Having Temporal Parts

To work in their role, temporal parts must have several characteristics. The first is obvious: they must *exist* or *be at the time*. A temporal part that is not at the time serves no role at all for the persistence of the whole to which it belongs. Another characteristic is that, beyond the time they exist, the temporal parts do not themselves *persist*. They not only exist in and at that time, but they also exist only at that time. They are temporary. They exist for that time and no other.

This does not mean that the temporal part does not persist for some non-zero duration. A particular temporal part can persist for the relatively fleeting period of time it occupies. However, to do so in this analysis, it must also do so by having its own temporal parts. If a persisting object has a temporal part on Tuesday and another on Wednesday, the part on Tuesday can be one that persists *through* Tuesday. However, if it does, it does so by having its own temporal parts—for example, a part on Tuesday morning, a part on Tuesday afternoon, and a part on Tuesday evening. If they occupy anything more than the briefest moment, even these parts have their own temporal parts.

Objection: Objects Are Continuants

This solution cannot work because persisting objects are *continuants*. They exist throughout the entire time they exist. If such time is dense or continuous, then there are an infinite number of times—moments—in it. At each moment, the persisting object must have its own temporal part. This means the persisting object has an infinite number of temporal parts.

Response 1: An Object Can Have Infinite Parts

The objection has force if objects cannot have an infinite number of temporal parts. Yet, it is not clear that something cannot have infinite temporal parts. One reason to deny infinite parts is that there is something special about time: time is continuous. Any arbitrary duration is composed of infinite moments of time. Then, we may argue that no object can occupy an infinite number of times, such as the moments that compose this duration. However, this is too strong: it is a problem for any of these theories—and its solution can be shared by all of them. If objects cannot occupy an infinite number of moments, and things must persist through those moments by being at those moments, then nothing can persist, whatever one's theory.

Perhaps the objection is that no object can have an infinite number of *parts*. However, this is also not obvious and extends beyond the thesis of temporal parts. For example, take spatial parts. Say that space is continuous, and an object fills that space. A solution to how it fills that space is that a part is at each location in the space. If objects cannot have infinite parts, then they cannot fill that space by having infinite spatial parts. And, if objects can fill space by having infinite spatial parts, then what prevents objects from having infinite temporal parts? Again, is there something special about time that is not special about space?

Response 2: This Objection Requires Continuous Time

The objection requires that objects persist by occupying infinite points in time. This depends on time itself being continuous or dense. A condition of continuous or dense time is that, for any two moments in a duration, there is another moment between them. Discrete time need not meet this condition; for discrete time, there are two moments in some duration that have no moment between them. This means continuous or dense duration have infinite moments, but discrete duration need not have infinite moments.

The specifics and arguments for and against continuous time (or dense or discrete time) cannot be detailed here (e.g., see Newton-Smith 1980). What is important is how the possibility of either plays a role in denying continuants or temporal parts.

If time is not continuous or dense, then an object cannot persist by occupying infinite times. If continuants require that objects can do this, then there are no continuants. In that case, the reality of continuants depends on the reality of continuous time. If, instead, continuants need not depend on continuous time, and can occupy a finite number of times, then this objection is irrelevant. Unless whatever justifies such finite occupancy denies the idea of temporal parts, temporal parts theorists can assume it as well.

The relationship between, on the one hand, concrete particulars—ordinary objects—and, on the other, temporal parts and wholes requires further clarification. There are two kinds of theory that accept the existence of temporal parts:

- Perdurance: Concrete particulars—ordinary objects—persist.
- Exdurance or Stage Theory: Concrete particulars—ordinary objects—exist only in each moment.

Perdurance: The Ordinary Object Is the Persisting Object

Objects persist by having different temporal parts. They are the *temporal wholes* that are constituted by the temporal parts. This is the theory of *perdurance*. Philosophers describe the ordinary object as *perduring* through the period of time in which they persist (see Figure 3.7).

The ordinary object is O. Its temporal parts are O_1, O_2, O_3, O_4, and O_5. None of these objects (O, O_1, O_2, O_3, O_4, and O_5) is identical to any of the others:

- $O \neq O_1 \neq O_2 \neq O_3 \neq O_4 \neq O_5$

An objection to this position is that ordinary objects as we otherwise understand them cannot be these perduring objects. Ordinary objects are concrete particulars. If they are the perduring objects, these concrete particulars are not wholly at any moment of time in which they exist. Only their temporal parts are wholly at any moment.

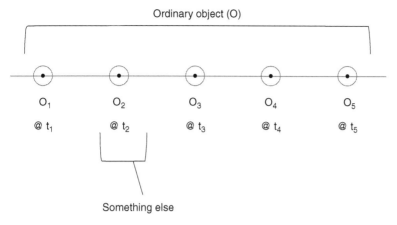

Figure 3.7 The Ordinary Object Perdures

For example, when I look at an apple sitting in a basket now, I see what seems to be an ordinary concrete particular at that time. However, whatever this thing I call "apple" sitting in the basket might be, perdurance requires that it not be an ordinary object or concrete particular. It is a *part* of an ordinary object or concrete particular. The ordinary object is the whole; this is its temporal part.

This objection turns on the *sortal* properties of objects. Sortal properties are properties objects have that allow them to be sorted into diverse kinds, classes, or groups of things. For example, say that an apple is any object that has the following characteristics: it is a fruit with a spherical shape and red skin. The collection of these properties (e.g., of shape and skin colour) and kind (e.g., fruit) can be thought of as *sortal* properties of an object. If the object has these properties, it can be sorted into the type of thing "apple".

The sortal properties of apples are properties that an object at a time and *wholly* at that time seems to have. That is, an object now, at this moment, can be spherical and red. In addition, what has these properties itself seems to be the ordinary object: an apple in the bowl just is the ordinary object. However, given perdurance, the object *now* with these properties is the temporal part. The persisting, perduring object is not; it is the whole the object with these properties is part of.

In some cases, when we conceive of what an ordinary object is, we think of it as the thing at a time. Yet, perdurance requires that the thing at a time only be part of the ordinary object.

Exdurantism (Stage Theory): The Ordinary Object Is the Object at Each Time

The intuition around ordinary objects is that ordinary objects are themselves at a time through which they persist. Another theory of temporal parts aims to satisfy that intuition.

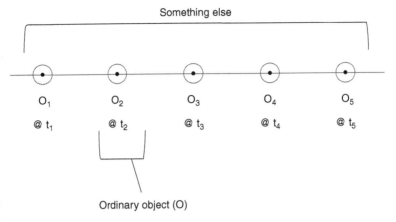

Figure 3.8 The Ordinary Object Exdures

This is *stage theory* or *exdurance*. Exdurance "identifies ordinary objects with brief stages instead of transtemporal sums of those stages" (Hawley 2015, 240). The temporal part is the ordinary object (see Figure 3.8):

> [O]rdinary continuants are instantaneous stages rather than temporally extended perduring "worms". Such entities persist by exduring (the term due to Haslanger, 2003)—by having temporal counterparts at different moments.
> (Balashov 2007, 143)

An exduring ordinary object itself possesses properties such as colour, shape, and size. It is, for example, the apple *now* in the basket (and, indeed, the basket now holding the apple). The ordinary object is any one of O_1, O_2, O_3, O_4, and O_5. None of these objects (O, O_1, O_2, O_3, O_4, and O_5) is identical to any of the others.

However, as with perdurance, these parts are not identical to each other. The exduring ordinary objects are the temporal parts, and distinct from one another. This makes exdurance unlike endurantism. For example, the apple and the basket are only the temporal parts two seconds ago or tomorrow morning, or any of the temporal parts between those two moments and now.

An immediate objection is that the exduring ordinary object is not the persisting object. The exduring ordinary object does not last. It only briefly exists, like all temporal parts. These are only parts of a perduring entity (the entity that Hawley calls the "transtemporal sum"). Instead, they are succeeded or preceded by other ordinary objects like them, what many metaphysicians call *counterparts* (e.g., Sider 2001, Balashov 2007).

This idea that the ordinary object only briefly exists violates another of the intuitive conditions of persistence and change for ordinary objects. Intuitively, ordinary objects are not temporary objects, but are identical to the persisting objects. Yet, intuitively, the ordinary objects directly possess the properties of the objects at each time. These two intuitions are incompatible given temporal parts and temporal wholes.

One response to this comes from a comment by Lewis (although Lewis was not an exdurantist). Lewis states that temporal parts of persons—what he calls "person-stages" are identical to persisting persons. The only difference is in how long they last:

> A person-stage is a physical object, just as a person is…it does many of the same things that a person does…it has a size and shape and location. [But] it does not last long … person-stages are related to persons as part to whole.
>
> (Lewis 1998, 205)

If stages or temporal parts are just like the perduring temporal whole by being physical objects with physical properties, then the reverse is also true. Perduring objects are also physical objects: the persisting person has many of the properties a person-stage has. They have size, shapes, and locations. The difference with perduring objects is that they *do* last long; they are related to object-stages as whole to part.

So, the perduring object can have a spherical shape, red skin; it can be an apple. Yet, this still raises the question about which object we see right now. When we are looking at an apple in a basket, do we see the perduring object or its temporal part?

Perhaps we see both. The persisting object has some of its sortal properties because its temporal parts have these properties. Similarly, a person, an apple, or a basket has a particular location because a temporal part has that location. But, then, a persisting object is sorted under a kind of object because its parts are sorted under that kind of object. If we say there are multiple temporal parts, then we have multiple instances of that kind of object. We have the ordinary perduring object, which is that object through its temporal parts, and we have each of the temporal parts.

The outstanding issue is that, during a period of time in which an object persists, how many ordinary objects are there? The intuition of persistence gives us the simple answer that there is just one object. This seems right. Yet, temporal parts give us multiple objects.

Should we then abandon temporal parts and return to endurantism?

Intuitions about Persistence

As discussed, endurantism holds that the whole object is at each time. There are not separate parts at separate times. It is intuitive in a way that the alternatives such as perdurantism and exdurantism are not. It satisfies Hinchliff's four conditions for change: an ordinary object can persist (unlike exdurantism) and itself have the properties at a time (unlike perdurantism). Does satisfying these intuitions mean that we should accept endurantism?

A response might that that intuitions are not always reasons to put aside alternatives. We look for "a believable account of persistence that vindicates as many ordinary beliefs as possible", according to Sider.

> But there are other considerations. The balance, I say, favours perdurance. That is why it is worth showing *how close* [perdurance] can get to capturing ordinary beliefs [...] Metaphysics is like horseshoes; close counts.
>
> (Sider 2001, 235)

On balance, it may be that we ought to accept counter-intuitive theories. All theories of persistence have problematic consequences. Endurantism violates Leibniz' law. This is why temporal parts are introduced in the first place. Theories with temporal parts obey Leibniz' law but violate other intuitions about the persistence of objects. However, Leibniz' law is arguably a deeper intuition; it is the intuition that no one thing can both have and not have properties.

Another response is that counter-intuitive results in the philosophy of time are not unusual and should not surprise anyone interested in the philosophy of time—or, indeed, just interested in time, whatever their level of study. Ordinary discourse about time can be perplexing and counter-intuitive. Even two people, having never studied philosophy or paradoxes in any formal way, can still wonder about time. Geach writes:

> [Q]uite ordinary people may find themselves bewildered when they think about time: worries about the reality of time do not require academic discipline of first learning to worry and then learning to get rid of your worries; they appear to be part of the human condition."
>
> (Geach 1979, 138)

Even so, it is not the most comfortable position that one's best philosophical theory is counter-intuitive. A consolation may be that it is more intuitive than its alternatives. But, having investigated the problems, it is hard to return to the original intuitions about changing objects.

Study Questions

1. Of Hinchliff's four conditions of change, which could you most easily abandon? Which *must* you hold on to?
2. Are you a *numerically different* entity to the person you remember being yesterday? Consider this under two scenarios: First, there is a difference in properties between you now and the person you remember being yesterday. Second, there is only a difference in time.
3. What is an example of an unchanging intrinsic property? What is an example of a changing property? Are these examples indisputably intrinsic properties?
4. Chapter 2 talks about real change as temporal passage. How does that affect the idea of change in objects? Does it mean objects must endure, or can they perdure or even exdure?

Notes

1 See Chapter 2.
2 See Chapter 1.
3 See Chapter 5 for more on language's role in the philosophy of time.
4 See Chapter 2.

Suggested Readings

The early noteworthy text on this is an extract from Lewis 1986. Although only published this century, the classic tenseless theory text on persistence is Sider 2001. Another comparable text is Hawley's 2004. Both texts argue for temporal parts over alternative theories. Both are also excellent at motivating the relations-to-times solution. Lowe 2003 and Haslanger 2003 offer adverbial accounts of persistence and change. Mellor, a tenseless theorist (unlike Lowe), argues in his 1998 against the idea that objects have temporal parts; his solution is similar (but arguably different) to the relations-to-times solution.

For a philosophical perspective that links to discussions outside analytic philosophy, an underappreciated Whiteheadian analysis of processes and persistence is found in Emmett 1992.

4   Philosophy of Physics and Time

Overview

An everyday, intuitive concept of physical things is that they are temporal: they exist in time, persist *through* time, and this existence has a beginning and an end. However, it has been argued that modern physical theory denies that time is fundamental, or even a real feature of the world at all. How can there be physical things that are temporal, yet physics denies there is time?

To understand where the argument comes from, we discuss two temporal concepts in modern physics: simultaneity and temporal order. According to modern physics, both simultaneity and temporal order are relative. After explaining "relative" and "absolute", we outline some reasons why each temporal relation is considered relative.

Simultaneity is relative because, in modern *relativistic* physics, the speed of light is constant, being the same in all *frames of reference*. Both space and time become relative to such frames to account for this. There is still an absolute structure in modern physics, with absolute locations and extents; however, this is space-time structure; time and space are only dimensions of this structure.

Like simultaneity, some temporal order is relative to reference frames. Some theorists think some temporal order is absolute. This is the temporal order of causal order. However, even here, there are physical reasons to deny such absolute order. The possibility of *backwards causation* requires that temporal order and causal order come apart. Yet, temporal order seems to be a fundamental feature of the world we encounter in our every day lives. How can this be explained? One answer concerns the relationship between causation and entropy, on the one hand, and perceived order on the other.

Some theorists deny that such temporal order and simultaneity can be features of a real time. Time and its features must be absolute; a "relative time" is no time at all. As such, one might conclude, relativistic physics *does* deny physical things are temporal things. To close, we examine the main reasons for such denials; it is suggested that they are based significantly on experience; they presuppose that such experience reveals everything there is to real time.

Introduction

Here is a common assumption about physical things: they exist in space and time. They are concrete particulars that "bear spatio-temporal and causal relations to each other" (Robinson 2017, online). The study of physical things is the study of things in space and time; physics is, "in its largest aspect, a tissue of laws expressing space-time linkages" (Neurath 1931).

Physical things' existence in time does not separate them from non-physical things. Non-physical objects—such as souls, propositions, or universals—"have this much in common: they all exist in time" (Markosian 2000, 377). Some philosophers think there are non-physical things outside of time: Platonists about mathematics hold that mathematical entities (such as π) are non-physical and do not exist in time. But at least some *non-physical* beings do exist in time.

So, this leaves space as a way of distinguishing the physical from the non-physical; only physical things exist in space: "The ones that exist in space, i.e., the ones that have spatial locations, are the ones that count as physical objects. Thus souls, if there are any, are objects with temporal locations but without spatial locations" (Markosian 2000, 377).

Again, this may not be exactly right. For example, Montero writes that the "stock example of a nonphysical entity is some sort of ghost", and ghosts exist in space; they appear in hallways and drift through graveyards. They do have strange properties, such as the ability to pass through solid objects. However, this does not make them non-physical: it is possible some physical entities can pass through solid objects as well, e.g., neutrinos can pass through walls (Montero 1999, 184).

As can be seen, distinguishing the physical from the non-physical is problematic. However, whatever non-physical things may be, at least physical things must be spatial and temporal. For example, a table is physical because the table has a spatial location (e.g., in the kitchen) and exists in time (it is made on Christmas Day and broken up for firewood on New Year's Day). A lightning flash is physical because, again, it happens in space (it happens over the mountains) and at a time (it lasts an instant). It is challenging to find further necessary properties of physical things. Actual physical things have many other properties. However, many of them are only present in some things and absent in others. For example, physical particles such as electrons have spin and velocity (or some combination of the same). These are properties of physical things; they may also themselves be wholly defined in terms of spatial and temporal properties. However, they are not necessary properties of physical things. To be physical, electrons themselves need not have spin. Spin is a property defined within quantum physics. Although quantum physics is part of the best modern physical theories, it could be false and yet physical objects exist.

Yet, many theorists take it that modern physics denies that there is time. For example, the most developed account of time in physics is found in the relativistic physics originally developed by Einstein. Relativistic physics has a general form (GR), covering the behaviour of all physical matter, and a special form (STR), which covers material objects that move at constant motion relative to each other (also known as objects that occupy *inertial reference frames*). Bergson, an influential philosopher of time, argued that STR denied the reality of time (Bergson 1999).

We will discuss Bergson's objections—and those of other philosophers—in more detail near the end of this chapter. For now, a first and ungenerous response to these objectors is that they are not physicists; as such, they do not fully understand the physics. If they did understand the physics, they would see that time as they conceive it to be is not denied by modern physics.

However, many physicists also hold that modern physics denies there is time. It is much harder to claim that these physicists do not understand physics. For example, in correspondence with a friend's widow, Einstein calls time "merely a persistent illusion" (Jammer 2006, 239). Quantum theory is often conceived as timeless (Healey 2002). In his book *The End of Time*, Barbour argues that there is no time in the physical universe (Barbour 1999). The physicist Smolin argues that time is denied or ignored in physics and needs to be taken more seriously (Smolin 2014).

At a Canadian Perimeter Institute conference attended by both philosophers and physicists, the physicist Elitzur pushed back against relativistic physics. According to relativistic physics, there is no real, fundamental, ontological difference between the past, present, and future. Elitzur objects: "I don't think that next Thursday has the same footing as this Thursday. The future does not exist. It does not! Ontologically, it's not there" (quoted in Falk 2016). Implied here is that this present Thursday *is* there, i.e., there is a fundamental difference between the present and the future and this difference is denied by relativistic physics.

Physics Without Time

If it is right that modern physics denies time in some way, then one can have a physical theory with no time in it.

If physical things are temporal things, then how can it be possible for physical theory to lack time? If physical things are temporal things, then, if physical things exist, time exists. In that case, physicists research temporal things. Yet, if physicists hold that time does not exist, then physical things do not exist. Thus, physicists research things that, according to physicists, do not exist. Does this make any sense?

One can research what one denies exists. Folklorists and anthropologists do this. Perhaps physicists are like anthropologists. Yet, that does not seem to be the case in practice. Many physicists deny there are ghosts because they are nonphysical; the implication is that existent things must be physical. But if physical things do not exist, then existent things are not physical.

Here is another possibility: some theorists think modern physics denies the reality of time because it contradicts some philosophical theories of time. However, this does not mean it contradicts them all. So, perhaps those who insist that there is no time in modern physics only think so because they presume a certain concept of time.

Substantivalism and Early Physics

Here is an example of how physical theory may contradict some philosophical theories. The substantival debate about time is between substantivalists, who hold that time is a substance, with its own independent substantial existence, and relationalists, who hold that time is in some way dependent on other things; in a universe with nothing else in it, there could be no time. For example, time is only a kind of property of things, such as simultaneity and temporal order.

This debate about time was live before the modern physical theory of relativistic physics. Both Leibniz and Mach argued against Newton's claim that time was a substance. In addition, Kant argued that there could be no such independent time—indeed, there could not even be mind-independent time.[1]

However, this debate is not exactly about the reality of time. It concerns instead how fundamental time is in the world or how independent time must be from other things. Relationalists who hold time to be properties and relations of other things still believe that time is real; they just do not think that it has independent reality. Whichever side the debaters come down, they each seem to think that it is right, in some way, to hold that time is real.

As said above, not so with relativistic physics. So, let us investigate why. We consider two features that relativistic physics is purported to reject: simultaneity and temporal order. We explain this relativity through STR and the physical concept of backwards causation. Then we outline why some theorists insist that, for time to be real, simultaneity and temporal order must be absolute.

As we will also see, the requirement that these features be absolute follows from some philosophical theories of time; it does not follow from all philosophical theories of time. The main conclusion of all this is that relativistic physics does not require that there be no time.

Relative Simultaneity

When something is absolute, it is not relative to different things. Such things can include size, location, and time. For example, say that a coin's three-dimensional shape is a *flat cylinder*. The coin's shape is *absolute* if this shape stays the same no matter which location you choose. No matter how I turn the coin in my hand, or where I stand relative to the coin, it is cylindrical. It does not matter if I am human or ant-sized; the coin is cylindrical.

This makes the coin's three-dimensional shape different to the two-dimensional shape of a facing side of the coin. If the coin's edge faces me, then its two-dimensional facing side is rectangular; if the coin's top faces me, then its dimensional facing side is circular.

This does not mean an absolute thing must always remain the same. It can change or vary. It is just that the change cannot be different according to different things. One example is discussed in Chapter 3; this is a change in intrinsic properties of the object. But, as they are commonly described, this change does not depend on something. For example, the property is not persistent to something else and changing for the object itself.

Another example is discussed in Chapter 2. This is the tense theory concept of temporal passage. Temporal passage is absolute: an event just changes from being in the past, to the present, to the future. This change is not relative to anything; for example, the change is not relative to some position in the B-series.

However, some things we often treat as absolute are, in physical theory, relative. The most significant for this chapter are simultaneity and temporal order. There are others less significant to this chapter; for example, in STR, also counter-intuitively, the three-dimensional shapes of objects are relative. However, to ease us into this, let us briefly consider intuitively relative properties.

Say that a train passes through a station at great speed. It is natural to treat the station (and the landscape around it) as not moving, while treating the train as moving.[2]

In physical terms:

- The station and landscape do not move. They are *at rest*.
- The train moves. It is not at rest.

The train's motion and the station's rest help explain changes between train and station. For example, in one moment, the train engine is passing the ticket office while one of its carriages has yet to reach the station. In the next moment, the engine moves out of the station while one of the train's carriages passes the ticket office.

Relative Frames

The description of this scene as the train in motion and the station at rest is not the only way to describe the motion of these objects. It is just one way of describing what moves and what is not moving, that is, *at rest*. The accuracy of each description depends on what it is we use to define motion and rest.

A passenger is sitting on the train. The passenger pours some milk into their coffee. The milk pours straight down into the cup, just as it does if they sit in the station café. The table on the train, and the cup on the table, are all at rest for the passenger.

For the passenger and the coffee cup, and the train itself, the *train* is at rest. For the passenger, the cup, and the train, the station speeds by; the *station* moves. That is, what moves and what rests is different between a train passenger and someone waiting in the station.

In physical terms, the motion and rest of station and train are *relative*:

• Both train and station are *at rest* to themselves—as is anything not moving relative to them.
• The station moves *relative* to the train. It also moves relative to anything at rest in the train, such as the passenger and the cup.
• The train moves *relative* to the station. It also moves relative to anything at rest in the station, such as someone standing on the platform.

In physics, this relativity of speed and rest is defined according to *reference frames*.

Reference frames are coordinate systems for calculating values of spatial and temporal location and extent, with an origin defined by the frame. They are defined by their *velocity*. Velocity is speed *and* direction. As such, a reference frame is defined by speed and direction. This has significant consequences for thinking about values according to different frames.

For example, two things can have the same speed but different directions. Instead of one train, say that two trains move through the station. For the platform, both move at the same speed. However, one moves in the opposite direction to the other. In that case, it moves at a different velocity and has a different frame.

Note here that the two trains move at the same speed (but different direction) to the station. The station is in a reference frame of its own. This frame defines the values for how fast things move. According to the station's frame, the two trains move at the same speed, for example. But it only defines how fast things move in that frame. In a different frame, things do not move as they do for the station's frame. They move at a different speed. For example, each of the trains has its own reference frame. From each of those frames, the station, and the other train move at different speed to their speed for the station.

Let us ignore the second train, and just focus on the station and the first train. Let us take those two reference frames, A (the train) and B (the station):

• In frame A (the train's reference frame), things in the world move at certain speeds.
• In frame B (the station's frame), things in the world move at speeds different to those in A.

Based on how frames define motion, what is in the frame is never in motion in that frame; it is always *at rest* in that frame. That is, it always has a zero speed. For example, according to A, the reference frame of the train, the train is at rest and has zero speed; according to B, the reference frame of the station, the station is at rest and has zero speed.

Furthermore, in modern physics, no individual frame is unique in defining motion or rest; no frames are *privileged*. No matter what is in either frame, the values for speed in B are as real values as different values in A. If, in frame A, the station moves (and the train rests), then this is as real a motion (or rest) as, in frame B, the station's rest (or the train's motion). There is nothing special about one frame's set of values over another frame's set.

That is, the frames we use to define speed and motion are *arbitrary* and *conventional*. We can choose the frame from which things move and are at rest. The frame from which motion is defined can be a matter of convenience, and yet be no less special than any others. For example, we might choose the frame in which we ourselves are at rest. Or, finding ourselves in complex motion relative to the Earth, we might choose the Earth because the maths is easier. It does not matter, so long as we pick some frame from which to define motion and rest.

Relative Is Neither Private Nor Subjective

Importantly, a relative property need not be a *subjective* property (Power 2018). It is relative to something, but that something need not be a subject or a person. Something can be defined relative to something else, without people being in any way involved. Writing on Einstein's view of physics (and thus on STR), Morrison suggests that STR is "afflicted by a most unfortunate misnomer":

> [I]n some quarters the term "relative," is identified with that which is private, pluralistic, and subjective. [However,] Einstein's science and his relativity theories do not relativize or subjectivize our knowledge. Instead, [they] provide monumental reinforcement for the principles of invariance and of objectivity.
>
> (Morrison 1987, 54)

Although a relative property is not an absolute property, it can be a *real* or *objective* property. The property can have a value in the absence of a subject. And a subject can be wrong about it; it is not merely up to each subject to decide on its value.

Say that I and my cousin each have a slice of cake. My cousin claims that his slice is smaller than mine. But this claim is false; his slice is bigger than my slice. His claim is *objectively* false. My slice of cake can really, objectively, be small, compared to (relative to) my cousin's. It can also really and objectively be *big*, compared to the crumbs. Even if these slices existed in the absence of people (however that might happen), it is objectively true that one slice is bigger than the other; and, no matter what my cousin claims, this is true; he is wrong.

Since Newtonian, pre-Einsteinian, physics, many physical properties are defined as relative to arbitrary and conventional reference frames. These include location, speed, and direction (and thus also velocity). However, in the special theory of relativity (STR), the most significant relative properties are space and time.

Relative Time

Return to the different frames of the train (A) and the station (B). According to the train and your frame (A), the station frame (B) has a particular velocity: it moves at a particular speed in a particular direction (e.g., at five miles an hour to the left). According to B, to a person on the station platform, A, the train, is in motion in the opposite direction (to the right).

For each frame—A and B—the other is in motion. But, for each frame, each is itself at rest. When you pass through the station, you start pouring the milk *at the same time that* the train hits a bump on the track. Everything leaps up for a moment, including the coffee cup. The cup flies into the air and lands perfectly, unbroken. The only difference from a moment before is that the coffee and milk is on your coat.

Two events happen at the same time: the train hits a small bump when you are pouring the milk. If two things are at the same time, then they are *simultaneous*; your milk-pouring is simultaneous with the train wheel striking the bump.

In addition, those two events happen *before* a third event: the coffee and milk soaking your coat. In fact, they not only happen before the soaking; they are a *cause* of the soaking. If the train had not hit the bump, the coffee cup would not have leapt, throwing the coffee and milk over you. If you had not poured in the milk, you would not have milk on your coat.

Furthermore, these events are all separated from each other in space: the wheel bump is several feet from where you sit; you pour the coffee a few inches from you; the spill on your coat is a few inches from that.

So far, this is intuitive. However, the physics of STR introduce physical elements that are not obvious. These elements make the physical situation counter-intuitive. According to STR, along with the velocity, distances between objects and the duration between events are different for different frames.

The Constant Speed of Light

The speed of light is constant or invariant in all reference frames. Lightspeed is roughly 3 by 10^8 metres per second or, as it is commonly called, c. Every instance of light—every photon—travels at this speed, no matter the frame, origin, or direction in which it is emitted. (To use a concept introduced in Chapter 3, the same *numerically identical* photon of light travels at c, that is, 3 by 10^8 metres per second.[3])

This speed is absolute. It is not relative. It is the same in all frames. Unlike the speed of the train or the platform, and people and objects on it, the speed of each photon does not vary by frame. It is this condition of lightspeed that drives the theory of relativity for space and time.

To accommodate this constant value of lightspeed, in each frame, the simultaneity and spatial distance between events must be different. This is illustrated in Figure 4.1 (Frame A) and Figure 4.2 (Frame B).

While a person goes by on the train (A), another person stands still in the middle of the platform (B). Thus, each person is in a different frame.

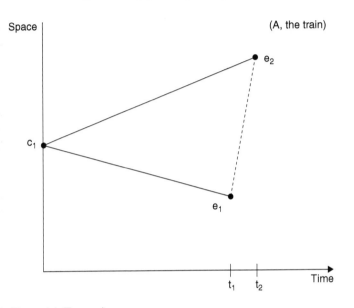

Figure 4.1 Frame A

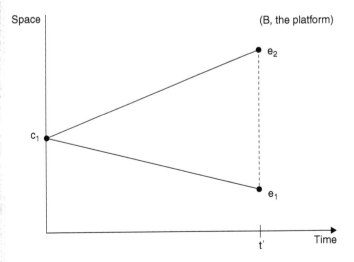

Figure 4.2 Frame B

At each end of the platform is a perfectly reflecting mirror.

The person standing on the platform lights up their phone, causing a flash (c_1) that casts light in all directions. Along with other photons, two photons of light travel in opposite directions along the platform. Each bounces off a mirror at either end (e_1 and e_2).

Figure 4.1 illustrates the timing of events according to A, the train's frame. Following the flash, the platform changes position relative to the train and the passenger on it. This includes the mirrors on the platform:

- One mirror approaches the passenger, the one nearer the engine at the front of the train. In doing so, the distance between it and the passenger is shorter than when the phone originally flashed (at c_1).
- The other mirror moves away from the passenger, the one further from the engine. In doing so, the distance between it and the passenger is longer than when the phone originally flashed (at c_1).

As such, during the time it takes for them to strike the mirrors, each photon of light travels a different distance.

However, the speed of the light in both directions is the same (c). Because of the difference in their distances, one photon of light takes a shorter amount of time to reach and strike one mirror ($c_1 - e_1$) than the other photon does to reach the other ($c_1 - e_2$). Thus, one photon strikes one mirror at t_1 and the other photon strikes the other mirror later at t_2.

So far, so intuitive. Different distances between mirrors and train; different times for light to travel them. However, from the frame of the platform, the description of space is different—and thus, because lightspeed is constant, time is different.

Figure 4.2 illustrates the timing of events according to the platform's frame (B). Following the flash, the mirrors, being at rest in the platform, are *equidistant* from the source throughout the time it takes for both photons to travel. There is no change in the distance travelled by either photon of light.

Again, lightspeed is constant (c) and thus the same for both photons. Moving at the same speed, each photon strikes each mirror (e_1 and e_2) at *the same time* ($t_{1'}$).

Thus, the two events e_1 and e_2 are simultaneous.

However, e_1 and e_2 are the exact same events in all frames. The event e_1 in frame A is numerically identical to the event e_1 in frame B. The event e_2 in frame A is numerically identical to e_2 in frame B. There are only two events here. They are both an event of a particular photon hitting a particular mirror.

What is different in each frame is their behaviour in space and time relative. For example, there is a difference in how much duration there is between the events. This varies between frame A and frame B. In frame A, there is some duration between these events; in frame B, there is no duration; the events are simultaneous.

That is, what is simultaneous for the platform (e_1 and e_2) is successive for the train (e_1 and e_2). This holds for any two events separated in space. The difference in speed between frames changes the distance according to each that lies between spatially separated events, and thus the amount of time it takes light to travel.

This relativity applies both simultaneity and to *succession* or *temporal order*. Some events are successive according to only some reference frames (the train) while, in other frames, they are simultaneous (the platform).

This description requires two qualifications.

Inertial Frames

Throughout this, frame A and frame B are different *inertial* reference frames. An inertial reference frame is one in which there is no acceleration, for example, there is no change in speed. A *non-inertial* frame is one in which there is acceleration: for example, it speeds up (accelerates) or slows down (decelerates).

The trains pass through the station without slowing or speeding up. Thus, the trains are in inertial reference frames relative to the station. And the station is in an inertial reference relative to the train.

However, a train that slows down and then speeds up again is in a non-inertial reference frame relative to the station. And, relative to the train, the station speeds up and slows down; thus, it is also in an inertial reference frame.

Non-inertial frames develop the discussion about time and physics for a wider range of physical interactions. However, there is enough in inertial frames to conflict with an idea of absolute time.

Possible Absolute Simultaneity and Temporal Order

In STR, there are exceptions to relativity of simultaneity and temporal order:

- There can be absolute simultaneity between *spatially coincident* entities, entities that occupy exactly the same points in space. If coincident entities are simultaneous in any inertial frame, then they can be simultaneous in all inertial frames.
- For many philosophers, the only absolute temporal relations between spatially separated entities are the *succession* of cause and effect (e.g., Mellor 1998). No causal relata are simultaneous in an inertial reference frame. A causal chain can extend over space, e.g., between the phone light and mirror-flashes. Thus, in STR, some spatially separated events—causes and effects—are always temporally ordered in all frames.

These exceptions aside, according to STR, time is not absolute. In different inertial frames, different durations hold between the same two events. What the duration between any spatially separated events depends on is something defined by speed or velocity. A different speed (or velocity) is a different reference frame. A different reference frame is a different duration and distance between spatially separated events.

Minkowski Space-Time

The discussion so far has concentrated on one sense in which time is not how folk commonly conceive of it. It is relative. However, there is another sense in which physical time may be thought of as unlike our folk idea of it.

As discussed in Chapter 1, a time without space is conceivable. Temporal passage can happen to events in space, such as a birthday party at a restaurant. It can also happen to events that are not clearly located in space, such as a feeling of uncertainty followed by a flash of mental insight.

However, a physical conception of space and time relationship arises out of STR. This conception undermines that view of time independent of space. This is a concept of both space and time being dimensions of something more fundamental. Space and time are not independent of each other; instead, they are like depth and width for space.

As depth and width are dimensions of space, space and time are dimensions of a four-dimensional manifold often called *Minkowski space-time* (e.g., Dainton 2001, Balashov 2005).

Specific terminology exists to refer to the features of space-time:

- Points in space-time are referred to as *events*. They are like spatial locations and temporal moments. However, unlike events in time, they are not just what happens at a time. They are what happens at a point in *space-time*.
- The extensions between space-time events are *intervals*. They lie between space-time events. They are like distances in space and durations in time.

Unlike space and time, space-time *is* absolute. It does not vary—it is *invariable*—from frame to frame. A space-time extent is like distance in ordinary concepts of space. In the ordinary concept of space, for a particular spatial extent, the values of depth or width can vary by frame, but the distance remains the same. For a particular extent of space-time, it is the distance and duration that can vary by frame; however, the space-time intervals remain the same.

We do not discuss space-time much in this book, or the terminology associated with it. Any reference to events here is reference to a more ordinary concept of events, of events being *what happens at a time*. Space-time is mentioned here, however, to make two points.

First, given space-time, time is no longer a fundamental feature of the world. That is, it is not independent of everything else, with its own substance or identity. It is an aspect of something else. In that case, a substantivalist theory of time may seem necessarily false: how can time be a substance if it cannot be independent of space? However, although it is false that time alone is a substance, it need not be false for space-time. There is no space to discuss it here, but some philosophers argue that space-time can still be a substance (for discussion, see Le Poidevin 2003).

Second, Einstein argued that all inertial frames are equivalent, arbitrary, and conventional. This claim became *The Principle of Relativity*:

> [T]he unsuccessful attempts to discover any motion of the earth relatively to the [ether] suggest that the phenomena of electrodynamics as well as of mechanics possess no properties corresponding to the idea of absolute rest. They suggest rather that [...] the same laws of [physics] will be valid for all frames of reference for which the equations of mechanics hold good.
>
> (Einstein 1905, 891)

However, as evident from the quote, some things are not relative—the laws of physics. They are the same in all frames of reference. As such, this is still an objective absolute model of the world.

Relative Temporal Order

Whatever their views of the truth about temporal order, almost everyone accepts that, intuitively, temporal order is *fundamental*. It is not derived or reducible to something else. It is not merely apparent or subjective; it is not merely a product of our relationship to the world in some way, or a local feature of the world. The temporal order of events belongs to the objective world. If events are temporally ordered in some way, they are temporally ordered this way whatever our relationship to them or our position or perspective in the world.

For example, it is an objective fact that the sun dies *after* it has burned for millions of years. Furthermore, this death is many millions of years *after* the moon became tidally locked around the Earth. Your reading this paragraph lies between the moon's tidal lock and the sun's death. The order of the moon's settling in its position, *then* your reading this, and *then* the sun's demise is the case whether you are a human reading this or an alien in the Andromeda galaxy. Indeed, given our intuitions of temporal order, even if the world lacked humans or aliens, it is the case that the sun dies *after* the moon has tidally locked.

Here is an illustration of how mere difference in temporal order can dramatically change the apparent nature of otherwise identical sequences. Consider some events involving an egg, a table, and the ground. The events can be ordered in two sequences. Call the two different sequences F and G:

- Sequence F: A whole egg rests on the table. *Then*, the whole egg travels between the floor and table. *Then*, the egg is in pieces on the floor.
- Sequence G: An egg is in pieces on the floor. *Then*, the whole egg travels between the floor and table. *Then*, the whole egg rests on the table.

F and G both appear to describe different chains of physical events. Yet, they share many similar events. For both F and G:

- $t_=$: The egg travels between floor and table.
- $t_<$: The egg is in pieces on the floor.
- t_2: The egg is a whole egg on the table.

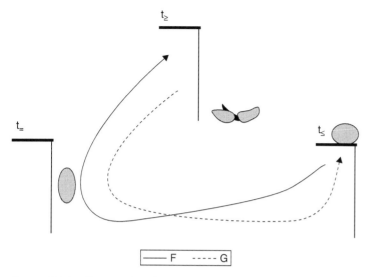

Figure 4.3 An Egg Moving through Space

The difference between them is the *temporal order* of events. As illustrated in Figure 4.3:

- **F:** the egg (t_2) rests on the table, ($t_=$) travels through the air, and ($t_\leq$) is in pieces.
- **G:** the egg ($t_\leq$) is in pieces, ($t_=$) travels through the air, and (t_2) rests on the table.

In ordinary intuitive, folk thinking about temporal order, this difference in these sequences is significant. For example, F, the first sequence, is a common (if unfortunate) sequence. But G, the second sequence, is not common at all. Indeed, were it to happen, it would be hard not to interpret it as a trick of some kind. One might say: broken eggs simply do not reassemble on the ground, then rise back on to the table.

Furthermore, this difference is *not* something that varies by any kind of reference frame. It does not matter if I see this from a train, a platform, or the Andromeda galaxy: either the egg is on the table, falls, and cracks on the floor or it reassembles on the floor, rises, and lands whole on the table. That is, it is absolute.

Yet, as with simultaneity, many physicists and philosophers of physics hold that temporal order is not fundamental like this. It is relative, just like simultaneity. So, why is it relative?

First, some reasons why it is not relative. F is more common than G. Falling and cracking eggs are common; self-assembling and rising eggs are not. This makes G stranger and rarer than F. However, rarity is not a reason for why one sequence is significantly different to the other. Otherwise, if the world contained one such sequence as often as the other, then we could not tell their order apart.

Second, the physical or non-physical nature is not enough to explain the differences in sequences' temporal order. Many common physical sequences are the reverse of other common physical sequences. One's starting point is the other's ending point, and vice versa. Indeed, it seems that we can take any group of physical events and order them without contradiction. For example, a red light can change to orange and then to green; a green light can change to orange and then to red (Mellor 1991, 196). Maudlin gives the example of an asteroid travelling between Mars and Earth. The asteroid travelling *from* Mars *to* Earth is a physical sequence of events. The sequence in the reverse direction, the asteroid travelling *from* Earth *to* Mars, is also a physical sequence of events (Maudlin 2002, 265–266).

The physical laws governing such physical sequences are *time-reversible*: we can reverse any physical sequence of events and still have a physical sequence of events. But we can still tell those sequences apart by their temporal order. For time-reversible sequences, each event at each point in time is in both sequences. In Mellor's example, the traffic light's events of being orange, being red, and being green are in the sequence red-orange-green and the reverse sequence green-orange-red. In Maudlin's example, each sequence has the asteroid at Mars, the asteroid at Earth, and the asteroid in transit between both.

So, a difference in a sequence's temporal order is not reducible to a difference in a sequence's frequency. Nor, indeed, is it a difference in the separate physical events in stages of the sequences, because these are shared by both.

Such reasons may tempt one to conclude that temporal order is irreducible to anything physical. Indeed, for some philosophers, temporal order is an inexplicable feature of time and the world. This is what Earman calls the *Time Direction Heresy*: if there is temporal order, it is "an intrinsic feature of space-time which does not and cannot be reduced to non-temporal features" (Earman 1974, 20).

STR and Relative Temporal Order

An immediate reason to hold that temporal order is relative is just because of relative simultaneity. In some frames, two events are simultaneous; in other frames, one of those events comes after the other, i.e., they are temporally ordered. We see this with the example of the trains: e_1 is simultaneous with e_2 in the frame of the platform, but temporally ordered in the frame of the train.

Since these events are simultaneous relative to some but not all frames, then they are relatively simultaneous. By the same reasoning, since these events are temporally ordered relative to some but not all frames, then they are relatively simultaneous.

As such, it follows that there is relative temporal order: the order of events such as e_1 and e_2 relative to a train speeding through a station.

Does this mean, then, that our sense that the sun's death is later than the moon's tidal locking is merely relative? Is this the temporal order that seems to conflict so forcefully with common folk intuitions about time?

Objection: There Is Absolute Temporal Order in STR

Not exactly. The events of e_1 and e_2 are not causally related. They have a common cause (c_1); they even have a common effect (my seeing them as two bright flashes of light). However, one does not cause the other.

As discussed earlier in this chapter, according to STR, if two events are causally related, then they can be absolutely temporally ordered. They are not forced, given STR, to be ordered in one frame and not in the other. For example, c_1 is earlier than both e_1 and e_2 in both the frame of the train and the platform. Indeed, given STR, this order holds in any other inertial frame. At least, according to STR.

As such, given the moon's tidal locking is in the causal history of your reading this, and the sun's death, it is earlier than your reading this, and the sun's death.

Are these events part of a causal sequence? Plausibly, yes. The moon's activity at some point in time causes things to happen—events—amongst the activity of the Earth and the sun. Those effects may be miniscule (especially for the sun), but they are still effects. And being effects, they are later than the events on the moon that cause them. Similarly, activity on the Earth and on the sun cause effects on the moon—and, indeed, cause effects on each other. Lastly, many other objects in the universe cause things to happen to the moon, the earth, the sun, and each other.

If this is right, then we might say this: the moon settles into tidal lock, causing an effect that is itself the first cause in a long and complex causal chain of events. This chain interacts with other causal chains, such as from the Earth and sun, or other material bodies. All these chains cause things such as your reading this; your reading this has its own effects, which join in with such causal chains. Until, somewhere far down the lines of these causal chains, there is the effect of the sun dying.

Response: Not All Earlier Events Are Causally Related to Later Events

This account requires that events that are not obviously causally related *must* be causally related. Otherwise, they are not temporally ordered. For example, perhaps your reading this is part of why the sun dies. But, if it turns out that it is not, does this mean the sun's death is not after your reading this? Surely, whatever we say of the causal relationship, the temporal order must survive it?

Causal Order and Perceived Temporal Order

Mellor proposes a solution. He uses causation between perception and the world to explain how, at least for subjects such as ourselves, there can appear to be a temporal order that does not involve causation.

Mellor begins by asserting that at least one event C causes another event E.[4] Thus, causation is not only an idea in our minds. For example, the whole egg on the table, along with some other event (such as my rolling it), causes the egg to fall to the ground and then shatter. This is the case even if no one observed it happening. Then, following Reichenbach (1928/1958 and 1956), he defines a cause C of event E as any event that increases the likelihood of A happening. "[A]n effect's chance must be greater than it would have been *in the circumstances* if its cause had not occurred" (Mellor 1991, 199[5]). For example:

> If C is *I roll the egg off the table*,
> and E is *the egg shatters*,
> then C is a cause of E
> iff C increases the likelihood of E.

The event E (*the egg shatters*) may happen anyway, sitting there on the table. However, the event C (*I roll the egg off the table*) increases the likelihood of E.

   Then, Mellor argues, we have a perception of temporal order.[6] He uses this perception of order to explain how temporal order arises:

> Suppose I see that one event, *e*, happens precedes another, *f*. My seeing this is itself an event, which I shall call S(*e*<*f*), where "S"(*p*)' represents a perception that *p* and "<" means "precedes". But what is S(*e*<*f*)'s structure; *how* do I see that *e* precedes *f*?
>
> (Mellor 1991, 194)

Mellor's answer is illustrated in in Figure 4.4. There is a causal order and an apparent temporal order. The direction of apparent temporal order arises out of the causal order.

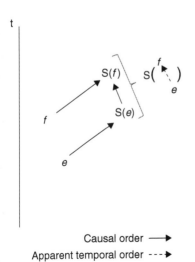

Figure 4.4 Causal Order Explains Temporal Order

The perception S(e<f) has two elements or parts: one part S(e) is a perception of e and the other part S((f) is a perception of f. Then, he causally links the two parts:

S(e) is one of the causes of S(f).

That is, one part of the perception is one of the causes of another part of the perception (from Chapter 3, we can think of these as stages or *temporal parts*). It is this causal order—between the parts of our perception S(e<f), which is of e<f—that temporally orders what we perceive:

- There is a causal relationship between the two parts of the perception.
- From this relationship, the perceptual part that is a cause (S(e)) appears to us as earlier than the perceptual part that is its effect (S(f)).

Furthermore, for each perception, the event that is perceived appears to occur at the same time as—to be *simultaneous with*—the perception of it:

e seems to be at the same time as S(e)

and

f seems to be at the same time as S(f)

As a result, *because* S(e) appears to be a cause of and so earlier than S(f), e appears to be earlier than f.

Causal Order and the Intuition of Temporal Order

The events that we perceive need not appear to be causally related. They only appear to be temporally ordered. Other than appearing temporally ordered, they need not appear in any way related. We can see a supernova followed by buoy's flashing light. We can hear a seagull and see a plane fly overhead. They can all appear to be temporally ordered without one seeming to cause the order. That is, what appears to be temporally ordered need not appear to be causally ordered as well.

This also explains why there can be Hume's epistemological question about how we know about causation through temporal order (see Chapter 1). Although causation explains how our perception of temporal comes about, it is not apparent to us *as causation*. It appears, instead, to be temporal order.

In addition, the above account does *not* mean that the events e and f are temporally ordered as they appear in our perception of them. As Mellor notes, time-lags between our perceptions of events and the events themselves mean that the events can have any number of possible durations between one another. These possible durations can lead to the inversion of order.

For example, at night, I see a blinking buoy's light on the horizon, then see a supernova beyond it in the sky. In my perception, it seems to be that the blinking light is *earlier* than the supernova. However, the stellar explosion is hundreds of years before the flashing light on the sea. Thus, the apparent order of these events (a blinking light then a supernova) is not their actual order (a supernova then a blinking light).

However, this apparent order is explained by the temporal order in perception: it is because of causal order in the structure of perception itself (Mellor 1991, 194; see also Power 2018). Furthermore, if events that appear to be temporally ordered are simultaneous with yet other events, those other events can appear to be ordered as well. We see this in the perceived events seeming to be ordered because of their relationship to the parts of perception.

It can also explain how many events seem to be temporally ordered. No matter how many events we perceive there to be, so long as they appear to be simultaneous with parts of our perceptions, and those perceptions appear to be ordered, then those events will seem to be temporally ordered amongst themselves. So, how does this explain the intuition that we can have temporal order without causal order?

Many events that we seem to us to be temporally ordered are not, in fact, causally ordered. They cause our perceptions of them, and so stand in causal order to something happening in us; their apparent order is due to actual causal order between parts of our perceptions. But this does not mean one of these perceived events is the cause of the other. The buoy's flashing light does not cause the supernova, nor the supernova the buoy's flashing light.

Furthermore, these events need not appear to be causally ordered. The buoy's light need not appear to cause the supernova, nor vice versa. All that needs to appear to happen is that one part of perception causes the other. As such, through a complex perception involving causal order between its parts, there is an appearance of temporal order between events that neither appear nor are, in fact, causally ordered. This explains the intuition that our own activities can be earlier than the sun's death without having to partly cause it.

Yet, Mellor's account of temporal order through causal seems to be undermined by another concept in modern physics: *backwards causation*.

Backwards Causation

Backwards causation is any instance in which a later event *causes* an earlier event. This is common in time travel stories,[7] that is, science fiction. This does not mean it is possible in the actual world. For example, faster-than-light speed is also science fiction, but it does not mean it is actual.

However, some theorists also find backwards causation useful for explaining the actual world. For example, Price uses backwards causation to explain some puzzling features of quantum physics. This involves EPR-violation, a phenomenon originally described by Einstein, Podolsky, and Rosen (hence, EPR).

This is a complex issue, which cannot be satisfactorily detailed here. But, briefly, in quantum physics, some particles can be quantum entangled. Those particles can also be separated in space. For such particles, changes to one of these particles seem to instantaneously change the other.

This violates relativistic physics because a way of conceiving of the relationship between these changes in these entangled particles is that one change is an event that *causes* the other change. However, in this scenario, the cause and effect are simultaneous events between spatially separated particles. In physics, this instantaneous causation involves something travelling faster than light between the particles. However, given relativistic physics, nothing can travel faster than light. In addition, it is not clear how the simultaneity described here relates to STR's requirements of relative simultaneity between spatial separated events.

Price argues that, if we use backwards causation, then we can avoid the violation of relativity. We describe the causal relationship between stages of the particles' existence before, after, and through the changes in a way that is entirely explicable in relativistic terms. We need only do one thing: reverse the direction of causation. Instead of the particle's problematic changes being caused by events *earlier* than the changes, they are caused by events later *than* the changes (Price 1997). That is, the direction of causation is from a later cause to an earlier effect.

However, Mellor argues that such backwards causation is impossible. For him, causal order *defines* temporal order. A is earlier than B just because A causes B (or appear simultaneous with a cause of B, e.g., the supernova with a perception of it). No event can be both a cause and an effect of another event. As such, no event can be earlier and later than another event.[8]

Entropy

Earman considers backwards causation to be a non-starter. He lists a set of reasons for holding there is backwards causation and none convince him. We can explain all such "backwards" causation as "forwards" causation (Earman 1967, 212–214). The kind of forwards causation may be uncommon (216) and be the reverse of a common sequence of events. But that does not mean we should interpret it as backwards causation:

> [O]ne often sees cream mix with coffee but one never sees cream spontaneously unmix from coffee; the latter process does not violate any laws of nature—indeed, all the fundamental laws which govern such a process are believed to be completely time symmetric; but it is "abnormal" in our present sense because the probability of the realization of the initial conditions necessary for such a process is very low.
>
> (Earman 1967, 216)

This is no reason to hold that the cream unmixing from the coffee is backwards causation. "A more felicitous thing to say might have been 'The improbable happened; cream unmixed from my coffee today'" (Earman 1967, 216).

Earman's example of cream mixing into the coffee raises another type of explanation around temporal order. This is entropy. *Entropy* is a decrease in order in a system—such as separate cream and coffee becoming mixed together. Where two physical sequences are otherwise identical, the sequence in which entropy increases—and so order decreases—is by far the more common sequence in nature. We see that with all the examples so far: eggs roll and smash more often than they assemble and fly; cream mixes with coffee more than they separate.

What does entropy have to do with temporal order? According to the *second law of thermodynamics*, the total entropy of the universe overall or an isolated system always increases over time (or can never decrease over time). That is, the second law states that disorder increases and order decreases over time (North 2002, 122).

Although entropy is a fundamental part of thinking about temporal order, it is not so obviously problematic for the relationship between time and physics. It is an explanation of why most events appear to have a particular temporal order, such as why cream mixes into coffee but such a mixture does not spontaneously separate into both. Or why an egg may suddenly roll off a table and but not jump on to the table. These explanations do not need claims involving backwards causation nor need they involve a denial of absolute temporal order.

However, entropy does play a role in explaining why, in a world in which backwards causation is possible, and there is neither absolute temporal nor causal order, we can yet seem to observe temporal order.

Bardon's Entropy Account of Perception

As discussed earlier, Mellor proposes that the temporal order in perception is because of *causal order* within the structure of our psychology, e.g., in our perceptions. If this difference between apparent temporal order and actual causal order is acceptable, then there is no problem—at least, no *obvious* problem—with substituting causal order with some other non-temporal order.

For example, we could explain order by order in entropy. The non-temporal difference is a difference in entropy.[9] However, it is not a difference in entropy in what is observed as happening in the world (such as eggs rolling, then smashing; coffee and cream mixing). The difference is in entropy in the underlying physical processes within us.

The proposal here is that entropy can play the role in perception that causation plays in Mellor's account. Like Mellor's account, it is a psychological and perceptual explanation. However, it can also accommodate the challenges of backwards causation.

Entropy need not increase everywhere, on every scale. It can decrease locally in a system. However, this decrease occurs at the cost of increasing entropy around it. If we decide to separate the different liquids of a mixture, we do so by expending heat into the environment. For example, to cause the separation, we may heat a mixed liquid by burning some flammable material; the flames reduce the material to ash and dissipate heat into the surrounding air. Whatever complex ordered structure the material had is now disordered heat and ash.

Perception may have causation behind it. The appearance of temporal order may be due to causal order within perception. However, contrary to Mellor's position, this need not block backwards causation. It can also provide another motivation for a physical concept of relative temporal order.

According to Bardon, developing a thought from Hawking, the processes underlying our perception are like the processes underlying the separation of a mixture into different parts. In creating a perception, the physical structure of neurons becomes more organized. However, it does so at the cost of order in what goes into creating that structure. For example, we break down complex chemicals in food to get the basic chemicals we need, and throw away what we cannot use. As such,

> [T]he formation of memories is related to a larger thermodynamic trend [...] In forming a memory, we reconfigure our neurons. This creates a local increase in order (within parts of our brain responsible for memory), but only at the expense of a slight expenditure of energy [...] an overall entropy increase. [...] Our brains getting themselves in better order happens within the context of the trend toward overall heat dissipation.
>
> (Bardon 2013, 120–121)

This allows psychological temporal order and entropy difference to be linked.

However, in a universe where entropy decreases, that is, not the one we find ourselves in, "our brains couldn't be getting themselves into better order". For example, heat would not dissipate but collect, squashing locally structured things, such as neural structures, into something more disordered, e.g., a mash of the materials that previously constituted the neural structures. This is an increase in local entropy.

In that universe, this increased local entropy prevents the formation of such complex entities as neurons (and perceptions associated with them). At least, it prevents it where the *organizing* of neurons and perceptions is in the direction of entropy's *decrease*. However, it is different for an organism that exists in the opposite direction in time to us in this universe, for example, its perceptions are formed on top of *backwards* causation. For that organism, there is a local entropic decrease—a local increase in order. As such, there can be a local organization of material into neurons and perceptions. Their perceptions form in the opposite direction in time. Their perceived arrow is reversed to ours; for them, global entropy in that universe increases.

If we were such reversed creatures in a universe where entropy is decreasing "we would remember the 'future' and anticipate the 'past'. *But the past, in that universe, would be just like our future, and the future, and vice-versa.*" (Bardon 2013, 121).

This is illustrated in Figure 4.5. Again, we have a perception $S(e{<}f)$. However, here we have two situations: one (the left side of the figure) in which the entropy

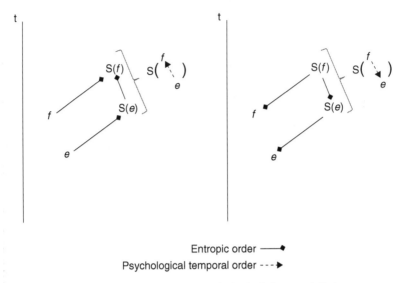

Entropic order ———▸
Psychological temporal order ---▸

Figure 4.5   Entropic Order Explains Psychological Temporal Order

increases in one direction, and the other (the right side) in which entropy increases in the *opposite* direction.

There is an entropic order and an apparent temporal order. The direction of apparent temporal order arises out of the entropic order. Because the entropic order on the right is the opposite of the entropic order on the left, the apparent temporal orders on both sides are also opposites of each other.

Such an account offers a response to denying relative temporal order based on perceptions and any intuitions or sense we have in line with them.

For subjects in a universe with backwards causation, and reversed entropy, the correct direction of temporal order is undetectable. For such subjects, they would perceive events in the opposite direction to it. Their perceptions would be reversed because they are determined by causal order, and that is backward. But they would also observe increasing entropy in that universe—because, for them, it is increasing.

Once we account for both, there seems to be nothing observable left to explain with absolute temporal order. Anyone in that universe who insisted there was such absolute order would insist it runs in the exact opposite to the direction we would accept. For example, for us, the sun in that universe dies before the moon tidally locks. But, for subjects in that world who, relative to *us*, exist backwards in time, the sun dies after the moon tidally locks.

There are other features of absolute temporal order that have been raised against the physical concept of time as a whole, that is, as it applies to time on the cosmic physical level, from the Big Bang to the Heat Death of the universe. Temporal order on this scale is sometimes called *global* temporal order. And there are responses to claims that there is absolute global order. For example,

Price appeals to initial conditions and temporal *anisotropy* to explain how temporal order is locally possible in the absence of global order (Price 2013, 292).

However, similar to the concept of time rejected by Kant's antinomies (see Chapter 1), these features are not as obviously problematic with respect to our intuitions about time. As such, although interesting, we do not discuss them here (but see Price 1997 and 2013). Instead, let us turn to objections against relative time relevant to more local and lived time.

Objections to Relative Time

The general position in modern physics is that time is relative. Does this relativity mean that, according to physics, time is unreal? Does time depend on absolute simultaneity and temporal order? This is a problematic outcome for any physical theory to take.

Let us consider arguments that such relativity does mean that time is unreal. First, we consider objections from Bergson, a philosopher who was a contemporary of Einstein. Then we look at more recent objections, from tense theorists and tenseless theorists.

Bergson's Objections to Relative Time

According to Bergson, a relative conception of time cannot be a conception of real time. In his view, there can be only one real time—with only one real duration and real simultaneity.

Objection 1: Real Time Is Continuous

First, according to Bergson, physical time is discrete or discontinuous—*divisible*. It must be divisible because we can measure it; it "seems to us to be wholly a measurable magnitude, just like space":

> I say, e.g., that a minute has just elapsed, and I mean by this that a pendulum, beating the seconds, has completed sixty oscillations. If I picture these sixty oscillations to myself [...] I do not think of sixty strokes which succeed one another, but of sixty points on a fixed line, each one of which symbolizes [...] an oscillation.
>
> (Bergson 1889, 104)

However, according to Bergson, real time cannot be divisible. Real time cannot be divided like pendulum seconds. It is a continuous and unmeasurable duration of past flowing into the present. In real time, there is "pure duration" but this duration lacks "a homogeneous medium or a measurable quantity" (Bergson 1889, 105). He bases this on time in everyday life. In particular, time in immediate experience is not broken into parts. It is a continuous stream. We can, perhaps, artificially impose some points in that stream (such as ticks of a clock), and so seem to take a measure of the stream itself. However, this is a measure of the points, not the stream. The stream is more than just the sum of these points, and it cannot be captured by such limited measures.

If time is continuous, and physical time is discrete, then Bergson makes a convincing case. One cannot strictly identify a discrete quantity with a continuous quantity.

However, it is unclear that relativistic physics is threatened by this need for real time to be continuous. Modern physics does not require discrete time. Indeed, it is typical to conceive of relativistic time as continuous.

For example, it is possible, given relativistic physics, for one reference frame's duration between two events to be π-times another reference frame's duration. Such a difference in values requires time to be continuous in at least one of these frames. If, in the first frame, we treat time as discrete, then, in the second frame, we cannot.

Whatever the duration might be in the first frame, say n, it is n/π in the second frame; n/π is not a value in a discrete series (we cannot get to it, for example, by dividing moments by countable values such as 3, 4, 5 ...). As such, a discrete conception of time is not found in STR.

Objection 2: Relative Time Is Merely Imagined Time

Physics' concept of time conflicts with experience because it relativizes simultaneity. This is the main objection to the physical concept of time; it not merely Bergson's. However, one of Bergson's specific objections to physical time's relativity is not often found explicitly in later objections. According to Bergson, relative time is not because of anything observed in real life, but because of the imaginings of physicists. It is only an abstract idea, applying to nothing physically real.

According to Ray, Bergson thought:

> [W]hen a space traveller or a clock moves away from us at high speed the moving objects are no more than phantoms of the physicist's imagination. The mathematical calculations of STR apply only to such phantom images. [...] [T]here may be a "multiplicity of imaginary times" in STR but there is nevertheless "a single, real time". [...]
>
> (Ray 1991, 25)

In this case, his view is in direct conflict with relativistic physics. STR (and general relativity as well) is a position committed to time itself being relative.

But why does Bergson think relative time is merely imaginary? Perhaps one reason is that, at the time of his writing, there was little evidence of relative time. The evidence was experiments that initially prompted Einstein's theory and a later experiment from the physicist Eddington about Mercury's movement around the sun (for a brief history, Yourgrau 2005).

However, there seems to be a great deal of evidence now for such STR. The behaviour of gold atoms in CERN's large hadron collider and the operations of GPS both need calculations using relativistic time (Galison 2003). The simplest explanation for this necessity is that time is relative. So, what other reason could prompt one to insist that time is absolute?

Objection 3: Experienced Time Requires Absolute Time

For Bergson, relative time *must* be only imaginary because our *experience* of time does not match it. Our experience is of absolute time. And Bergson insists that the physical concept of simultaneity must match our experience of this relation. Otherwise, the physical concept has no *raison d'être*: it does not describe the relationships we experience between things and events, but some mathematical relation which we do not, nor cannot, experience. Thus, for him, this mathematical relation is not simultaneity. Whatever it is, it must be something else (Bergson 1999, 46).

As an example of STR's conflict with experience, Bergson offers the experience of the simultaneity of two flows. Say that you watch a tightrope-walker crossing the centre of a whirlpool. His rope bisects the circle of spinning water. You stand on the ground near one end of the rope. On the far side, the water flows left; on the near side, the water flows right. The water is flowing in opposite directions and you are aware of both. Here, you experience two motions—that is, two flows.

There are two questions about this experience:

- Do you experience simultaneous events in experiencing the two movements of water?
- Is your experience of the water flowing left simultaneous with your experience of the water flowing right?

According to Bergson, the answer is trivial: you experience the flows together; thus, they are simultaneous. Two instantaneous perceptions are simultaneous that are "apprehended in one and the same mental act" (Bergson 1999, 35). He then adds:

> [I]t is obvious that simultaneity implies two things: first, an instantaneous perception; second, the capacity of our attention to divide itself without being split up. I open my eyes for a moment. I perceive two flashes in that instant coming from two separate points. I call them simultaneous because they are both one and two at the same time. They are one in that my act of attention is indivisible, yet they are two in as much as my attention is at once shared between both of them, divided and yet not split up.
>
> (Bergson 1999, 156)

Thus, this simultaneity "is absolute" but it also "does not depend on mathematical convention, or upon any physical operation such as the setting of clocks"

(Bergson 1999, 156). That is, Bergson rejects STR's concept of relative simultaneity because it does not capture our experience of simultaneity.

We can also apply this to experiences of temporal order. The experience of temporal order is of absolute temporal order, such as seeing an egg fall and break, and coffee and cream mixing (as opposed to eggs falling and breaking, and coffee and cream separating).

For Bergson's objection to work, the relativity must conflict with the experience of simultaneity. We discuss experienced simultaneity in more detail in Chapter 7. Here, let us look at the experience of something being absolute. For Bergson's objection to work, the experience of absolute simultaneity must be distinguishable from the experience of relative simultaneity.

However, counter-examples suggest that experiences of absolute and relative things need not be distinct. For example, there is motion. What would it be like to experience rest or motion as absolute, that is, as not depending on any reference frame? This question for motion is answered through two theories of the Earth's place in the universe:

- A (geocentric) view: The Earth is at absolute rest and the centre of the universe.
- A (centre-less) view: The Earth is relatively in motion or rest, like everything else.

Yet, to tell these two theories apart, we cannot turn to our experience; our experience cannot show if the Earth is at absolute rest or merely relatively at rest.

Similarly, Power argues that, in general, something can appear to be *absolute* just if its relativity is not apparent. As experiences of motion show, we can be ignorant of our own frame of reference in our experience. This lack of awareness can account for the apparent absoluteness of experienced simultaneity (Power 2010, 2018).

As a last point on Bergson's objections, it must be noted that he raised these challenges with the very physicist who produced the idea of STR. In 1922, he responded to a talk by Einstein, detailing his reasons for rejecting STR based on the experience of simultaneous flows. In response, Einstein said little. And some researchers argue that Einstein was dismissive of Bergson's arguments, and they have not been taken as seriously as they should (for discussion on the social and political issues around this debate, see Canales 2016).

Tense Theory Objections

Several other philosophers of time have difficulties with the physical concept of time. For tense theorists, relative time is incompatible with necessary features of time, such as temporal passage and a fundamental distinction between past, present, and future.

Tense Theory and Temporal Order

One reason to hold that there is absolute time—especially temporal order—is an important feature of time according to tense theorists. Tense theory requires that temporal passage be a real and fundamental feature of the world. And temporal passage requires absolute temporal order.

As discussed in Chapter 2, the temporal passage of tense theory is the change in event's positions in a unique A-series. The passage is change through *the* present, *the* past, *the future.* This real A-series is neither indexed nor relative.

For example, events in the A-series change in a particular way that gives this order. E_1 occurs *then* event E_2 occurs because:

(a) E_1 is future *then* E_1 is present *then* E_1 is past.
(b) E_2 is future *then* E_2 is present *then* E_2 is past.
(c) E_1 is present and E_2 is future; E_1 is past and E_2 is present.

According to Kroes, such passage "is an aspect of physical reality". Therefore,

> [T]he flow of time is a legitimate physical concept which in principle can be explicated without making an appeal to "extra-physical" concepts such as "consciousness" or "mind".
>
> (Kroes 1984, 424)

This change is not merely in our beliefs or experience. It is something in the world, even if we were not in it. Even if no conscious or thinking beings existed, so long as the moon tidally locks and the sun dies, it is an objective fact that the moon tidally locked in the past, and the sun will die in the future.

For example, the theory of the "moving spotlight" (or, as Savitt calls it, the "moving now"; Savitt 1996, 349), the present moves along events, making each one present for a time; those over which it has yet to move are future (or later than the present); those over which it has passed are past (or earlier than the present).

However, physical theory does not include such a moving present. Squires notes that, when all the physical facts are described, there is no special "now" in the description. "Now", like "here", is only an indexical "now", defined relative to a tenseless time (Squires 1990, 139). This is the case even in pre-STR physical theory; for example, Newtonian physics lacks a special now. If a moving now is what is missing, it was lost before relativistic physics came along.

What relativistic physics does is relativize this order. An order that arises out of backwards causation or that depends on different reference frames cannot be an absolute order. As such, it cannot be the absolute order behind a tense theorist's concept of temporal passage.

Tense Theory and Relative Simultaneity

The fundamental A-series of tense theory is also challenged by relative *simultaneity*. Tense theory's single fundamental A-series defines the B-series. It also defines the B-series relation of simultaneity. As such, it requires that simultaneity be absolute. Simultaneity holds between events if and only if those events are at the *same time*.

If tense theory is true, then this "same time" is a position in the A-series. This position can be the present. However, it can also be any other A-series position. For example, it can *three weeks from now* (a future A-series position) or *1,000 years ago* (a past A-series position).

For tense theory, what is important is that there is only one real series for such events. For example, there is only one present; there is also only one position that is *three weeks from now*. So, if an event is present, then it is not also *not*-present; and, if an event is *three weeks from now*, then it is also not *not-three weeks from now*.

However, if simultaneity between spatially separated events is relative to different frames, then the "same time" of events is relative to only some frames and not others. If, for some frames, the "same time" is the present time, then the multiple events are present only relative to some frames. Multiple events that are present to each other in some frames are, in other frames, *not* present to each other. In those other frames, at least some of the events are past and some are future.

We see this in the example of photons striking two mirrors while the train passes. For the platform, both of those events (e_1 and e_2) are present when the other event is present. But, for the train, when one of those events is present (for example, e_1 is present), the other event (e_2) is not present. Instead, e_2 is either past or future.

A unique A-series cannot have this. There can be two ways of dividing the same events between A-series positions. There is only one A-series, and so only one way to divide them.

As such, only one of these descriptions of the pastness, presentness, or futurity of events can be a description of their positions in the *real* A-series. Tense theorists must hold that one of these descriptions of events' A-series positions is mistaken—or, at best, merely derived or unreal.

Presentism

The need for this is especially pressing given *presentism*. Presentism holds that only the present is real. Yet, if the difference between the present and past is relative to different frames, then (given presentism), what is real is relative to different frames. Recall that such frames are connected to such properties as velocity—speed and direction. If two things move at different speeds to one another, or in different directions, their frames are different. As such, given presentism, what is real is different between them, and only because they are in different frames.

That is, given presentism and relativistic physics together, reality is different depending on how fast you move.

In any case, the problem is there for all tense theorists, not just presentists. The tense theory requirement is like Bergson's demand: he thinks of relative simultaneity (and any time series arising from it) as learned or imaginary. It is not a *real* time series.

Similarly, say that tense theory is true, and e_1 and e_2 are in the same real present. That is, they are simultaneous—at the same time. Yet, relativistic physics suggests that there is a frame in which they are not simultaneous; say, one (e_1) is present and the other (e_2) is past. Given tense theory, the non-simultaneity of these events is not in a *real* time series. The real time series has them simultaneous (and present).

However, unlike Bergson, tense theorists cannot appeal to a lack of physical evidence to hold that other frames are merely imaginary. So, how can they explain the evidence while also holding that there is still a single, real A-series? How can they accept the physics while also holding that there is absolute simultaneity and absolute temporal order?

Privileged Frames of Reference

By far the most common tense theorist response is that not all frames of reference are equivalent. There is a *privileged* frame which is distinct from the others, which amongst themselves continue to be equivalent. This unique, privileged frame matches real space and time. The time measured in the privileged frame is absolute time; from this frame, the measured simultaneity is the real, absolute simultaneity; the measured temporal order is the absolute temporal order. Through this, we also can have a single real A-series: there can be a single absolute division of time into past, present, and future.

In recent philosophy, Tooley and Lowe both argue for such a privileged frame (Tooley 1997; Lowe 2003). However, this view is not just from philosophers more recent than Bergson. As Galison describes it, several pioneers in 20th-century physics, Bergson contemporaries, held such a view. Their mathematics resembled Einstein's relativistic physics, but they continued to assume that there was still absolute time. Instead, there was a privileged frame.

Why did such theorists hold a privileged frame? They did not explicitly demand an A-series (McTaggart's paradox did not obviously play a role in their deliberations). One reason is that the privileged frame was the frame of the *ether*.

The Ether

The ether was a concept in 19th-century physics introduced, in part, to explain the movement of light. Its details need not concern us here; we need only know that, in physics of that time, it was held to be *absolutely at rest*. No matter if it is measured to move by some arbitrary frame, the ether never *really* moves.

The ether could seem to move because of one's frame of reference. However, this is mistaken. If, for example, a train station moved relative to the ether, then the ether may seem move, just as a train moves relative to the station. However, this is a mistake. The ether is absolutely at rest; no matter how one interacts it, it does not move; other things do. What moves in relation to it is always what is really in motion. Thus, although, for the station, the ether may seem to move, and the station to be at rest, the ether is really at rest and the station is really moving.

Thus, the ether occupies a privileged frame of reference for motion. The measure according to the ether's frame is the real measure of motion. No other frame gives such values. When it came to thinking about the evidence that prompted relativistic physics, theorists continued with this approach:

> [S]ome of the greatest physicists of the nineteenth century were beginning, out of desperation, to experiment with mathematical variations in the way the time variable t transformed in different reference frames. But all of them—Poincaré, Lorentz, Abraham—kept firmly to the notion of a true ether rest frame, and none of them accorded equal weight to [other reference frames] and the true (absolute) physical time of the ether rest system.
>
> (Galison 2000, 374)

That the ether is at absolute rest raised problems with trying to describe it as a physical entity. For example, how can a physical entity interact with an ether that neither resists nor moves against anything (Lange 2002)?

Part of Einstein's revolutionary thinking was that he dispensed with its necessity in physics. As discussed, Einstein claimed that all inertial frames are equivalent, arbitrary, and conventional. This came from *The Principle of Relativity.* No frame is privileged. There is no privileged ether frame.

To get the single A-series, the tense theory must deny this principle. The same laws are not valid for all frames of reference. Not all frames are equivalent. There is a frame that matches real time, including an absolute division between past, present, and future.

Objection: We Cannot Detect the Privileged Frame

Rest relative to the privileged frame is not really "relative" at all. It is not simply at rest relative to something else. Nor is it really moving. If it seems to move, then that is a mistake. However, we cannot detect this particular frame. The laws of physics look the same in it as other frames.

Some reasons have been advanced for why this is so. For example, Lorentz proposes that light—which does not really have a constant speed in all frames—propagates in such a way that, from all frames other than the privileged frame, it contracts in the direction of motion. This contraction gives light the same speed as it has in the privileged frame (Galison 2003). To save tense theory, the earlier Newtonian idea of absolute rest is reintroduced, with no physical evidence to support it.

However appealing this may be, it has its own counter-intuitive consequences. Unlike other frames, from which motion and rest are merely relative, rest in the privileged frame is absolute rest. If something moves relative to the privileged frame, then it really moves. Even something at rest in the privileged frame seems to move (because the observer moves relative to it), it does not really move. This is the case despite, with respect to all other physical properties of entities in it and in non-privileged frames, there being no difference in their behaviour.

So, it may seem to me that, when I run quickly relative to the privileged frame, I am moving. However, if it seems to me that I run quickly but I am at rest in the privileged frame, I am not really moving. Despite pumping my legs, being out of breath, and feeling the strain of motion, I am not moving at all.

However, if tense theorists consider absolute time undeniable by physical theory, then they may accept such counter-intuitive consequences. To accept relative time, they may think, is much worse. For example, Prior discusses two people moving relative to each other, and the question of who first saw a flash of light. According to relativistic physics, outside each's reference frame, there is no sense to this question:

Now I don't want to be disrespectful to people whose researches lie in other fields than my own, but I feel compelled to say that this just won't do. I think we have excellent grounds for insisting that the question in question is not a meaningless one [...]. People who are doing relativity physics are concerned with the relations of before and after and simultaneity, but these aren't the first things as far as the real passage of time is concerned—the first thing is the sequence of past, present, and future, and this is not just a private or local matter, different for each one of us; on the contrary, pastness, presentness and futurity are properties of events that are independent of the observer [...]

(Prior 1998a, 105)

Tense theorists may be happy to follow Prior and dismiss the physics. However, there are problems with separating time from physical time. Physical time has the time in changes within physical objects, including rocks, people's bodies, chairs, and fundamental particles. If tense theorists grant this physical time to physicists, then there seems little left for tense theorists. Perhaps independent or substantival time is still available. However, other aspects of time are found in the physical world.

Metaphysicians may respond that metaphysical time just *is* the time in changing physical things. A physical description of time is just inadequate for capturing it entirely. And if a description of time conflicts with this metaphysical idea of time, then it is not really time.

Such a metaphysical response requires time be blocked from empirical investigation. Tense theorists who are metaphysicians may be happy with this.

Tenseless Theory

According to the tenseless theory *B-theory*, time is real. Time is fundamentally the B-series, the series of events in terms of before/after and simultaneity. Change is merely differences in things or properties at different points in the B-series. Temporal order is the before/after relation, e.g., there is a difference in temporal order between E *before* F and F *before* E.

B-theory has less problems with relativity about time. That physics relativizes A-series positions is not a challenge to B-theory. B-theory does it as well. A-series positions are relative, derived from the positions of events in the B-series.

As such, generally, tenseless theory is considered more compatible with relativistic physics. However, relativistic physics can raise problems for B-theory. Relativity theory not only relativizes A-series positions; it relativizes B-series positions as well. The B-series is the series of positions ordered by *temporal order* and *simultaneity*. And these are relative according to relativistic physics.

Thus, a B-series ordering of events is also relative. If a B-theorist holds that there is an absolute B-series, then they must deny relativity theory. They must do so for the same reason that A-theorists must deny relativity theory. Time is relative; there is no absolute temporal series, be it a B-series or A-series.

Almost no current tenseless theorists (B-theorists or otherwise) deny relativity theory. The closest, perhaps, is Mellor (e.g., Mellor 1991, 1998). As discussed in the section on causal order, Mellor holds that backwards causation is impossible. If backwards causation is required for relativity of time, then Mellor must be a tenseless theorist who denies relative time. Yet, even in that case, he does not. Indeed, he argues from STR against A-theory (Mellor 1998).

However, as said, he does want to deny some relativity—the relativity of causal direction. Causation cannot run in one direction only in some contexts. It absolutely runs in one direction. And his attitude toward the possibility of backwards causation resembles what a tense theorist might think of relative time more generally.

Like Prior, Mellor is not swayed by the mere possibility of some consequence of physical time. On physics allowing backwards causation, Mellor writes:

> But this assumes that anything which is "physically possible" (i.e., compatible with physics) is really possible i.e., that only physics can limit metaphysical possibility. And that's nonsense. For example, the physics of a simple pendulum only constrains its period of oscillation to be proportional to the square root of its length, an equation which has negative solutions. But this doesn't entail that, unless some *physics* rules it out, a pendulum could only oscillate in literally less than no time! We need no *a posteriori* physics to rule that out. We can rule it out *a priori*, because it makes no sense.
>
> (Mellor 1991, 197)

For a tense theorist, like backwards causation, perhaps relative time is also merely a physical possibility. Perhaps it is also a concept that, metaphysically, makes no sense.

They may do more. They may turn from metaphysics to defend their position. Bergson defends his view of time by experience; he draws on phenomenology, not metaphysics. As we discuss in Chapters 6 and 5, there are other kinds of philosophical objections to such claims from physical theory.

Study Questions

1. Consider an ordinary, everyday physical object, such as a table or an apple. Can such an object exist outside of time?
2. Describe two main elements in physical theory that give rise to relative simultaneity. Do you need both? Could you deny one and have *absolute* simultaneity?
3. What, do you think, is the best reason to hold that temporal order is relative? Now reverse it: what is the best reason to hold that temporal order is absolute?
4. How does perception explain why we might believe there is *absolute* temporal order? Are there similar reasons to believe in other kinds of absolute values, such as absolute motion? If not, what do you think is the most important difference?
5. Let us say that all instances of simultaneity are absolute. Is there any way you could discover or show there is such absolute simultaneity?

Notes

1 For discussion of a specific aspect of the substantivalist debate, and a brief discussion of Kant's argument see Chapter 1. For more on the debate in general, see, e.g., Forbes 1991; Dainton 2001; Lange 2002; Le Poidevin 2004.)
2 This thought-experiment is an update on one from Einstein. However, the specific form is based on Dainton 2001, Power 2010 and 2018. The figures here are from Power 2018 (similar figures can be found in Power 2010).
3 See Chapter 3.
4 Mellor prefers facts as the relata of causation, rather than events, but also holds that his argument is the same whether it involves facts or events (for Mellor's work on tense and facts, see Chapter 5).
5 Also, versions of this account are found in Mellor 1981 and 1998.
6 Mellor also argues that this perception of temporal order is not of tensed order, but tenseless order. In the content of our perceptions of temporal order, nothing looks past or present; "there is nothing tensed" (Mellor 1991, 194). We look at this again in Chapter 6.
7 See Chapter 10.
8 As with the events e_1 and e_2 in the section on relative simultaneity, the events here are particular events, numerically identical events, not events that are only similar to each other.

9 This may be better thought of as a version of Mellor's theory, and not an alternative theory. Mellor follows Reichenbach's concept of causation (Mellor 1991). Reichenbach proposed that causal order (or asymmetry) could be reduced to entropic asymmetry (Reichenbach 1956; for discussion, Frisch 2013, 295).

Suggested Readings

Putnam (1967) is an earlier philosophical commentator on relativistic physics and its implications for the philosophy of time. Mellor's 1981 and 1998 also provide good introductions to arguments with respect to the metaphysics of time. Dainton 2001 is an excellent thorough philosophical text on the physics of time, in all its possible forms. Lange 2002 is also a good introduction, as is Lockwood 2005. For a historical and philosophical discussion on physics and time, see Yourgrau 2005.

Mellor's work on temporal order and perception is found in his 1981, 1991, and 1998. The case for backwards causation is thoroughly argued by Price 1997; it involves delving into entropy and quantum mechanics much further than is done in this chapter; see also his 2013. Bardon 2013 is a good discussion on the perceived arrow of time in a world without absolute order.

For philosophical objections to relativistic physics, see Tooley 1997. For historical context, including reasons for its popularity, see Galison 2003. For a similar thorough examination of Einstein's work, but which focuses on and considers Bergson's objections from the social and artistic context at the time, see Canales 2016. Finally, Capek 1991 for a physicist's thoughts on modern physics' view of time, one which is sympathetic to Bergson's ideas.

5   Philosophy of Language and Time

Overview

One approach to problems in the philosophy of time is to examine the language in which these problems are expressed. This comes out of an approach to philosophy of language that many theorists in the last century considered productive. This is to first or, even, *only* analyse the language of what seem to be metaphysical problems. In doing so, the intent is to understand these seeming problems instead as puzzles of language and grammar.

Applied to time, some philosophers attempt to use analyses of our temporal language to dissolve philosophical problems. One approach is to criticize the literal metaphysical meaning of temporal language. In particular, some metaphysical ideas about time, such as temporal passage, seem to be less literal metaphysical expression and more metaphorical expression. However, a more common approach in the philosophy of time is to criticize descriptions of time for ignoring the necessity of time in these descriptions. Some philosophers argue that tenseless theorists incorrectly use language in their descriptions of time. When the need for time in the language is taken seriously, many of the metaphysical problems around time are revealed to be problems of expression.

In addition, a common argument is that language supports allegedly intuitive concepts of time, such as tense facts and tensed change. One way it supports those concepts is that tenseless descriptions of events cannot capture the language we use to describe such tenses. In particular, they cannot capture the meaning of tensed language. However, tenseless theorists argue that they do have means of capturing such tense language, through token and date theories of meaning.

Lastly, there is a conception of temporal talk as a form of logic. This is sometimes taken to motivate a view that language supports one theory over another. However, even here, the language does not obviously support one position in time over another. The general point is that language does not obviously decide the philosophical debates around time.

Time and the Linguistic Turn

One investigation into language and philosophy concerns the difference between linguistic expressions—such as words, sentences, and phrases—and other phenomena. There is the question of how to distinguish words cut in a tree from marks left by wood-boring insects. The generally agreed answer is that the difference is not in obviously physical properties, such as location, shape, or size. Words can be carved where insects burrow. The marks of wood-boring insects can look exactly like a sentence. A sentence in an appropriate alphabet can resemble insect marks in wood. And like any written words, such expressions can have any size at all.

The most direct and immediate answer philosophers agree on is that what differentiates linguistic expression from other things is *meaning*. Something is meant by linguistic expression; nothing is meant by other non-linguistic physical things. Words cut in a tree have meaning. Marks from insects do not.

Another philosophically relevant aspect of language is that meaningfulness of language can conceivably challenge any philosophical theory at all (or even theories from other disciplines). One may have a theory of some X—whatever X may be (here, we are interested in time, but it can apply to space, colour, or anything whatsoever). We may ask, does one's theory capture the apparent meaning of expressions about X? If not, does it have an explanation for why there seems to be such meaning? Furthermore, can how we express concepts of X help solve philosophical problems about X?

These questions took on particular force from the early 20th century. At that time, many philosophers began to take a linguistic approach to philosophical problems. In this *linguistic turn* in philosophy, they first treated metaphysical problems as matters of language and grammar. Investigations into the problems of metaphysics were to involve how we *express* them—how we formulate our questions and phrase our answers. As the logician and philosopher Prior put it: there may be "genuine metaphysical problems" but "you have to talk about grammar at least a little bit in order to solve most of them" (Prior 1991, 35).

Some philosophers, such as *verificationists* and *logical positivists*, took a harsher approach to metaphysical problems. They denied that there were any genuine metaphysical problems at all. They argued that metaphysical problems are reducible to puzzles and mistakes of language. Metaphysical expressions are taken to literally refer to something in the world. However, independent of linguistic puzzles and mistakes, they have no meaning at all. Instead, they are meaningless pseudo-expressions (Carnap 1932, 61). Any metaphysical expression has as much meaning as the statement that "the even numbers are darker than the odd numbers" (Carnap 1932, 72).

But why are metaphysical expressions, in *particular*, so meaningless? Most of them certainly seem as meaningful as other expressions, and nothing like statements about the colour of numbers. Carnap answers: metaphysical expressions are meaningless because they have neither a literal meaning nor a metaphorical meaning. Expressions only acquire literal meaning through tautologies or experience (including empirical evidence). For example, we might acquire the meaning of concepts such as "apple" and "ripe" by empirical observation: seeing apples in different seasons, and observing their different states, including their being ripe. We grasp the meaning of "apples are fruit" by grasping the concept of apples, the more general concept of fruit, and seeing the trivial connection between them.

Metaphysical expressions do not acquire meaning this way. For example, say we make metaphysical statements about time's substance. We do not grasp the meaning of such a statement by trivially understanding "time" and "substance", and seeing how these are connected. Nor do we grasp its meaning by empirically observing time and substance as we might an apple and its ripeness. Otherwise, their "metaphysical theses would become simple propositions of experience of the same kind as those of physics". However, according to Carnap, metaphysicians provide no other criteria of meaning for their statements (Carnap 1932, 65).

Instead, Carnap states, in most cases, the metaphysicians use terms with ordinary literal meanings. They also *mean* what they say literally. However, they use the terms metaphorically, and not literally. Through this move, the meaning is lost. The "meaningless words of metaphysics usually owe their origin to the fact that a meaningful word is deprived of its meaning through its metaphorical use in metaphysics" (Carnap 1932, 71).

Why do metaphysical terms lose meaning just because they are used metaphorically? It is because metaphysicians do not intend to use the metaphorical meaning. They take the metaphorical language as if it is meant literally; in doing so, the language metaphysicians use has no meaning at all. It does not have the ordinary literal meaning; it is metaphysical language, not ordinary language. It does not have the metaphorical meaning, because it is meant to have a literal meaning.

In 21st-century philosophy, this sceptical view of metaphysics is no longer generally held. Many (if not most) 21st-century philosophers consider the verificationist project of reducing all metaphysical problems to linguistic puzzles to fail. Yet, the point still has force when we consider specific uses of language in philosophical discourse.

We can see this with time. In particular, we see it with some metaphysical descriptions of time. Terms are used that have ordinary literal meanings, but they do not have those literal meanings. Instead, the terms seem to be used in their metaphorical sense. However, they are used as if they are not metaphorical. This raises the question: what *are* the intended meanings of such terms? And, if we do not know, how can we say we understand our arguments?

Metaphors of Temporal Passage

The linguists Lakoff and Johnson argue that our language of time is, in many respects, metaphorical language. Our conceptual systems are grounded in our experiences of the world. These concepts come in three kinds.

Some of our concepts are about the physical world or experienced things, such as ordinary objects spread out around us in space. When we use these concepts, or describe the subjects of these concepts, we mean what we say literally. For example, we see two objects and say that one of the objects is larger than the other; we mean what we say here *literally*.

Other abstract concepts are not about experienced things. The contents of these concepts are described metaphorically. For example, we have abstract concepts of numbers. And we say that one number is *higher* than another. *Higher* is a spatial concept. No numbers are literally higher or lower than others. None have actual or literal elevation of any kind; they do not exist in space at all.

Finally, there are concepts that are not obviously of abstract things. They are in some way related to the physical world. However, we do not experience them and we use metaphors to describe them. For example, we have concepts of emotions, such as happiness—and we refer to them metaphorically, e.g., "My mood is low today" uses a spatial concept, "low", metaphorically.

Lakoff and Johnson commonly use talk about time to illustrate the last type of concept. They hold that, often, when we talk about time, we use metaphorical language that, meant literally, is talk about space. Time is often "metaphorically conceptualized in terms of space" (Lakoff and Johnson 1980, 128).

Note that they do not claim that all temporal language is metaphorical; a description of time as extended (i.e., as having duration) or ordered (i.e., temporal order) is a literal description. Other linguists agree; for example, Boroditsky writes that we do experience time as a continuous unidirectional change "marked by appearance and disappearance of objects and events". As such, this aspect of time does not require metaphor to describe it; it can be described literally (Boroditsky 2000, 3–4).

However, such linguists do think temporal language is metaphorical with respect to an important disputed feature in the philosophy of time—temporal passage. Here are two of Lakoff and Johnson's (1980) examples (uppercase type indicates the metaphor's name):

- TIME IS A MOVING OBJECT: For example, "the time will come when [...] By virtue of the TIME IS A MOVING OBJECT metaphor [...] the future is facing toward us as it moves toward us" (43–44).
- TIME IS STATIONARY AND WE MOVE THROUGH IT: For example, "we go through the years [...] We're approaching the end of the year" (45).

These are metaphors of *temporal passage*: "in one case, we are moving and time is standing still; in the other, time is moving and we are standing still. What is in common is relative motion with respect to us, with the future in front and the past behind" (Lakoff and Johnson 1980, 45).

Again, it is because we do not experience such temporal passage (these linguists claim). Temporal passage is among aspects "of our concept of time that are not observable in the world".

> For example, does time move horizontally or vertically? Does it move forward or back, left or right, up or down? Does it move past us, or do we move through it? All of these aspects are left unspecified in our experience with the world. They are, however, specified in our language—most often through spatial metaphors. Whether we are looking *forward* to a brighter tomorrow, falling *behind* schedule, or proposing theories *ahead* of our time, we are relying on spatial terms to talk about time.
>
> (Boroditsky 2000, 4)

If this is right, then one might argue as follows: temporal passage is only, if anything, a metaphorical passage. It does not matter whether the change is a movement through time of the present (as in the "moving spotlight" theory) or movement of the moments of time itself (as in McTaggart's change of events' A-series positions). This passage is not a *literal* passage.

This raises a problem for some forms of the tense theory of time. As discussed in the first metaphysics chapter, tense theory asserts that temporal passage is real. However, if a description of such passage is merely metaphorical, the description of it as passage is not a literal description. As such, if tense theorists mean it literally then, given Carnap's attack on metaphysical language, what they are saying is meaningless.

Indeed, some tenseless theorists do charge tense theorists with treating a metaphor as a metaphysical thesis. According to Smart, that "old age and death lie in wait for us is to speak in metaphor" (Smart 1963, 17). In addition, at least one tense theorist agrees. Discussing problems around thinking about time, the philosopher and logician Prior writes:

> A natural first move towards extricating ourselves from [perplexities about time] is to admit that talk of the flow or passage of time is just a metaphor. Time may be, as Isaac Watts says, like an ever-rolling stream, but it isn't really and literally an ever-rolling stream.
>
> (Prior 1991, 35)

Objection: Metaphors of Passage Have Meaning

Tense theorists might respond that their talk about passage has always been metaphorical. It has never been literal. "Temporal passage" of course never means something like literal passage through space. However, although we must speak metaphorically, the meaning of the metaphor is clear. And the metaphor in some way gets at a metaphysical truth about time.

If the way we talk about these features of time is metaphorical, then it raises the question: why must we talk metaphorically? In contrast, we can literally refer to and describe motion in space. So, can we not provide a more literal reference or description for this important feature of time (according to tense theorists, anyway)?

For Prior, the reason we *do* talk metaphorically is because the events that are described as changing do not really change at all. Only objects change. However, the way we talk about events means the surface grammar of our statements resembles statements about objects. We return to Prior's kind of answer later in this chapter. For now, although it may explain why we talk metaphorically as if time is space, it does not explain why we must do this.

Perhaps we can provide some literal talk. Let us try this: the metaphorical terms around temporal passage such as "time passes" and a "spotlight" have the following literal meanings:

- What is metaphorically temporal passage is literally events changing position in the A-series.
- What is metaphorically a spotlight is literally a unique present.

In this case, the literal language avoids accusations of misled metaphorical talk. A tense theorist speaking like this is not subject to Carnap's accusations of meaninglessness. They do not treat as literal what is, in fact, metaphorical. They literally mean change here; they literally mean a unique present.

This may be enough to satisfy accusations of metaphorical language. It still leaves the question of where the literal meaning comes from. One proposal is that the linguists above are mistaken. We grasp our understanding of temporal passage from experience itself. That is, we *experience* events changing position in the A-series; we experience a unique present.

If this is right, then a tense theory statement about temporal passage, being based on experience, gets its literal meaning from that experience. It is not, in fact, a metaphysical statement. It is about the world we observe.

We discuss the case from experience for various theories of time in Chapter 6. Here, we turn to another challenge from language to certain metaphysical positions of time.

Merely Apparent Metaphysical Meaning

Carnap likens metaphysical language to the pseudo-statement that "the even numbers are darker than the odd numbers". This is obviously a meaningless pseudo-statement. However, the comparison opens one initial response to Carnap's attack. Unlike the nonsense about number colours, metaphysical language is *not* obviously meaningless. Metaphorical or not, it *appears* to have meaning. So, why does it appear to have meaning?

One common answer from critics of metaphysics is that the apparent meaning comes from the way the metaphysical pseudo-expression is structured. Language itself has a structure, a structure that has nothing to do with how the world is metaphysically. Instead, the structure itself can suggest a metaphysical interpretation. However, it does not mean that there is anything metaphysical to match it. It is just a feature of the structure or grammar of the language itself.

For example, the question "is time real?" resembles the question "is an apple green?" The grammar of the questions suggests that time is somehow similar to apples, reality is somehow similar to colour, and how time is real is somehow similar to how apples are green.

However, so this account goes, the similarity between these questions has nothing to do with time, reality, apples, and colours themselves. It has to do only with the grammar of the language in which the questions are asked. For example, the question needs a subject ("time", "apple") and predicate ("is real", "is green"). This does not mean that time resembles an apple in any way, nor that being real resembles being green. For example, that *time* and *real* can appear in sentences like this does not mean that they are, respectively, an object or a property.

Instead, when we consider the actual role time or reality play in language, we see they do not have a role like those of apples or colours. Time does not have the role of an object and reality does not have the role of a predicate. Instead, they have different roles in the grammar. For example, in language, they are *modifiers*.

Modifiers

Modifiers *modify* other terms, such as references to objects or properties. An example of a modifier is "slowly"; it can modify verbs such as "climb", as in "she slowly climbs the hill". Prior states that "putting a verb into the past or future tense is exactly the same sort of thing as adding an adverb to the sentence".

> "I was having my breakfast" is related to "I am having my breakfast" in exactly the same way as "I am allegedly having my breakfast" is related to it, and it is only an historical accident that we generally form the past tense by modifying the present tense, e.g. by changing "am" to "was", rather than by tacking on an adverb.
>
> (Prior 1991, 40)

So, for example,

1. "TOMORROW, there is a cat in the kitchen" is similar to "ALLEGEDLY, there is a cat in the kitchen".
2. "There WAS a cat in the kitchen" is similar to "There is NO cat in the kitchen".
3. "I visit you AFTER I collect the groceries" is similar to "I visit you OR I collect the groceries".
4. "I VISITED you" is similar to "I COULD visit you".

Some modifiers are redundant. We can usually dispense with them, except where we want to help clarify something's relationship to something else. And, according to Austin, "real" is such a redundant modifier.

A "real goldfinch" means the same as "a goldfinch". When we use "real" to modify a term, "we should insist always on specifying with what 'real' is being contrasted: and then usually we find some specific, less fatal, word, appropriate to the particular case, to substitute for 'real'" (Austin 1979, 88). For example, hearing a goldfinch singing in the kitchen, we may state that there is a *real* goldfinch trapped in the kitchen; there is not merely a recording of a goldfinch's song.

The principle here of caring about the role a term has in grammar is that doing so allows one to avoid what seem to be metaphysical problems, such as paradoxes. We rewrite the terms of these apparent problems so that they have their correct grammatical roles. When we do so, the problems no longer arise.

Again, specific to problems around time, such a paradox may be McTaggart's paradox. Let us try this: the paradox treats A-series positions such as the past, present, and future as if they are instants of times, as if they are *dates*. For example, "yesterday" is treated as if it is similar to Tuesday; "the present" is treated as if it is similar to "six o'clock".

However, in a correct grammar, this is the wrong role for these A-series positions. They are not dates. "We are inclined to say that both 'now' and 'six o'clock' 'refer to points of time'", writes Wittgenstein:

> This use of words produces a puzzlement which one might express in the question "What is the 'now'?"—for it is a moment of time and yet it can't be said to be either the "moment at which I speak" or "the moment at which the clock strikes", etc, etc.—Our answer is: The function of the word "now" is entirely different from that of a [date].
>
> [...] One has been tempted to say that "now" is the name of an instant of time, and this, of course, would be like saying that "here" is the name of a place, "this" the name of a thing, and "I" the name of a man.
>
> (Wittgenstein 1958, 108–109)

Wittgenstein's suggestion that "now" is like "here" and "I" is a tenseless theory approach to the question. As discussed in Chapter 2, a tenseless theory concept of "present" is it being an indexical similar to "here". When properly understood, the grammar shows that the role of A-series positions in language is as indexes, i.e., as tenseless theorists argue it to be.

However, that an analysis of grammar supports tenseless theory is an outlier in the discussion about language in the philosophy of time. Most philosophers of time that appeal to grammar and language defend *tense theory*.

Temporal Properties of Linguistic Expressions

What determines the meaning of what we say? One answer is that meaning is determined by particular instances of linguistic expression—for example, particular spoken utterances or written sentences. These exist in particular points in space and time; for example, words are carved in a particular location: halfway up a trunk of a particular tree. I tell someone my sandwich order at lunchtime, and when I tell them is a particular time.

However, it is generally agreed that such particular linguistic expressions—such as *that* written sentence on *that* page, that utterance about my sandwich—cannot be what determines meaning. Such particular expressions vary in their spatial and temporal structure. Yet, they can all share the same meaning. My statement about my sandwich can have the same meaning as what is carved in a tree; yet, my utterance and the carved words occur in different times and places, and last different amounts of time.

Tokens

Particular instances of linguistic expression are *tokens*. Examples include such expressions as utterances and written phrases. Tokens include the precise sequence of meaningful syllables when we speak; they also include the exact layout of printed ink when we write words on a page.

Along with tokens of linguistic expression, there are *types* of linguistic expression. Types are abstract entities under which different tokens may fall. If there are two individual robins in one tree, then there are two *tokens* of a bird (the two individual robins) but one *type* of bird, the type *robin*.

Furthermore, tokens can fall under a variety of different types. For example, a sentence written in black ink in English can be a token of type *English* and of type *black ink writing*. The same sentence can share one of its types with other tokens, and not others. For example, the above sentence can be the same type (*English*) as another sentence, but not the same type of ink (the other is written in blue ink), and be the same type (*black ink*) as yet another sentence, but that other sentence is a different language type (it is in Spanish).

Importantly, two tokens of the same *linguistic expression* can have the same *meaning*.

For example, the following two written sentences are both tokens of one linguistic expression:

(a) The cat is in the kitchen.
(b) The cat is in the kitchen.

There are two tokens—(a) and (b)—of a sentence. However, there is only one *type* of linguistic expression here.

Importantly, tokens need not share the same spatial and temporal properties to have the same meaning. For example, in Shelley's *Ozymandias,* the narrator finds the following lines carved beneath a statue in the desert:

My name is Ozymandias, King of Kings;
Look on my Works, ye Mighty, and despair!

If the narrator reads these lines out loud, his speaking it is a particular token—an utterance—that merely takes a second. Yet, that brief token has the same meaning as the millennia-old token carved in stone on the statue's base.

Meaning is not merely something that belongs to each of the particular tokens of a linguistic expression. And differences in meaning do not require differences in linguistic expressions' spatiotemporal properties. Because the particular tokens of linguistic expression can vary so much between them, yet have the same meaning, many theorists propose an abstract entity that bears the meaning. This might be thought of as a specific type under which these tokens fall. But what is the nature of this type? One influential theory is that types that bear meaning are *propositions*.

Propositions

Propositions are abstract entities that are expressed by tokens of linguistic expression. Although abstract, some of their defenders hold that they are very familiar to us. Moore writes: "what happens when you hear a sentence, which you do understand, from what happens when you hear a sentence which you do not understand":

> Certainly in the first case, there occurs, beside the mere hearing of the words, another act of consciousness—an apprehension of their meaning, which is absent in the second case. And it is no less plain that the apprehension of the meaning of one sentence with one meaning, differs in some respect from the apprehension of another sentence with a different meaning.
>
> There certainly are such things as the two different meanings apprehended. And each of these two meanings is what I call a proposition.
>
> (Moore 1953, 73–74)

That is, we apprehend or are aware of propositions when we understand or grasp the meaning of some expression.

Like other abstract entities, propositions do not occupy space. Only their tokens do. (a) and (b) both occupy different locations in space; one is above the other on the page; but, other than that, there is nothing else. The proposition that bears their meaning is not *also* located in space. As an abstract entity, it may be conceived of as a type—or, at least, something like a type.

Propositions may not occupy space. But do they occupy time? Certainly, their *tokens* occupy time. Say that the proposition "The cat is in the kitchen" is expressed by both a shout and some chiselled stone. And say that the shouting lasts a second and the carved words last a millennium. Is there also some moment or time in which the proposition itself exists? Does it flash into existence just *after* it is shouted? Or does it occupy the moments of its tokens? Say that I carve it into stone some time after I shout it. Does the proposition exist at the moment of the shout, ceasing when the shout ends—then, when I carve it into the stone, does the proposition begin to exist again, lasting as long as the carving?

These questions indicate the strangeness of holding that a proposition exists in time (again, not its *tokens*). They may suggest that holding that propositions exist in time is implausible. If propositions are types, then they suggest that it is even less plausible that they exist in time. Particular token robins may be born, live, and die; the *type* robin does none of these things, or anything temporal. So, one might think, particular tokens of linguistic expression are created, last some time, then end; the propositions that have these tokens' meaning do none of these things. Propositions are not temporal.

However, if propositions are not temporal, then there is a problem. Some theories of time attempt to explain such features of time as temporal passage by appealing to changing propositions. The changes are in truth-values of propositions. Yet, if propositions do not exist in time, then how can they change?

Changing Propositional Truth-Values

Say there is the following sequence of events during a week:

i.   On Tuesday, I shout "The cat is in the kitchen".
ii. On Wednesday, I write down "The cat is in the kitchen" on the kitchen noticeboard.
iii. On Thursday, my friend reads my sentence on the noticeboard—"The cat is in the kitchen".
iv. On Friday, my friend signs in American Sign Language (ALS) to me "The cat is in the kitchen".
v.   On Saturday, I sign back "The cat is in the kitchen" to them.

On each day, there is a different *token* of the linguistic expression. In addition, on each day, each of these different expressions (i–v) is a different *type* of linguistic expression:

- *i* is of the type *auditory speech act* or *utterance.*
- *ii* and *iii* are of the type *written sentence.*
- *iv* and *v* are of the type *ALS signing.*

Yet, all of these tokens have the same *meaning*. They are all tokens of the same proposition. They all mean that the cat is in the kitchen.

However, it can be the case that these tokens are not all true and false *at the same time*. For example, say that the cat is in the kitchen on Tuesday, not on Wednesday, but comes back into the kitchen again on Thursday. In that case, we have the following truth-values for tokens at different times:

- On Tuesday, the token in *i*—my shouting—is true.
- On Wednesday, the token in *ii*—the written sentence on the noticeboard—is false.
- Yet, on Thursday, the very same token in *ii* is also in *iii*—the written sentence—is, again, true.

Different tokens (the tokens in *i* and *ii*) of the same proposition have different truth-values. Furthermore, a single token of that proposition—the written sentence in *ii changes* truth-value from Wednesday to Thursday.

So, does the truth-value of the proposition *itself* change? Does the proposition expressed by "The cat is in the kitchen" *change* from being true on Tuesday, to false on Wednesday, back to true on Thursday? Again, not if propositions do not exist in time. Something that is not in time cannot change.

Truth-Makers and Facts

As discussed in Chapter 1, according to truth-maker theory, *truth-makers* make propositions true or false. This allows an explanation of how propositions can vary in their truth-values.

An important class of truth-makers is that of *facts*. Facts are specific kinds of entities, similar but not identical to events. They are not concrete particulars such as talking donkeys, but ways in which talking donkeys are. For example, in some possible, non-actual world, if talking donkeys are loud, then it is a *fact* that talking donkeys are loud.

Facts can be true or false, or the case or not the case; the terminology can vary. For example, it is the case or it is true that talking donkeys are loud; that is a *fact*. Furthermore, some facts are true in all possible worlds. For example, it is a fact in all possible worlds that the square root of 2 is irrational; there is no possible world in which the 2's square root is rational.

Furthermore, some but not all facts are true in the actual world (and some are only true in the actual world). For example, in the actual world, it is a fact that the speed of light is finite. In some other possible world, light travels instantaneously, the speed of light is infinite, and it is *not* a fact that the speed of light is finite. (And, in the actual world, it is not a fact that talking donkeys are loud, or anything else.)

Truth-Makers for Propositional Variation in Truth-Value

Some possible-world theories use truth-makers (including facts) to explain variations in proposition's truth-values across different worlds.[1] These typically involve concrete particulars[2] with a specific relationship to propositions about them. Briefly,

- Each possible world has a different set of concrete particulars in it. Many of these particular fall under different types, types that are absent in other worlds.

   For example, one possible world *W1* contains a set of particular talking donkeys; another world *W2* does not have such donkeys but has non-talking donkeys.

- These concrete particulars are *truth-makers* for certain propositions. That is, in the world containing them, they make certain propositions true; they can also make other propositions false.

For example, the proposition P^W *donkeys can talk* is true in *W1* because *W1* has talking donkeys in it; the talking donkeys are truth-makers for P^W in *W1*. However, in *W2*, P^W is not true, P^W is false, because there are no talking donkeys in *W2*; there are no talking donkeys to be truth-makers for P^W in *W2*.

Given this account, we can have a theory of propositions varying in truth-value over possible worlds. A proposition varies in truth-value across worlds if one world has the truth-maker and another world does not. P^W varies in truth-value from *W1* to *W3* because *W1* has talking donkeys and *W3* has not.

Perhaps we can apply similar reasoning to time. Each moment of time is an analogue of a possible world, leading to the following:

- Each time has a different set of concrete particulars in it. Many of these particulars fall under different types, types that are absent at other times.
- For example, one time *T1* contains a set of dinosaurs; another time *T2* does not have such dinosaurs but has horses.
- These concrete particulars are *truth-makers* for certain propositions. That is, in the world containing them, they make certain propositions true; they can also make other propositions false.

For example, the proposition P^T *there are dinosaurs* is true at *T1* because *T1* has dinosaurs in it; the dinosaurs are truth-makers for P^T in *T1*. However, in *T2*, P^T is not true, P^T is false, because there are no dinosaurs in *T2*; there are no dinosaurs to be truth-makers for P^T in *T2*.

In this way, we might say, propositions can change value by having different truth-makers at different times:

- P^T is true at one time, when there are dinosaurs.
- P^T's truth-maker at that time are the dinosaurs. P^T is also false at another time when there are no dinosaurs (such as 2020). There is not one dinosaur to make P^T true at that time.
- So, the proposition P^T changes because it is false at one time (*T1*) and true at another (*T2*).

Similarly, we can explain the variation in truth-values of propositions about objects and their changing properties. For example, say that there is a proposition P^{Ripe} that *the apple is ripe*. Then, similar to above, we have this situation.

If an apple is raw at one time (t_1) and ripe at another time (t_2), then:

P^{Ripe} that *the apple is ripe* is false at t_1 (when the apple is raw) and true at t_2 (when the apple is ripe).

From this account, it follows that different propositions are true or false at different times. For example, along with P^{Ripe}, there is P^{Raw}, that *the apple is raw*.

P^{Raw} is true at t_1 (when the apple is raw) and false at t_2 (when the apple is ripe).

However, there is an outstanding question here. It is the original question: how can propositions be *true at a time*?

Objection: Propositions Are Abstract and Not in Time

Lots of things have lots of properties in time. Donkeys talk loudly on a Tuesday. Similarly, it may be apparent that the proposition *donkeys talk loudly* is true on a Tuesday.

However, if propositions are abstract entities, then they are not *in time*. If propositions are not in time, then they cannot be anything *at a time*. If they cannot be anything at a time, they cannot be true or false at a time. If they cannot be true or false at a time, then they cannot vary their truth-value from one time to another.[3]

Truth-Makers and Tokens

Mellor (1998) argues that truth-makers (especially facts) make propositions true or false through the propositions' *tokens*.

Say that there is the following proposition:

K: the cat is in the kitchen.

Say there is also this possible fact:

M: there is a cat in the kitchen.

Furthermore, there is a cat in my friend's kitchen. However, there is no cat in my own kitchen.

Then we can say the following about propositions and tokens.

- I utter "the cat is in the kitchen" at a specific time and place. My utterance is a token U of K.
- There can also be other tokens of K, such as a sentence written on a noticeboard.
- As may be obvious, M can be a truth-maker of K. However, we cannot simply infer that K is true because M is a fact. It depends on *where* and *when* M is a fact.

Using such linguistic tokens, we can give the following account:

1. My utterance U "there is a cat in this kitchen" is a token of K.
2. U is at a location L in space and time.

3. At L, there is either a truth-maker or there is no truth-maker for K.
4. If there is a truth-maker (M) at L (e.g., L is my friend's kitchen), then K is true.
5. If there is no truth-maker (no M) at L (e.g., L is my kitchen), then K is false.

Then, the proposition K is true if the following conditions are met:

- The token U of proposition K is at location L.
- The truth-maker M is at L.

If these *truth-conditions* are met, then we can say:

- K is true at L.

That is, despite being an abstract entity, the proposition K is true at L because it has a token U and a truth-maker M at L. However, if the token U is not at L, then K cannot be true at L.[4] The truth-conditions depend on the token being there.

This is intuitive. Consider a different proposition K' composed of two phrases: "there is a knat" followed by "in the kitchen". If there is never a token of K (for example, no one ever speaks or writes K) when a knat is, in fact, in a kitchen, then K is never true. K *could* be true if someone just said it *in a kitchen* around some *knat*. But, as of this writing, they have not.

Implicit Context

Implicit, unspoken context matters to meaning. There is often an implicit understanding that, despite using terms that seem to refer to when or where we speak, we are not, in fact, referring to those times and places.

We often talk about things as if we are around them when we are not: in our own houses, we talk about cats in kitchens in other houses, and say "there is a cat in the kitchen". We do not lie nor are we mistaken. Or, at least, we are not taken to be lying or mistaken. For example, you visit me and are concerned about your cat. While having coffee in my kitchen, you phone home. Afterwards, with relief, you say to me "the cat is in the kitchen". I do not think you mean the kitchen we are in. But I believe you speak the truth.

That is, the time one refers to in a token can be *implicit*. It presumes recipients already grasp the context. When I say "the cat is in the kitchen", the implicit context can be the kitchen we are sitting in, for example, my own.

Token-Reflexive Truth-Conditions

However, the implicit context need not be that of either the individual expressing the proposition or the recipient. We can refer to other kitchens and cats without giving an explicit relationship between dates and places.

For example, I say to a friend K':

K': The cat is in the kitchen.

I do not mean the kitchen we sit in and he knows that. The kitchen here is, implicitly, a different kitchen to the one we are in. The truth-conditions of K' are met if the kitchen is other than the one we sit in. However, it otherwise resembles K. The difference is in the implicit context we share.

We can also make the contexts explicit. For example, instead of K or K', we have

> K": The cat is in another kitchen (*my friend's* kitchen) and not *this* kitchen (the kitchen in which my friend and I are talking).

Or even more explicitly:

> K#: On the second Wednesday of 2020, in the house four doors down from the Melkweg, Amsterdam, the cat is in the kitchen.

K" is true if there is a cat in a different kitchen to the one in which there is the token of K".

But K# has different truth-conditions. It does not matter where the token is. It is true if there is a cat in the kitchen four doors down from the Melkweg. But it does not matter where the token is. I can say it just outside the door of that address, or on the moon, or three hundred years from now, when the Melkweg no longer exists. K# is always true anywhere and at any time.

The table summarizes the four different kinds of propositions made true by their truth-makers and tokens.

Locations of Proposition's Tokens	Example
A. Tokens must be at the same time and place as their proposition's content.	K is true if the truth-maker is at the same and place as the proposition's token.
B. Tokens must be *implicitly* at a different time and place to their content and reference.	K' is true if its truth-makers are not at its tokens' times and places.
C. Tokens must be *explicitly* at a different time and place to their content and reference.	K" is true if its truth-makers are not at its tokens' time and place.
D. Tokens reference the time and place of their content but do not reference their own time and place.	K# is true if the truth-maker is at the time and place given in K#. It does not matter when and where tokens of K# themselves are.

Note the explicit differences between these tokens with respect to their reference to the token's own time and place:

A. K makes no reference to tokens; it contains only references to other objects and events.
B. K' also makes no reference to tokens. It only references the time and place of objects and events. However, another location is implied from the context.
C. K" explicitly references the truth-maker's time and place *and* the token's time and place. The proposition explicitly references its token's time and place by "this" or implicitly references it by "another". "Another X" has built into its meaning that there is an X with which our reference is compared. The token of K"'s own location is a referent.
D. K# makes no reference to the token *itself*.

B and C are significant here. The truth-conditions of K" involve explicit *reference to the token itself*.

Mellor calls truth-conditions that explicitly the token itself *token-reflexive* truth-conditions (Mellor 1998). Token-reflexive truth-conditions are truth-conditions of a propositions which include properties of the tokens themselves.

Such tokens are relevant to linguistic debates in the philosophy of time. They offer a tenseless theory response to challenges from propositions around tense. To see this, we must first look at a tense theory of language. This theory concerns how we naturally or must think of language. It also purports to dissolve apparently metaphysical problems of time while avoiding metaphysics.

Linguistic Responses to McTaggart's Paradox

Some philosophers argue that McTaggart's paradox is based on a mistake of language. In describing the fundamental nature of time and change, McTaggart fails to describe them in *tense* terms. He mistakenly uses tenseless language to describe time. He *detenses* descriptions of time—that is, removes tense from statements that should have it.

These philosophers claim that all language, including temporal language, is fundamentally tensed. If we ensure that we describe time in tense terms, and avoid describing it as an object with properties, then McTaggart's paradox does not arise.

For example, Prior writes:

> McTaggart's underlying assumption, which generates each of the moves that lead us to a contradiction, appears to be that "has been", "will be", and the strictly present-tense "is" *must* be explicated in terms of a *non*-temporal "is" attaching either an event or a "moment" to a "moment".

(Prior 1967, 6)

The solution involves only language. There is no need to bring in metaphysics. We need only discuss the language and ensure that we use language correctly.

The first philosopher to propose this solution is McTaggart's contemporary, C.D. Broad. According to Broad, despite McTaggart's belief that the A-series is fundamental to time, his argument is a *tenseless language* form of talk. However, tenseless language is neither an ordinary nor fundamental way of talking. The ordinary or fundamental form of language is *tensed*.

An event is never just past, present, or future. When we describe an event's position in the A-series, there is always a *temporal copula* built into the description. A temporal copula has time built into it. For example, "is" is a temporal copula because it refers to a present state of affairs. It has the same meaning as "is now". Similarly, "is past" and "was" have the same meaning, as do "is future" and "will be" (Broad 1938).

Neglecting this temporality in the language is central to the paradox. For example, take the statement "It was raining". This describes a particular event— the event of *raining*—at a particular time, in the past. So "It was raining" is the same as the raining being past, or:

(a) *The raining* is past.

According to McTaggart, the raining is also present and future. This leads to the following contradiction:

(b) The raining is past, present, and future.

However, McTaggart assumes that the correct understanding of the phrase "the raining is" is as a form of *tenseless* expression. The "is" in "the raining is" is not itself placing the event in the past, present, or future.

According to tense theorists, such a tenseless description misleads. Linguistic expression has time built into it, and this time is tensed. If X *is* Y, then X *is* Y *now*. As such, (a) is the same as (a'):

(a') The raining is *now* past.

And (b) is the same as (b'):

(b') The raining is *now* past, present, and future.

This allows us to avoid paradox. (a') may be true: all it needs to be true is that it is not raining now but it *was* raining, and so is past.

However, (b') is *false*. No event is *now* in several positions in the A-series. It is in just one A-series position. It can only be that:

(b'') The raining is now *either* present, past, or future, but *not all three*.

Or:

(b*) The raining *is now* present, it *will be* past, and *it was* future.

There is no contradiction in holding (a') and (b'') or (a') and (b*). These statements are of the same form as statements about any event in the A-series, and any position it might have in the series.

If this analysis is correct, then there is no contradiction in holding that events are in the A-series. As such, there is no paradox.

Irreducible Tense

This analysis rests on the position that tense is an irreducible feature of language. When we state, "A is B", the "is" is the same as "is now". To state that "A is B in the past" or "A is B in the future", we are more accurate and explicit to say that, respectively, "A was B" and "A will be B".

It works if we must talk about time in tensed terms, and there is only one way we can correctly describe events in these tensed terms. It does *not* work, however, if tenses are relative to different moments of time, and the ascriptions of "is", "was", and "will be" are as correct from one time as they are from another.

For example, if it is as correct to describe the weather from a past position in the A-series as it is to describe it from the present, then the tense of the weather, of the day's raininess, has the following contradictory A-series positions:

- The raining is past (according to the present).
- The raining is present (according to the past).

Again, the contradiction in (b). As such, this proposition must either be true or false according to one A-series. Picking out a single A-series makes this a tense theory approach. It is analogous to solving the paradox by appealing to a metaphysically special or privileged A-series and present. However, there is a significant difference: the solution comes from a claim about time in language, and not about time *outside language*, as a real metaphysical time would be.

One might be tempted to think of this as a purely linguistic solution. It is the kind of solution, one might claim, that avoids metaphysics. It merely points out a feature of the grammar we use. Through this, we solve problems around what seem to be metaphysical paradoxes of time. But once we get the language right, these apparent paradoxes disappear.

How does it relate to explaining propositional truth-values through tokens and truth-makers? What are the tokens and truth-makers of a tensed proposition such as *it is raining now*.

And is this solution purely linguistic? Does it avoid metaphysics, or does it require metaphysics to work?

Tense Language and Tokens

In a tense theory, a truth-maker in time is itself tensed. Everything in time is tensed. If that truth-maker is a fact, then (following Mellor 1998) call it a *tensed fact.* And call the token of a proposition made true by such a fact a *tensed token.*

For example, take the proposition P that *it is raining.* P has a token at a particular location in time: someone utters P out loud. Given tense theory, P is made true by the tensed fact *it is raining.* The "utters" of the token and "is" of the fact indicate that both are present. Thus, the token is a *present* token—and thus, a tensed token.

This gives us the following:

• P is true if it is a fact that *it is raining* and P's token is present.

In the A-series, the token and the truth-maker (such as a tensed fact) can be at different times. Like other places, other times than the token's time can be referenced by the token.

For example, P# is the proposition that *it was raining.* It is true in the following situation:

• P# is true if it is a fact that *it was raining* and P#s token is present.

Similarly, P* is the proposition that *it will be raining.* It is true in the following situation:

• P* is true if it is a fact that *it will be raining* and P*s token is present.

This provides a straightforward explanation of how a proposition can change truth-value. The proposition changes truth-value by what it references changing position in the A-series. If P is true when the truth-making fact *it is raining* is present, then P is false when that fact is past or future. (However, when the fact is future, P* is true, and, when the fact is past, P' is true.)

In this analysis, the *facts change* and the propositions' truth-values change with them.

Objection 1: Propositions Cannot Change Truth-Value in Tense Theory

This analysis so far presupposes that the propositions' tokens are present. But such tokens themselves exist in time. They are not always present. Indeed, most tokens are only *temporarily* present. For example, I mutter on Tuesday that *it is raining.* Whether or not that is true, the token itself—my muttering—is past by Wednesday. So, the tokens change their position in the A-series. Does this make any difference to their truth-value?

Hopefully, it does. Otherwise, this analysis risks a contradiction similar to the one it is meant to avoid. We get different propositions at different times that contradict each other, yet all must be true.

A token's truth-value is not given by the token's A-series position. Tokens only change their A-series positions and nothing else. Yet, if that is right, then a proposition does not change truth-value when its tokens change A-series positions. For example, P is true when

(a) P's token is present and it is presently raining

and

(b) P's token is past and it is *not* presently raining.

Yet, P is not true on Wednesday. It is *not* raining and P is the statement that it *is* raining. P has changed from being true to being false.

However, if a token was true on Tuesday, when it was uttered, and only changes by undergoing passage, i.e., changing tense, then it does not change truth-value as well. As such, P must be true even on Wednesday—despite being past on Wednesday.

Response: Tense is a Modifier

Tense is a modifier. It changes linguistic expressions. Just like "indirect", "unreal", and "possible", tenses such as "past" (or "was") and "future" (or "will be") modify the truth-values of propositions. They do so by changing the tokens and not the propositions.

Past tokens do retain their truth-value. However, they do not do so *without qualification*. They retain their truth-values through qualification by their tense—their pastness or futurity. The tense modifies the token:

• Past (P's token, e.g., uttering "it is raining")

It also modifies the tense of the truth-maker, to get:

• Past (P's truth-maker: it is raining)

The proposition's truth-value is thus modified. The token of P's *it is raining* is now past. And so, the token of P *was* true. The relevant tensed fact is that it was true that it is raining.

This is similar to tokens and their truth-makers in different possible worlds. In the actual world, the proposition Q "There are unicorns" is false. But, in a possible world with unicorns, Q is true. We can express that difference by having a token of Q in that other world. Then, from this world, we have this expression:

• Possibly (a token of Q, e.g., uttering "there are unicorns")
• Possibly (Q's truth-maker: there are unicorns)

This modification explains why there is no change in truth-values. Say that Q is true in worlds containing its token, that is, tokens of Q in worlds with unicorns. In a world with no unicorns, Q is false. However, in that world, Q, like unicorns, is possible. In that world, *possibly (Q)* is true.

Similarly, if P is true only when P is present, P is false when it is past. However, because it is past, *past (P)* is true. And within the "()" of "past", the token is still true.

In addition, in this answer, presentness changes nothing about a statement in this thinking. It is redundant, like real or direct. "Present" is similar to "direct", "real", and "actual". "Present" does not modify the truth-value of statements it contains. If Q is true, then *actual (Q)* is true; if Q is false, then *actual (Q)* is false. Similarly, if P is true, then *present (P)* is true; if P is false, then *present (P)* is false.

Objection 2: Tense Tokens Are Not Merely Linguistic Entities

Philosophers seeking to dissolve metaphysical problems cannot use this tense account of language. It draws on tense truth-makers. Tense truth-makers are metaphysical entities. They are real things in the world that are tensed. Tense theorists accept such entities. However, tenseless theorists deny that there are such entities. If the tense and tenseless debate is a metaphysical debate, what seems to be a merely linguistic solution involves taking a metaphysical position.

The issue is that this solution involves committing to *tense facts*. But, for a tenseless theorist, there is no need for such facts. As such, this solution brings in metaphysical entities, and so is not purely about language.

Response: The Tokens Only Undermine Mere Linguistic Solutions

Although tense theorists might need to posit metaphysical truth-makers, such as tensed facts, this only undermines a *verificationist* solution to the paradox. Tense theorists need not be verificationists. They need only be one with respect to McTaggart's paradox—and, given it is a paradox, have excellent reasons to do so. They can dissolve the paradox on linguistic grounds while accepting other metaphysical entities, such as tense facts.

Furthermore, given the reason for taking the linguistic approach, one might hold that this linguistic analysis supports tense theorists. It uses tense truth-makers. This use gives tense theorists the advantage over tenseless theorists. Tense theorists hold that events have real and fundamental tenses. That language's truth-values depend on tensed things is compatible with such a view.

Even so, this solution is not based merely on language. As may be expected, this account is a problem for tenseless theory. Although not a mere linguistic analysis, it turns on there being tokens and truth-makers with positions in the A-series. Can a tenseless theorist offer a solution that does not need tensed tokens and truth-makers?

Tenseless Facts

Tenseless theory has its own theory for propositions involving tense. It involves implicit and explicit reference to some aspect of the *tokens* of such tensed propositions. One such account is Mellor's early *token-reflexive* account of tensed propositions (Mellor 1981). Another is Smart's date-reflexive theory (see Smart 1963). The most developed account comes from Mellor (1998).

According to Mellor, what makes any proposition true or false is that its tokens are true or false. And what makes tokens of tensed propositions (which he calls *A-propositions*) true or false is something tenseless. These *tenseless facts* (or, in Mellor's terms, *B-facts*) are truth-makers of tensed expressions.

However, a tenseless fact is always true; it is always a fact. How can always true tenseless facts make true sometimes true *tensed* statements such as *it is raining* or *there is a cat in the kitchen*?

Mellor's first answer draws on token-reflexive statements. For example, a proposition P contains references to the following:

- Event *e*
- Tenses—present, past, and future
- A token of P itself, e.g., a particular utterance or written statement expressing P

These features allow P to have the general form of a token-reflexive expression for the tenseless fact of a tensed statement:

> Any token of P is true if and only if it is as much earlier or later than e as P describes the present is than e.
>
> (Adapted from Mellor 1998, 31)

For example, K^A is a true proposition and M is a fact:

- K^A: The cat was in the kitchen a day ago.
- M: The cat is in the kitchen.

For tenseless theory, K^A is true because of a tenseless fact described by the following tenseless statement:

> *Cat-Kitchen Tenseless Fact:* A token of K^A is true if and only if the token is a day later than M and K^A describes the present as a day later than M.

The "a day later than M" is how much longer K^A refers to the present as later than M, the cat being in the kitchen. The amount of time described in the proposition is a day, and the token itself is a day later than M. That is how much time a day ago is from the present. In this, the token and description of the present are at the same time.

The fact described by the *Cat-Kitchen Tenseless Fact* proposition is not tensed. However, the proposition K^A refers to does have tensed terms. In keeping with the tensed responses to McTaggart, the "is" and similar verbs in K^A are present terms. In terms of tenseless facts, this analysis aligns the tensed parts of grammar (such as in K^A) with tenseless facts, such as those containing tenseless relations of earlier and later.

These theories involve reference to entities and their place in time. They involve appeals to entities that are actual things in space or time. However, verificationists should be fine with tokens. Such an anti-metaphysical philosopher of language might think that language does not involve abstract entities such as propositions. However, they must at least grant that there are the kind of things that are tokens of language. These are such things as words written down somewhere and at some time, or said in different circumstances.

As indicated by the analysis above, tenseless facts are very little beyond such things as written words for tokens and cats in kitchens for truth-makers. If verificationists accept written words and cats, then they accept what is enough for tenseless theory.

Objection: Some Tensed Propositions Cannot Have Tokens

The token-reflexive account does have a particular weakness. Its propositions get their truth-value through the existence of their tokens at some point in time. By having a specific token at a time, the proposition has a specific truth-value. If a proposition has a truth-value at some time, then it must have a token at that time. However, some propositions can be true in cases in which it is impossible for them to have tokens.

From Mellor, call the following proposition ~u:

~u: There are no tokens now.

~u is false now. But it need not be false; it need not have been false nor need it be false in future.

Here are two situations when it can be true:

1. Ten billion years ago, when the stars had barely formed, there is no language at all; as such, there are no tokens of any proposition.
2. A billion years from now, after language-capable life has disappeared, there will be no tokens.

In both cases, ~u is true. That it is true then, but not now, seems a reasonable situation to be in. Propositions can be true, whether there is any token at the time or place they reference. "This is a cold empty void" is true in the Boötes void (one assumes), even if there is nothing to utter it out there.

However, a token theory cannot provide such truth-values. Drawing on the token-reflexive account of tensed propositions, take e to be the fact of *there being no tokens*. Since the statement is one about the present, substitute "as much earlier or later than e" with "simultaneous with e":

Any token of ~u ("There are no tokens now") is true if and only if the token is simultaneous with *there being no tokens* and ~u describes the present as being simultaneous with *there being no tokens now*.

If token-reflexive theory is true, then ~u cannot be true. It can be true only if its tokens are at a time when there are no tokens of at all. Since there are no tokens at all, it is never the case that there are tokens at that time. Thus, it is never the case that ~u can be true.

Yet, ~u can be true. It can be true billions of years before and after language. As such, this use of tokens to provide truth-conditions cannot capture the truth of all tensed propositions.

Response: Date-Reflexive Theory

A token-reflexive theory of meaning is only one kind of reflexive theory. If necessary, we can appeal to something else instead of the token. As the truth-conditions can be implicit or explicit, such conditions need not be built into the expression itself. We can specify the conditions implicitly.

A proposition such as ~u is never true because its tokens are true. Instead, something about the *time* which the proposition refers to makes ~u true.

Yet, what about the time makes the proposition true? Mellor writes "What then does make '~u' true at a time t when, as it says, there are no tokens? The answer can only be a fact about t itself, namely that there are no tokens at t" (Mellor 1998, 34).

This is a *date*-reflexive theory of tense language. We use a tenseless date referenced in the proposition, implicitly or explicitly, to provide some truth-conditions for it. The tenseless fact then includes that date in it:

~u: "There are no tokens now" is true if and only if the date at which it is true is simultaneous with *there being no tokens* now as P describes the present is to *there being no tokens now*.

But can we refer to dates? Here is a worry: the relevant dates in this context are not within human time, e.g., in the next few centuries. They are when there is no one. Indeed, we can pick a date when there is nothing of any significance happening at all, for example, a million years after the heat death of the universe.

Yet, if the original objection is even to work, we must be able to define such dates. The examples of times with no tokens are precisely dates that we have, somehow, described. And this is enough for a date-reflexive theory. "[T]imes [...] remain contentious", Mellor writes. "But not, fortunately, on grounds that matter here." Suppose

[W]e agree with Leibniz that to talk about time and space is really to talk about temporal and spatial relations between events. This is not to deny that times and places exist, merely to say that they depend for their existence and identity on events, whose temporal and spatial relations define them.

(Mellor 1998, 34)

If we are to have a time when ~u "There are no tokens now" is true, then we can use that time as a date. If there is no such time, then there is no time in which there is an absence of tokens or ~u is true.

Tense Logic

Some philosophers hold that time cannot be merely physical or even metaphysical. Physical or metaphysical conceptions of time are "dreams of our language" (Geach 1998). This is because tensed time is part of *logic*; anyone who casts doubt on time's part in logic is "sawing off the branch he sits upon" (Geach 1998, 198–199).

Prior argues that time is no more a thing than a possibility; the past and future are not tense properties, nor are they tense locations (such as positions in the A-series), nor temporal facts. They are no more these than negation is a negative property, negative location, or negative fact (Prior 1998b).

So, this is a *tense logic* conception of time. Tenses are logical entities or operators—*tense operators*. Tensed expressions are similar to expressions in classical logic or modality. Tense no more needs a fact (or any other truth-maker) than the OR operator needs a fact.

Logical Operators and Truth-Value

Earlier in this chapter, we discussed the concept of time as a modifier or adverb. In addition, the present was presented as a redundant modifier; it does not change truth-values of propositions, but the past and future do.

Tense logic captures these features. Tenses are modifiers or operators, taking in arguments, entities, or propositions as input, and outputting other arguments, entities, and propositions. And, just like other logical operators, the propositions' truth-values change.

Importantly, in logical expressions, adding operators can change truth-values, yet it is not obvious that *truth-makers* must change. For example, if I make the following two statements:

1. There are unicorns.
2. NOT (There are unicorns).

These are two different propositions with different truth-values. 1 is false and 2 is true.

However, in this world, the same fact—that *there are no unicorns*—makes 1 false and 2 true. 1 and 2 are differences in the language, but not in the world.

In accepting that there are differences between the above sentences—and that there are different truth-values for each—one need not accept that there are different things corresponding to each in the world. That is, 1 and 2 have the same truth-makers.

Perhaps, then, similarly:

1. There are dinosaurs.
2. WAS (There are dinosaurs).

There are two different propositions with different truth-values. 1 is false and 2 is true.

Again, the difference between them does not require a difference in *truth-makers*. In the world, the same fact makes 1 false and 2 true. It is only a difference in language. In admitting there are differences between the above sentences—and that there are different truth-values for each—one does not admit that there are different things corresponding to each in the world. That is, 1 and 2 have the same truth-makers.

Tense Logic and the Metaphysics of Time

Can this approach enable us to take sides in the philosophy of time while avoiding any metaphysical position? First, given tense logic, tense or tenseless arguments about tense facts are misled. We do not need OR, AND, or NOT *facts* to make propositions containing the OR, AND, or NOT operators true. Similarly, we do not need either tense or tenseless facts to make a tensed proposition true or false.

Objection 1: We Talk as if Tense are Properties, Locations, or Facts

Yet, we talk as if we need tense facts (or tenseless facts). More generally, we talk as if tenses—past, present, and future—are properties or locations. For example, we say "my birthday *is past*" (tense is a property); "the death of the sun is *in* the future" (a location); it is a *fact* that my writing this is present.

According to some proponents of this view, tenses (or at least, non-present tenses) are not properties, locations, or facts because, similar to negation, these tense-modified expressions describe things that do not exist, for example, my past birthday does not exist (it is an ordinary day for me)—nor does the sun's death (the sun is burning away just fine).

So, there is nothing that exists that has such a property or location; there is nothing in the past or future to be a fact. If nothing can have a property or location, or be a fact, then there is no reason to require there be such properties, location, or facts.[5]

Christensen writes:

[U]nlike the predicates "is round", "is an explosion", etc., the predicates "is past" and "is present" do not signify real attributes or qualities of anything. It would be a strange attribute indeed that an object or event could acquire only and always by ceasing to exist or to occur!

(Christensen 1974, 297)

Objection 2: Tense Logic Assumes Presentism

This conception of tense is consistent with *presentism*. This answer is not consistent with eternalism. How tenses work depends on there being no past or future things—events, objects, facts.

For this objection, tense logicians may heartily accept it. Proponents of such a conception of time are typically considered to provide arguments for supporting presentists (e.g., Prior 1998b; Christensen 1974). For example, according to Prior, if we say truly that there is a present boat trip, then that boat trip exists or is real. If we say truly that there is a past boat trip, then that boat trip does not exist or is not real.

Again, this is like *possibility*: if we say truly that a boat trip is actual, then that boat trip exists or is real. If we say truly that a boat trip is merely possible, then that boat trip does not exist or is not real.[6]

Objection 3: Tense Operators Do Not Need an Unreal Past and Future

However, asserting that time is a kind of logic does not solve the metaphysical debate. Tense logic, even if it *is* a form of logic, involves its own special operators. These may be compared to other operators. However, like any distinct operator, they do not share all their features with other operators. They are not simply variants of other operators, or other operators in a temporal disguise.

For example, take the past operator *WAS (boat trip)*. *WAS ( )* is like many other operators. It modifies its arguments. Tense logic supports presentism if the *WAS ( )* operator modifies its arguments like the *NOT ( )* operator does in a specific way:

- If proposition P asserts the reality or existence of some x, then *NOT (P)* negates the reality or existence of x.

Similarly, if *WAS ( )* is like *NOT ( )* by similarly negating P, then

- If proposition P asserts the reality or existence of x, *WAS(P)* denies the reality or existence of x.

However, this is only the case if tense operators share this negation with the *NOT ( )*. This is an assumption. Simply being a logical operator does not force the non-existence of the content (*x*) for the argument (*P*). There are operators that do not deny reality or existence. For example, there is the AND *( )* and OR *( )* operator. If we truly say:

- *AND (*There is a boat trip, there is a costume party*)*

Or

- *OR (*There is a boat trip, there is a costume party*)*

Neither denies the reality or existence of the boat trip or the costume party. What we need is more information, for example, for the *OR ( )* operator, we discover that there is no boat trip.

Similarly, a PAST () operator may require the existence or reality of the content of at least one of its arguments, like the *OR ( )* operator, or of the content *both* of its arguments, like the *AND ( )* operator. What we need is more information, for the PAST (There is a boat trip), we discover that such boat trips are real.

One might insist that past operators are *more* like *NOT ( )* than *AND ( )* or *OR ( )*. The *WAS ( )* operator may be like the *NOT ( )* operator. However, if it is not identical to the *NOT ( )* operator, then it functions differently to it. Those differences could make it more like some other operator than *NOT ( )*, along with the existential commitments involved.

Whatever we say here, in comparing tense operators to other operators, if we are to avoid taking a side in the philosophy of time before doing so, we must be carefully neutral. And, for tense logic to offer support to a side, it must not take that side to begin with. Furthermore, we should remain neutral if we wish to avoid metaphysical commitment, as many philosophers of language may wish to do.

However, remaining neutral about the metaphysics, while using tense logic, does not clarify which philosophical theory of time is preferable to the others. We may understand how the tense operator *WAS ( )* works and see similarities with *NOT ( )*. Yet, because we also understand there is a difference between them, the similarities are not enough to dismiss tenseless theory and support tense theory.

Some presentists agree with the idea that tense logic alone does not commit one to presentism. Nor, of course, does it commit one to any other theory of time (obviously, they are presentists).

In Chapter 2, we briefly discussed *nefarious* presentism's position that past statements are unanalysable. This makes it similar to tense logic: tense operators are not analysed away into other things. However, Tallant adds that "tense logic is (or at least can be read as) metaphysically agnostic as to the underlying ontology" (unlike nefarious presentism) (Tallant 2020, personal correspondence).

Indeed, philosophers who advocate tense logic, such as Prior and Geach, also express philosophical opinions that go beyond the language to other things.

They do not merely settle with language or tense logic. As seen in those other chapters, they make claims about physics and experience as well.

Study Questions

1. Is it possible to talk about temporal passage without using metaphor? Try and describe temporal passage literally. (Is the proposed description in this chapter sufficient?)
2. Can a proposition exist in time? Whatever your answer, consider how similar reasoning might apply to propositions about (a) space and (b) possible worlds?
3. Do you agree that the "past"—e.g., in "a past boat trip"—plays the same linguistic or grammatical role as "slowly" in a "a slow climb"? What differences are there? For example, is it possible to place "past" in a different place in an expression, where "slow" cannot go?
4. If the present is a redundant term, what does this mean for the *presentness* of experience[7] or the unique present of a moving spotlight theory[8]?

Notes

1 There is a lot more to this account. For example, possible world theories often play a role in accounts of the nature of propositions. We do not discuss that here (but see Lewis 1986 for a detailed and classic account.)
2 See Chapter 3.
3 Theorists about possible worlds and propositions propose another account. Specifically, propositions are sets of possible worlds (e.g., Lewis 1986). Again, there is no space to detail this here, and it is unclear how such sets may work for time and space.
4 There is more than this to how truth-makers and propositions are connected. Causation also plays a role in connecting truth-makers to what they make true. We discuss this perception in Chapter 1.
5 At least, no reason to require such properties be instantiated. For the purposes of this discussion, we assume this to be true. Metaphysicians may think otherwise.
6 So long as modal realism is false, of course (see Lewis 1986).
7 See Chapter 6.
8 See Chapter 2.

Suggested Readings

Lakoff and Johnson 1980 is the classical text on metaphorical talk; a common example throughout is metaphorical talk of time; they go into a great deal of detail about these metaphors, and some may be interesting to philosophers of language and time.

A lot of metaphysical work includes discussions of language. For example, Mellor's 1998 *Real Time II* is the main text for the tenseless theory of language, involving tense, truth-makers, and tokens. Sider's 2001 *Four-Dimensionalism* is also useful; although Sider's book focuses on persistence, chapter 2 "Against Presentism" includes a general examination on the reducibility of supposedly metaphysical time talk to non-metaphysical time talk (for tense logic, see section 2.1). Lastly, section I of Jokic and Smith 2003 is dedicated to the philosophy of tense language.

Prior's 1967 *Past, Present, and Future* is an excellent and lively work on linguistic solutions to time as alternatives to metaphysical solution. It also goes into detail on tense logic (be aware he uses logical notation—Polish notation—that is not standard in current philosophy). Perhaps more useful initially is Hasle and Øhrstrøm's work. Hasle and Øhrstrøm 1995 is a thorough look at historical and current ideas around temporal logic. And they have a recent interdisciplinary anthology on Prior's logic and philosophy of time—Hasle et al. 2017 and Hasle et al. 2019.

6 Philosophy of Mind and Time

Overview

Does the time depend on the mind, or is independent of the mind, having existence outside of it? Given that most entities that appear to be mind-independent also appear to change, the answer may seem obvious that it is mind-independent. However, St Augustine argued that time is mind-dependent. This is because, he holds, time needs duration—yet nothing mind-independent can have duration. Although the argument is compelling given some intuitive philosophical positions on the past and future, it is not so compelling given others. That time is mind-dependent or independent is based on one's philosophy of time.

Whether time as we *think* of it is mind-dependent or not, one might yet argue that at least the time we *experience* is mind-dependent. Again, for some aspects of time, this is not how it seems: the time we experience—in the change we experience—seems to be mind-independent. Yet, there are reasons to hold that the time we experience is mind-dependent; that is, the phenomenology of time is of a mind-dependent time.

First, our experience of time in mind-independent things is always mistaken in the following way: we do not experience a real duration (a "time-lag") between our experience and the external things that we experience. In reply, this only means the time we experience is not all the time there is; some time is hidden from us.

Second, just because time is apparent to us need not mean that time is mind-dependent. It can appear to us to be mind-*dependent*. In some cases of what might be called experience, this is compelling; for example, the experience of time that we learn about, such as the duration between now and the Big Bang, may be something of which we have an imaginative experience; as such, it may appear to be mind-dependent.

In reply, this does not capture the time we seem to perceive or directly experience. This is the time of perceived *change*. It includes the duration (what is sometimes called a 'specious present') and the temporal order of that change. In addition, there are even experiences of events with durations longer than what we perceive. In all cases, the duration and temporal order seem to belong to something mind-independent. Furthermore, that they do not, or that we are puzzled about how that can be, is again because of philosophical assumptions about time, similar to the assumptions that make St Augustine's argument compelling.

Third, the most widely accepted model of the phenomenology of time requires a distinction between mind-independent things and experienced time. *Retention theory* presents a model initially developed by the phenomenologist Edmund Husserl. It is unclear if experienced time in retention theory can be thought of as mind-independent. In reply, the last few decades have seen the development of an alternative theory to retention theory. *Extensionalism* allows the time that we experience to be mind-independent. It does so by holding that time we experience just is the time it takes for the experience to occur. Similar to the other objections, the main resistance to this solution seems to come from one's philosophical commitments.

Introduction

St Augustine of Hippo is puzzled by time: "What, then, is time?" he writes. "There can be no quick and easy answer, for it is no simple matter even to understand what it is, let alone find words to explain it" (Augustine 1961, 263–265, 11.14); "it is a problem at once so familiar and so mysterious" (Augustine 1961, 270). St Augustine decides that time cannot be in in the world. It must only be in the mind. It must be *mind-dependent*.

Other theorists make similar claims about time. For example, the phenomenologist Merleau-Ponty writes that time depends on the subject, that is, time is *subjective*:

> [T]ime [...] exists only for a subjectivity, since without the latter, the past in itself being no longer and the future in itself being not yet, there would be no time [...] nevertheless this subject is time itself [...] we can say with Hegel that time is the existence of mind.
>
> (Merleau-Ponty 1962, 280)

However, time seems neither merely mind-dependent nor subjective. Changes in the world seem to happen separately to any human or subject at all, and these take time to occur. We can talk about the duration of such events, the order of their stages or phases, or the simultaneity of changes in their parts. A house's decay may take decades of weathering, shifting ground, and weed growth; a star rises in the east before setting in the west; a kingfisher dashes over a deep quiet river when a branch creaks in the wind. These processes and events seem, at the very least, non-mental and non-subjective. They seem, at least, to be mind-*independent*.

Why then might one think time is mind-dependent? Is the claim that time is mind-independent a mistaken understanding of time? If so, is it a metaphysical error or an error based on our experience? If the former, perhaps we must look more carefully at the metaphysics. If the latter, we must look at our immediate experience of the world, at our phenomenology.

At least with respect to the phenomenology, it seems we have excellent reasons to believe time is mind-independent. After all, the time in our experience of kingfishers diving, of decaying houses, and of gradually turning stars seem to belong to these events, to that diving, decaying, and turning, and not to us nor our minds.

Time is Only in the Mind: St Augustine's Argument

St Augustine accepts that time seems to be in the world. He discusses time in changes that are not created by humans—for example, the movements of the stars (1961, 271, §13) or the moment of divine creation (1961, 262, §13). His argument for the mind-dependence of time engages with the time in these kinds of changes.

St Augustine considers time as primarily *duration*, that is, as an amount or period of time, a temporal *extent*. He then asks: how could there be anything with such a duration? He concludes that no such time or duration, and nothing with such a duration, could exist in the mind-independent world. Instead, it must be only in the mind. That is, time must be mind-dependent.

He thought that things in the world could not have duration because the present has no duration, and the past and future (and things when they are past and future) do not exist. As discussed in Chapter 1, Sextus had a similar argument. These views on duration spur the following argument:

1. The past and future do not exist.
2. The past and future have duration (i.e., time).
3. If the present has duration, then no matter how short this duration might be, for *any moment* in it that is present, all the other moments in it are either past or future. The moments before that present moment are past; the moments after that present moment are future.
4. The present has no past and no future moments in it.
5. (From 3 and 4) The present has no duration.
6. (1, 2, and 5) For any moment (past, present, or future), it either has duration and does not exist or it has no duration.

Thus, nothing that exists has duration: the existing present has no duration and the durational past and future do not exist. Although we seem to measure a duration of existing things, we must actually measure something else. But what? According to St Augustine, the "something else" is in the mind:

> It is in my own mind, then, that I measure times [...] For everything which happens leaves an impression on it, and this impression remains after the thing itself has ceased to be. It is the impression that I measure, since it is still present, not the thing itself, which makes the impression as it passes and then moves into the past. When I measure time, it is this impression that I measure. Either, then, this is what time is, or else I do not measure time.
>
> (1961, 276, 11.27)

As this "something else" is all there is to what we call duration, for St Augustine, time—if time exists—is mind-dependent.

Objection 1: Time Is Unreal Not Mind-Dependent

St Augustine's argument rests on claims that the past and future are unreal (and the present without duration). As discussed in Chapter 2, this is a *presentist* view of time. An initial objection is that the unreality of the past and future does not make time mind-dependent. It makes time unreal. There is no time because the only real moment is the present, and the present has no time in it.

That something is unreal does not make it mind-dependent. The *idea* of an unreal thing can be mind-dependent, but it does not follow that the unreal thing is as well. A unicorn is unreal, but unicorns are not mind-dependent; the idea of the unicorn is mind-dependent but is not identical to a unicorn.

St Augustine acknowledges this; in the passage quoted, he states that he either measures something in in the mind *or* he does not measure time. If that "or" is exclusive, then if time is mind-dependent, it can be real.

So, what would make time mind-dependent but also real? St Augustine does not give much of an answer. Again, he only notes that we do *seem* to measure time. And if this appearance is correct, then, because of his argument, time is not in the world. Time does not belong to things like decaying buildings, moving stars, kingfishers in flight; it belongs only to mental entities, such as our thoughts or experiences of such things as decaying buildings, moving stars, and kingfishers in flight.

However, this response runs up against a significant objection: it requires that mind-independent things do not change. Change needs duration. A change cannot happen in an instant. If something lacks duration, then it lacks change. Yet, again, many mind-independent things do seem to change; they have certain properties at some times; they do not have those properties at other times.

We might deny that they can change. We might hold that mind-independent things only *seem* to change. However, if we also insist that we measure time because we *seem* to measure time, we risk inconsistency. Without further reasons to distinguish them, it is inconsistent to appeal to appearances in one case and dismiss appearances in the other. We do this by denying that mind-independent things change, despite seeming to change, but insist we measure time, because we seem to measure it.

Furthermore, in the denial of change in ordinary mind-independent things, we deny the reality of those ordinary things. It is part of such ordinary things that they undergo change. This is especially true of living things. For example, trees grow and kingfishers fly. But non-living things also change—rivers flow, ice breaks. What is left of an ordinary object such as a tree, kingfisher, river, or ice if such a thing does not grow, fly, flow, or break?

Objection 2: The Past and Future Are Real

We may reject Augustine's original 1: the past and future do not exist. We hold that the past and future are real; they do exist. Something that exists—the past or future—also has duration. If the past and future are mind-independent, then duration—and thus time—can be mind-independent.

As discussed in Chapter 2, this is to admit the position of *eternalism*. If we deny 1, then we get a different conclusion to Augustine. There can be time because there is something real with duration—both the past and future.

Presentists cannot accept this solution, however. Furthermore, if we wish to remain *neutral* about the presentist/eternalist debate, we cannot accept this solution. To be neutral about this debate is to avoid committing to either eternalism or presentism. Holding that the past and future are real is being an eternalist; it is not being neutral.

Objection 2: The Present Can Have Duration

We could deny either 3 or 4—and through denying either one, deny 5. The result of this denial is that the present *can* have duration, and so something real can have duration.

However, to deny 3 or 4, we must also bring in thinking about metaphysics (as discussed in the first metaphysics of time chapter).

Tense Theory

If we deny 4, then the present does include *some* of the past and future. It includes a bit of the past just before a particular moment in the present and a bit of the future just after a particular moment in the present. These bits of the past and future combine together to give the present at least some duration.

Let us say we accept presentism, that the past and future are unreal (that, is the first premise, 1). If, as presentists, we also deny 3, then multiple moments of the present are not past or future. This allows these moments to be real, given presentism—just because they are not past or future, but present moments.

However, even as presentists, this kind of response runs into problems. These are problems it shares with tense theory eternalism, a general problem with having multiple present moments.

So, let us move on to eternalism. Eternalists generally can hold that there is a real present, past, and future. Thus, eternalists can deny 1. As such, they can have real durations. However, one of the reasons for holding that there is duration is that duration is in some way apparent to us. And part of St Augustine's problem is that we are not aware of the past and future. So, we may have a real duration because of a real past and future. But can that real duration also be apparent to us?

Not, it seems, if one is an eternalist and also a *tense theorist*. If an eternalist is a *tense theorist*,[1] then they cannot hold that the present is partly past or future— at least, a present they care about. As discussed in Chapter 2, tense theorists hold that time is fundamentally a single A-series of events or moments organized into the past, present, and future. This A-series includes a unique present that separates the past from the future. In such a series, the present is precisely not the future or past. Indeed, it is a single moment separate to both. As such, it has no part that is future or past. So, tense theorists must accept 4.

As also discussed in Chapter 2, tense theory can have other A-series, derivative A-series. Thus, one might hold that the present belongs to one A-series, for example, the fundamental A-series, while the past and future that are part of it belong to another (derivative) A-series.

However, that does not help the tense theory response. These other series are defined by either the fundamental A-series or a B-series, which is itself derived from the fundamental A-series. In either case, these other A-series positions are not really the positions of something, and any duration dependent on such A-series is not really its duration (for more on this, see Power 2016).

Tenseless Theory

Tenseless theorists do not need to accept 4. According to tenseless theorists, any A-series is derivative; there is no fundamental A-series. The B-series is fundamental to time. What is present is what happens at some B-series time; what is past is what is earlier than a B-series time; what is future is what is later than a B-series time. That is all there is to what makes something past, present, or future.

For a tenseless theorist, something's duration depends only on whether it is spread over several moments in the B-series. If it is spread out over multiple moments, then it has duration; if it not spread out, then it has no duration.

Given the tenseless theory, we ought not argue from A-series distinctions. We ought to rephrase such arguments in tenseless terms. Once we do, the argument quickly becomes implausible.

To rephrase this argument using B-series terms, we define the *present* as some moment in the B-series—call it T. This moment can be any moment. We also define the past as *any period earlier than T* and the future as *any period later than T*:

1. For any moment T in the B-series, any periods of time earlier than T and any periods of time later than T do not exist.
2. The periods of time earlier than T and the periods of time later than T have duration (i.e., have time).
3. If T has a duration, then no matter how short this duration might be, for *any moment* in T that is present, all the other moments in T are either a period of time earlier than T or a period of time later than T.
4. T contains no period of time earlier than T and no period of time later than T.
5. (From 3 and 4) T has no duration.
6. (1, 2, and 5) For any moment, it either has duration and does not exist or it has no duration.
7. Therefore, nothing that exists has duration: whatever is at T is too brief and periods earlier or later than T do not exist. Although we seem to measure a duration of existing things, we must actually measure something else.

Formulated this way—in tenseless theory terms—the argument is unsound.

First, 1 is false. Tenseless theorists are almost invariably eternalists. For eternalists, any period of time earlier or later than T *does exist*.

Second, 3 is also false—*by definition*: if T has a duration, then it has moments in that duration that do not belong to periods earlier or later than T. If a period of time is defined as earlier or later than T, then it is not *during* T. And any moment in T can have other moments in T earlier and later than it.

4 is true. However, 4's truth does not matter for tenseless theorists. If T has a duration, then any moment in that duration is in T, and not part of an earlier or later period. And T can have a duration. It can have a series of tenseless moments that constitute it.

Thus, for tenseless theory, St Augustine's argument cannot get off the ground. It only has force given tense theory.

This brief digression into the metaphysics of time shows that arguments like Augustine's do not simply mean that time is mind-dependent. We must first consider it from different metaphysical positions. The metaphysics of time can change how one thinks about time in relation to the mind.

What this discussion also shows is that certain ways of thinking about time may be more immediately compelling to some theorists than others. Perhaps St Augustine's argument is powerful because it rests on the intuitions about time claimed by tense theory (or, more specifically, presentism). If tense theory is true, these intuitions match reality. But if tenseless theory instead is true, then these intuitions mislead us.

However, perhaps there is more to tense theory and the mind than an argument like St Augustine's. Perhaps our experience of time (or *time-consciousness*) gives reasons to think that time is mind-dependent or that tense theory is true.

Temporal Experience

In the philosophy of time, a common class of arguments are what might be called *experience arguments* for some position on time (e.g., Miller 2019). As the name suggests, they are arguments that turn to our experience to justify certain philosophical positions of time.

The most common positions alleged to be justified by experience belong to tense theory: real change is temporal passage and there is a fundamental, unique present. According to many philosophers, the content of experience gives reasons for holding that real time has both features.

And so, we might say:

- The experience of change is an experience of temporal passage.
- The experience of the present is an experience of a fundamental, unique present.

For example, the tense theorist Craig writes:

> For we experience that world, not as a static tableau, but as a continual flux, as a tensed world. We do not experience a world of things and events related merely by the tenseless relations earlier than, simultaneous with, and later than, but a world of events and things which are past, present, or future. [...] [T]his stream of consciousness alone constitutes for us a temporal series of tensed events. Some of our thoughts are now past, we are aware of our present mental experience, and we anticipate that we shall think new thoughts in the future.
>
> (Craig 2001, 159)

Even tenseless theorists think there is some power to this view. Le Poidevin (2007) writes:

> Why does the A theory strike us as the natural view of time? What is it, pre-theoretically, that inclines us to suppose that there is something special, and not merely perspectival, about the present? Why do we say, and think, that time passes? Surely the answer lies in our ordinary perceptual experience.
>
> (Le Poidevin 2007, 76)

Falk writes that, if "the theory that time is [the] B-series (the B-theory) is to be justified, there needs to be an account of the appearance of passage (whoosh and whizz)" (Falk 2003, 211).

The importance of appearances and experience is consistent with this chapter's approach so far. We have already argued that a reason for resisting claims that time is unreal or mind-dependent is that it does not *appear* to be unreal or mind-independent.[2] So, if it appears that time includes temporal passage and a unique present, then is that not a reason for resisting claims that time is neither?

The Appearance of Time in the World

Here are two concepts of seeming or appearing. Call them the *cognitive* concept and the *phenomenological* concept:

1. *Cognitive*: By "seeming" or "appearing" is meant that we unreflectively *think* of time that way.
2. *Phenomenological*: By "seeming" or "appearing" is meant that we *experience* time that way.

A cognitive seeming is how we think about time, without reflection or philosophical analysis. It is a philosophically naïve thought. In this sense of "seeming", time seems to extend beyond our own immediate experience. There seems to be time in decaying houses and moving stars. When we think of this time, we think of something that happens even in the absence of human experience. We think of time as transcending the empirical or immanent—as not merely being confined within what we could experience. There is such time even in the absence of any possible experience at all.

Say that a nearby pulsar bathes the Earth in radiation, killing everything living, leaving only lifeless ruins. In the remaining dead environment, we think there is still time: the stars rotate up over the horizon at night and disappear in the morning. Beneath them, the ruins still decay. And so, there is still time.

This sense of time as extending beyond even possible experience is why there is a difference between how we think of time and how we experience time. The other, *phenomenological* sense of "appears" or "seems" concerns how we *experience* time. By definition, this is a sense of time as it is *experienced*. As such, this apparent time cannot transcend the empirical or immanent. It just is what we experience; it just is what is immanent.

Yet is time something we can experience? Throughout this book, I assume that we experience colours, shapes, and pain, and that this is obvious to everyone. Unlike colours, perhaps, we might think it obvious that we do not distinguish time from other features of the world through experience. If at all, we can only infer it from our experience.

Time We Do Not Experience

There are some aspects of time that we obviously cannot experience:

- Unless we are capable of mystical experience, we cannot experience the time that encompasses all change and persistence, for example, from the first moment of the Big Bang, through all other moments, to infinity or whatever the last moment might be.
- We cannot experience specific moments of time, for example, the moments of the Big Bang or the death of sun.
- We cannot see the *change* in mountains wearing from erosion. Nor can we hear oak trees grow in our nearby park.
- We cannot see change in the time it takes light to travel from the mirror on your wall to your eyes. Or the time between two flickers of light in a functioning neon tube. The flickers happen so fast that there appears to be no gap between them: there is just a single continuous glow.
- We also cannot experience the specific time-lag between the following events: the lag between light leaving a distant star and the light striking our eyes. We cannot even experience the temporal order of those events. When this happens, we only experience the distant star.

The times of such events, changes, and states are those no human has experienced. We can think about such times, of course. However, we do not experience them in any way like we experience colour, shape, or pain.

Time We Do Experience

Yet, a great deal of what is apparent to us appears to both be in time and to have temporal properties. Here are some examples of experience in which time seems to play a part:

- *Clock time*: I look at a clock on the wall before starting to write. A few hours pass, then I look again. The hour hand has moved.
- *Duration*: Waiting in the hour before a job interview, time drags. In the hour afterwards, the hour flies by. I also have some kind of sense—what does not concern us here—that some durations last different lengths to others. For example, I have some kind of sense of how long an hour normally feels and can compare it to how long a minute normally feels. I can tell from this sense that one (the hour) is *longer* than the other (the minute).
- *Change through memory*: In a familiar place, you notice something has changed since you were last there. It can be anything: the location of a vehicle, ambient temperature, the colour of leaves. Recalling how these things appeared before, you remember the actual event when you were last there. You also anticipate the future changes of such things, for example, if a vehicle will change location again, if the temperature will fall or rise again, if a colour will fade.

- *Involuntary anticipation*: Hurrying to leave my house, I knock a full cup from a table and seem to *feel* the cup hit my bag, the hot coffee splash against my skin, before it does, in fact, do that.
- *Hearing change*: Listening to a piece of music or feeling its rhythm, I am aware of the changes in it and myself.
- *Feeling change*: I move a part of my body. I pay attention to something moving in my environment. I wave my hand in front of my face, observe my heartbeat, and my breathing.
- *Seeing change*: I catch the flash of a kingfisher's wings as it wheels below us across the river.
- *Experiencing simultaneity*: I attend to more than one thing at once. I focus on my breathing and feel the temperature in the room, while hearing the sound of a bicycle passing by.

These different experiences are all experiences in which time plays a part. Indeed, any experience we have is similar to the above examples in this respect. Most of our experience seems to be temporal, to have time as part of its content and character.

How might we resolve this difference between experienced and non-experienced time? Perhaps it is a matter of *scale*. To adapt the story of Goldilocks (and its use in astronomy), we can experience time only if it is neither too large nor too small, but only "just right":

- We do not experience the whole of time because it is too vast. Similarly, the Big Bang and the sun's death are too far away in time.
- We do not experience the flickers in the pulses of neon tubes because they are too short.

Objection: Time-Lag

Scale is not enough to distinguish temporal experience from other kinds of temporal cognition. There are cases in which the scale of what we experience is on the same scale as the too-large events above, such as the death of the sun. There are also cases in which the scale of what we do NOT experience is on the same scale as what is "just right".

The light of distant stars takes time to reach us, for example, it takes over six hundred years for light from Betelgeuse to reach us. This duration is a "time-lag" between any distant star and our seeing it. We do not experience the duration. It is a hidden duration. However, we do see, at the other end of this duration, distant stars (or it seems to us we do, which is all that matters here). If we do not experience the sun's death only because it is too far away in time, then we should also fail to see a distant star because it is too far away in time. But we *do* see distant stars at remote times. So, it is not that there is a long duration between something and us and, thus, we cannot see it.

Similarly, if we see the moon shining the sky, we see light emitted from it just over a second ago. There is a time-lag in that experience as well. Yet, despite it falling within a Goldilocks period, we do not experience the duration of that lag.

Response: Apparent Time

The time-lag objection is based on when what we experience *actually* happens. However, we are interested in when what we experience seems to happen. We do not *seem* to experience these events as being at those scales. Moonlight does not seem to be a second ago when we see it; the distant star does not seem to be thousands of years old. They just seem to be present, to be happening now.

That is, when it comes to the difference in this chapter, the question concerns *appearances* or *seemings*—the *phenomenology*. In terms of appearances, we do not seem to experience events as occurring thousands or millions of years from the present. In phenomenological terms, it is possible to pick out the durations we do not experience by whether or not they fall within a certain period. This period lies somewhere longer than a lightning flash and shorter than a century.

However, scale still is not enough here. The moonlight's lag is not too long or too short. It falls within a Goldilocks duration that is longer than a lightning flash. We might respond by changing the Goldilocks limit. But there are durations of all lengths that we do not experience. Say we increase the lower Goldilocks limit, so it omits the duration of moonlight. There are still other cases that are above this limit, such as the time it takes sunlight to each us.

For all scales, there are similar durations between what we do seem to experience and what we do not. Duration alone does not separate apparent time from time that is not apparent (for further discussion on time-lag, see Houts 1980, Power 2013, 2018).

Apparent Reality

Perhaps it is this: The difference between time that is not apparent and time that is apparent is that the time that we experience appears to be real. The time that we do not experience does not appear to be real.

Again, what we experience might very well be unreal. We might be hallucinating or under an illusion. The point here concerns what is apparent, not actual. So, what time appears to be real?

Phenomenological Presentism

It may be that only what appears to be present appears to be real. This is an appearance that is in line with presentism—the philosophical position that, in fact, only the present is real. Here, we are only concerned with appearances. The suggestion, then, is that we only experience what appears to be present. Call this *phenomenological presentism*.

Given phenomenological presentism, the time that is apparent to us can only be the present time. As evident in the examples above, many apparent times are not in the present. They include experiences of year-long durations, change, and of the past.

So, maybe it is this: we do not just experience the present. Although presentism requires that the past be unreal, this is an accurate description of our experience. As such, the time that is apparent to us is not merely what appears to be real. It includes, given presentism, unreal times such as the past.

We might deny phenomenological presentism and hold that the past and future appear to be real. Call this *phenomenological eternalism*—again, because of the philosophical position that all times are real. However, phenomenological eternalism also fails to separate times that we do not experience from those that we do. Many of the times that we do not experience are not present. But, again, many that we do experience are also not present. As such, the reality or unreality of times does not determine whether we experience them, or not.

Appearance of Actual Times

The times that are not apparent to us are merely possible times. They may be plausible or likely, such as prehistoric times or the death of the sun. However, we cannot say that they are, strictly, actual. They are ways things could be.

In contrast, the times that we do experience appear to be actual. Even if temporal experience is profoundly misled (e.g., we hallucinate our past), it appears to be of actual times, not merely possible times.

This distinction separates the appearance of time from time we only think about. Again, it is not about what *is*, in fact, actual. It is about what appears to be actual. It is not that the Big Bang did not actually happen several billion years ago. It is that our experience does not include the appearance of it as actually happening. We get to our certainty about it through thinking about it, not through experiencing it.

One worry about this answer is that it does not explain what it means for something to appear to be *actual* (be it time or anything else). How is an apparently actual thing distinct from an apparently possible thing or an apparently real thing? For this answer, we must carefully distinguish reality and actuality in experience, perhaps indicating some phenomenological characteristic that matches one or the other, but not both.

However, there is another way to answer this. Chapter 5 outlines an argument that words such as "real" and "actual" are redundant words that describe something without further modification. The *real* and the *actual* pick out nothing until we contrast something in relation to them. Reality is contrasted with unreal; the actual with what is either impossible or merely possible. As such, we can take the experience of real times to be the same as the experience of actual times. But how do we distinguish an unreal time from a merely possible time? In this answer, one is a time we experience, the other one we can only think about.

But, other than that difference, is there anything else? For reasons of space, we must leave that question unanswered.

The next question is this. We may say that time is apparent to us. However, time can be understood in many different ways. What understanding of time matches our experience? Further, time is complex; it has many different features, such as duration and temporal order. So, what specific features of time do we experience?

Duration

Waiting for a job interview, we have a sense of an hour and the sense of a minute. We seem to experience such duration live; we live through it, are aware of it. These seem to be in some way direct or immediate experiences of duration.

Similarly, memory experience includes a sense of a duration between when we remember and when what we remember happens. For example, I remember a vivid conversation at breakfast this morning. In remembering the conversation, I experience it as past; I also experience myself now remembering it. As such, I experience duration composed of at least two moments: the past of the remembered event and the present of myself remembering.

Temporal Order

No event succeeds itself. Temporal order is between at least two moments of time. If event E is followed by event F, then the moment of E is different to the moment of F. Because there is temporal order between E and F, there are two moments (one for E and one for F). Furthermore, duration is a length of time. Multiple moments constitute a length of time. As such, two moments constitute a length of time, and so a duration.

That temporal order requires two or more moments, and that two or more moments give a duration, is part of the concept of temporal order and duration. It is part of a basic description of temporal order. This includes descriptions of temporal order in experience. If there is an appearance of temporal order, then there is an appearance of at least two moments in time—and so, also, an appearance of some duration.

At the very least, then, memory experience gives us an experience of duration and of temporal order. If I have a memory experience of a past event while also being aware that I am in the present, there are two times in the content of this experience:

1. Some of what I experience is past.
2. Some what I experience is present.

If what I experience is a combination of 1 and 2, then I experience both the past and present. If something is past, then it is earlier than what is present. If an event E appears to be past and another event F appears to be present, then it appears as if E is earlier than F. That is, there is an appearance of temporal order between E and F.

Are there any other kinds of experience that give us duration and temporal order? Some philosophers think we experience duration, and even temporal order, as *present*. If that is true, there are problems for some philosophical theories of time (although not others).

Experiences of Change

As discussed in earlier chapters, the present is a single moment in the A-series. There is only one present, and it lies between several past moments and several future moments. If this is right, then if we experience the present, we experience it as a single moment in the A-series.

This moment is what Le Poidevin calls the *experienced present* (e.g., Le Poidevin 2007, 76–77). It is the single moment that we experience as present. However, some philosophers think that the experienced present is not enough to capture our experience. In their view, no experience can be of a single present moment. Any typical experience is of multiple moments. For example, even as we have immediate experience of the present—of things we see, feel, hear, and so on—we are also remembering past events. We experience multiple moments, and not only of a single present.

This view only undermines a tense theory if we hold that the experience is of times that cannot be in a single, fundamental A-series. An experience of both a past and present does not obviously deny this. Even presentists are not threatened by this. Our experience of the past events need not be of events that appear to be real.

However, there is a further complication that some theorists insist upon. It concerns what we immediately experience—for example, what we see, feel, or hear. Despite being of present or immediate events, they insist this is of more than a single moment in time. They hold that what we see, hear, and feel is over multiple moments in time. This is the experience of time that is the experience of *change*.

Perceived Change

Change is at the very least variation over time. Like temporal order, change requires multiple moments—and so, change requires duration. In addition, changes are distinguished from each other by the order in which they occur.

For example, a ball bouncing from the left to the right is a change. It is a change that is almost identical to the change that is a ball bouncing from the right to the left. However, these two changes are different. In one, the ball is on the left before it is on the right; in the other, the ball is on the right before it is on the left.

This description of change provides two temporal features:

- *Temporal order*: The changes are distinguished by the order of their constituting events, that is, by the order of where the ball is at separate times (left then right; right then left).
- *Duration*: Two events at two different times—the ball is on the left and the ball is on the right. This gives us duration.

If this is right, then experiences of change are experiences of temporal order and duration.

Some of our experiences of change are slow change, such as the change in the seasons. We are aware of them over periods of time, over several weeks or months. We could also include events earlier in the day or week, such as a journey earlier in the week or getting out of bed this morning.

However, other experiences of change are of much shorter duration. Indeed, they are so short they seem to be immediate. These are *perceived* changes.

Perceived changes are common and numerous. We hear a quickly dripping tap, feel our own pulse, see someone waving their arm from a boat by the shore. We hear the lilting climb of a tune or feel the throbbing pain of a toothache. These examples are all immediately experienced changes—changes felt, seen, or heard.

Importantly, these changes seem to be experienced as *present*. They do not seem be changes between the past and present—such as a tree's leaves since last season. Nor do they seem to be changes between the present and future—such as the door opening after you wait to be invited in for an interview. No, these perceived changes seem to be happening *now*. The person is waving now, the particular lilting tune is happening now, the throbbing pain is now.

Such experiences motivate the argument for what is known as the *specious present*. The specious present is the apparent present in which these perceived changes seem to occur (Power 2012). It contains the duration and temporal order of those changes.

These changes, like any change, extend over a duration. However, these changes, and their durations and temporal order, appear to be present because they lack the following features:

- They do not seem to be past. They have not already happened.
- They do not seem to be future. They are not about to happen.

They do, however, seem to happen in time—in fact, they seem to happen *now*. And this is enough for them to seem present.

However, durations and temporal order require multiple moments of time. As such, such appearances of present changes are appearances of a present with multiple moments—*and* with temporal order between those moments. That is, these are instances of the specious present.

Perceived Change and Philosophical Theories of Time

Tense theory is either challenged or made no different to tenseless theory by perceived change and its specious present. The challenge comes from it being a present with duration. As discussed previously on St Augustine's argument, tense theory has difficulties with present duration. This is because tense theory holds that time is of events in a single fundamental A-series. Any other time series—including the B-series of tenseless times—are derived from this fundamental A-series. This series includes a single fundamental present.

If we perceive change in the present, and thus in a specious present, we perceive a duration that is in the present. A duration is a multiple of times. This gives one of three scenarios:

1. The multiple times of the specious present are present moments in the fundamental A-series.
2. The multiple times of the specious present are tenseless moments.
3. The multiple times of the specious present are times in a derived A-series. The specious present is not the fundamental present.

Tense theory must deny 1 because, according to tense theory, there is only one unique fundamental present. So, there cannot be multiple presents.

Tense theory can accept 2, so long as the experienced specious present is a moment in a derived A-series. Derived tense series can come from a tenseless B-series (which is derived from the fundamental A-series). In that case, we are in the same position as 3.

Tense theory can accept 3. However, 3 does not uniquely support tense theory. It places tense theory on the same level as tenseless theory with respect to experience. Given 3, we do not experience a fundamental present. We experience a *derived* present, that is, a present defined in relation to several tenseless moments in time. Both tense theory and tenseless theory allow a derived present. Tense theory gains no advantage by taking this position.

Tenseless theory is not threatened by a present with a duration. It can accept a derived present. For tenseless theory, if we perceptually experience a change as present, then we can perceptually experience the change as happening over a multiple of tenseless moments. For tenseless theory, these tenseless moments can constitute a derived present.

As such, perceptual experiences of change—and the duration of the specious present containing them—give us reason to hold that our experience of time is tenseless. Or, at least, these experiences give no reason to prefer tense theory over tenseless theory.

However, our experience allegedly is not only of such changes but of temporal passage. This experience is a reason to hold tense theory to be true. However, such an experience is not the kind of perceptions of change described above. So, what could such an experience of passage be?

Temporal Passage

One afternoon, in my early career in the philosophy of time, I caught myself doing something odd while muttering to myself. I passed my hand back and forth across my desk in front me, asking under my breath questions such as: "Does it seem to be become present? Does it seem to disappear into the past? Do I experience it *purely becoming* from the future?"

I even found myself unconsciously slowing down the movement of my hand—as if, in seeing my hand pass each point of the desk, I could see whatever I was looking for. As if what I sought was something like the change in the colour or position of my hand.

It makes sense to slow my hand down to spot the change in colour or position. However, it does not make sense to slow my hand to spot other properties of such motion. For example, if my hand moves so rapidly it blurs, I may think I can slow my hand down to see the blur more clearly. However, that does not work. In slowing down, the motion blur disappears.

I was not looking for such changes. They are changes in objects, in their properties. These are changes accepted by tenseless theory, and—if the above discussion is correct—what is perceived in a specious present.

What I was trying to see—that is, to immediately experience in some way—was what tenseless theorists cannot accept. This is the temporal passage of events through a single A-series, from the future, to the present, to the past. That is, by paying close attention to the phenomenology, I sought the immediate data of experience that support the existence of temporal passage.

As shown earlier in this chapter, many philosophers of time (from all sides) allege that we experience temporal passage. Not only that, but they claim the passage is obvious and common. It is not supposedly like such things as experiencing the divine, seeing the Aurora Borealis, dreaming of chocolate, imagining worlds, or having strong synaesthesia. The experience of passage is not supposed to be difficult to describe, rare, hard to detect, of something unreal, or impossible to show to others. Everyone has it, it appears real to everyone, and everyone can point it out to each other. This is why tense theory is said to succeed in matching experience but tenseless theory fails. However, again, this passage is not the change in things that we perceive. And I must confess, I cannot detect it. All I perceptually experience are changes in things.

One quick response to my scepticism is that I was naïve—and still am—if I think that actions such as closely watching my moving hand is the only way to check experience. Temporal passage is not obvious as perceived change is obvious. Yet, that is not how the tense defence from experience is advertised. The passage is supposed to be obvious; it is part of its allegedly intuitive appeal. As such, it is exactly something a naïve observer should detect.

There is a possible candidate for experiences of temporal passage. Kelly 2005 calls perceived change "pace perceived". He then gives examples of two other kinds of temporal experience:

- Listening to an opera singer holding a note
- Watching a plane taxi along a runway, then lift off

In both, we are aware of a change or an event that has been going on for some time: the singer's sustained note and the plane's motion. So, here is one way to describe what both have in common: these experiences include a sense of a change between our own location in time and the moment that the sung note or the plane's travel begins. This change is a growing or increasing duration, for example, it feels like the note is being held for longer and longer, or the time from which the plane began travelling along the runway is getting further away (Kelly 2005, 208–209; for comment, see also Noë 2006 and Le Poidevin 2007).

Perhaps this is tense theory's temporal passage. It is of the beginning of long changes which are still going on. Tenseless theorists must account for this experienced change to meet the challenge from tense theory. Yet, no matter how this experience is explained, it is not as immediate an experience as the immediately perceived change. This change in events themselves, or in the present in relation to these events, is not a kind that anyone can have as present. It is of a past event becoming more past.

Illusionists and Veridicalists

Many tenseless theorists argue that the experience of temporal passage is an illusion. Given there is an illusion, they then offer explanations for it (e.g., Falk 2003, Le Poidevin 2007, Paul 2010, Prosser 2012). Yet, if experienced passage is not perceptually immediate change, then there is not even an illusion. There is nothing apparent to be illusory. And, recently, some philosophers have pushed back on the assumption that we have an experience of temporal passage.

Miller distinguishes between *illusionists* and *veridicalists* (Miller 2019). Illusionists hold that we do experience passage, but it is illusory. Veridicalists deny that our experience is even illusory. We do not experience passage. The illusionist answer requires an explanation of why there is such an appearance of passage. The veridicalist position does not. However, even for veridicalists, there is still something requiring explanation: if there is no experience of passage, why does anyone hold that there is?

One approach to answering this is to carefully look at all the features attributed to passage and describe those that are compatible with tenseless theory. An example is change, at least the perceived change in object properties. However, there are also other properties of such passage.

For example, temporal passage is change in *a single* A-series (the fundamental A-series). It is not a change through multiple A-series, as tenseless theorists would need it to be. So, we might try to explain this appearance of a single A-series in terms of actual multiple A-series that are mistakenly taken as one A-series.

Another feature is passage's *fundamentality*. Something that is fundamental, one assumes, is ubiquitous and outside anyone's control. We can control whether some particular objects change or not—such as my hand and its location. However, whatever temporal passage through an A-series might be, we cannot choose to stop or reverse it. Take the death of the sun and all the events simultaneous with it (such as the ending of the solar system). Whatever brings these events about, they are in *the* future and, at some time, will be *present*. If they will be simultaneous, then, when they are present, they are simultaneous and, when past, were simultaneous. Such events and their passage together cannot be prevented.

Deng argues that this latter feature of temporal passage, its inevitability, is because we feel *passive* with respect to the time-series in which we exist (which, for her, is the B-series). Unlike our experience of space, we cannot cause a change in our location in time. Yet, whether we act or not, because we are part of a world in which things change, we *do* change location in time: for example, we change from being awake in the morning to asleep at night. As such, we experience the temporal aspect of change as unavoidable and out of our control. This change in time seems independent of us, and anything that we do or is done to us (Deng 2013).

Finally, return to the idea that temporal passage is the changing duration of a held note or an object in continuous motion. A tenseless theorist must explain experiences of *changing duration*. This requires more thought than there is space here to express (for an attempt, see Power 2018).

Phenomenological Models of Time

A significant part of the study of temporal experience is in the development of models that describe the structure of temporal experiences. To close, we consider two such models: the retentional model and the extensional model.

Husserl's general model of time-consciousness still influences the current thinking of phenomenologists, cognitive scientists, and analytic philosophers. It is a *phenomenological* model, that is, a model that falls out of the *phenomenological method*. At the heart of the phenomenological method is an attempt to reveal the necessary features of consciousness.

An important part of the method is the suspension or "bracketing out" of all metaphysical commitments, both explicit and implicit. This not because one doubts them (unlike, say, Pyrrhonian sceptics[3]). Such commitments include unexamined or folk metaphysics (such as the "natural attitude"), and these are to be avoided in correctly describing consciousness.

What remain are non-metaphysical features of consciousness. These features are the focus of phenomenology. The phenomenological description is of those remaining features. As such, a phenomenological model of something is a non-metaphysical descriptive model of it.

The resulting description is not necessarily sufficient for understanding the world. However, ideally, it provides a necessary part of any further philosophical and scientific investigation.

Applied to time, the method requires that the metaphysics of time be put aside, including unexamined folk metaphysics of time. A phenomenological analysis of time is inherently "the exclusion of every assumption, stipulation, and conviction with respect to objective time (the complete exclusion of all transcendental presuppositions concerning what exists)" (Husserl 1991, §1, 4). This leaves only non-metaphysical descriptions of time. A phenomenological model of time is a non-metaphysical descriptive model of time. The account of time does not assume "the existence of a world time, the existence of a physical duration, and the like, but appearing time, appearing duration, as appearing" (Husserl 1991, 5).

So, the resulting description is neither idealist nor anti-realist about time; both are metaphysical positions on time. The phenomenological investigation is about the time that it would be meaningless to doubt the existence of. It is "immanent time of the flow of consciousness, not the time of the experienced world" (Husserl 1991, 5).

Husserl did not publish his work in his lifetime. It was published by his student Heidegger, however, and his model has been taken to be an accurate and insightful phenomenological description of time-consciousness. Yet is the model of time based on Husserl's work a genuinely non-metaphysical descriptive model of time?

Retention Theory: The Tripartite Structure of the Phenomenology of Time

Husserl's phenomenological model of time varies over several of his unpublished texts and is inspired by his teachers (such as Brentano) and his contemporaries (such as Bergson and James). It has been developed by those who follow him into what is now called *retention theory* (also known as *retentionalism*).

Retention theory holds that consciousness has a *tripartite* temporal structure. It has three parts relevant to time:

1. *A primary impression*: the immediately perceived data of consciousness. What appears to be perceptually present.
2. *A retention*: the "just-past" perceived data of consciousness. It contains what perceptually appears to be "just-past".
3. *A protention*: the "about-to-happen" perceived data of consciousness. What appears to be perceptually "about-to-happen".

Why this structure? A central problem of time-consciousness is that we need to explain an experience of change that is more immediate than experiences involving memory. That is, we need to explain that experience of change in the specious present—an immediate, perceptually present change.

However, according to Husserl, if we only had primary impressions of all stages of a change, then these stages would not seem to constitute a change. They

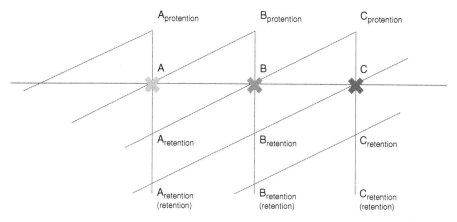

Figure 6.1 Different Theorists' Depictions of Husserl's Protention-Primary Impression-Retention Model

would seem to constitute a combination of simultaneous events: for example, listening to a sequence of notes, we would hear a "chord of simultaneous tones, or rather a disharmonious tangle of sound, as if we had struck simultaneously all the notes that had previously sounded" (Husserl 1991, §3, 11).

Husserl posits the tripartite structure to explain how, in one experience, we can experience the stages without the tangle. The model is illustrated in Figure 6.1. The figure represents experiencing a succession—say, a change—of some events that occur in the following order: A then B then C. (The diagrams are adapted from diagrams by Husserl 1919/1991, Merleau-Ponty 1962, and Gallagher 2012.)

A, B, and C can stand for any stage in a three-stage change or series. For example: three notes of a melody; a traffic light's green, amber, then red; a cough, a lightning flash, a freezing wind. What matters is the order: A *then* B *then* C. Here I discuss the different elements depicted in the figure.

Physical Time and Phenomenological Time

The horizontal line with Xs marked on it stands for *physical time*. This is the time marking consciousness's occurrence in the physical world (e.g., A-B-C). Phenomenological time is shown by the diagonal lines (e.g., $A_{retention}$-B-$C_{protention}$). Physical time and phenomenological time need not be the same, but they can be (which is important in the next section).

Primary Impressions in Husserl's Retention Theory

At each moment in our experience of time, we have a *primary impression*. This is an experience of something immanent and immediate. It is hearing a bell ring or seeing a flash of lightning. Usually, the primary impressions are also constantly changing. We have a sequence of primary impressions. For example, in

Figure 6.1, there is the change in primary impressions represented by the horizontal line running through all three Xs:

1. We experience A as a primary impression. (We do not experience B or C as primary impressions.)
2. We experience B as a primary impression. (We do not experience A or C as primary impressions.)
3. We experience C as a primary impression. (We do not experience A or B as primary impressions.)

However, so this account goes, this is not enough for our experience of ABC (A then B then C). Given this description so far, *at each moment in time*, we only experience the one event: in 1, only A; in 2, only B; in 3, only C. This is a succession of experiences of events; it is a succession of primary impressions. It is not itself an experience of change or succession.

To give the experience of the order of the events, Husserl's model includes the following structure: when experiencing the primary impression of any events, we also in some way experience the events preceding and succeeding these events. As discussed, the "in some way" is not by having a primary impression of those events. Primary impressions together give us the problematic experience of ABC as *simultaneous*. Instead, we do it through protentions and retentions.

Protentions and Retentions

We experience change through primary impressions connected to *protentions* and *retentions*. The figure represents the connection by the diagonal lines running through each of the Xs:

1. We experience A as a primary impression.
    We experience B as a *protention*.
2. We experience B as a primary impression.
    We experience A as a *retention*.
    We experience C as a *protention*.
3. We experience C as a primary impression.
    We experience B as a *retention*.

Furthermore, we are also aware of the *protention of protentions* and *retentions of retentions*. This is detailed in the figure by the diagonal line running through the third X.

1. We experience A as a primary impression.
    We experience B as a *protention*.
2. We experience B as a primary impression.
    We experience A as a *retention*.
    We experience C as a *protention*.

3. We experience C as a primary impression.
   We experience B as a retention.
   We experience A as a *retention of a retention*.

This is not Husserl's full model of temporal experience. He also discusses memory experience (which he sometimes calls *secondary memory*) and anticipatory experience (such as imagining tomorrow). But these are not part of the tripartite structure itself. They are not fundamental to consciousness. and the tripartite structure is.

The structure is also meant to include the *perceptual experience of change*. The protention, retention, and primary impression are part of perceptual experience. Less clear from discussions on the models are that such elements as *retentions of retentions* are also part of it.

So, if we experience time, then its appearance has this underlying structure. This should be a structure common to all experiences of time.

Objection: Nesting

Dainton criticizes Husserl's model on several points. A main one is that retention theory involves *nesting*. Say that ABC is a sequence of notes. Given Husserl's model, the subject has the following sequence of auditory experiences:

1. A primary impression of A (the earliest note), a protention of B (the next note), and a protention of (a protention of C) (the latest note).
2. A retention of E, a primary impression of G, and a protention of A.
3. A retention of (a retention of E), a retention of G, and a primary impression of A.

However, our experience also contains the totality of our previous experiences. As such, in each experience, we have the sum of all our previous experiences. At 3, we not only have what is in 3, but also what is in 2 and 1:

> We retain not only past primal impressions, but our preceding total states of awareness. The latter include not only retentions of the primal impressions which preceded them, but the total states of awareness and their retentional complexes, with these retentions themselves containing retentions of previous total acts and their retentions, and so on.
>
> (Dainton 2000, 157)

Retention theory posits all these nestings of retentions and protentions. Yet, Dainton responds, this is not how it *appears* to us. The phenomenology of hearing ABC is not so complex:

> [A] consciousness which contained this degree of internal complexity would be clogged with different contents to a nightmarish degree. It is manifestly

obvious that in the perception of a simple tone, our consciousness is remarkably clear: all we are aware of is the tone itself as an enduring auditory item.
(Dainton 2000, 158)

We just hear A, then B, then C. We hear the notes succeed each other, but we do not hear each note along with hearing another note retained and yet another protended. (Never mind also hearing the earlier retentions of retentions and yet later protentions of protentions.)

In response, perhaps the retention theory model describes how our experience of successive notes comes about. There is a retentional structure underlying our phenomenology, or one of the causes of it. However, as Dainton notes again, this does not matter for a *phenomenological* theory. A phenomenological theory gives us how things seem, not how things are. Whatever this tripartite retentional model is intended to be, and however it might succeed, it must successfully capture the phenomenology to meet the demands Husserl himself sets for the theory.

Response: Descriptive Abstraction

Gallagher responds to Dainton by stating that Husserl's concept of retention "is a phenomenologically legitimate descriptive abstraction":

> The phenomenology of listening to a piece of music is such that when a series of notes in a melody are played, for example, I hear the melody and not just one note and now another, and now another, etc. Previously sounded notes are retained in the intentional experience so that as I hear the note that is now being sounded I hear it as part of a continuity of notes. [...] Based on the experience and the descriptions of it, Husserl proposes the idea of retention as an attempt to characterize just such aspects of experience. It's a descriptive abstraction [...] the only relevant question for the phenomenologist is whether it is close enough to the experience or introduces any distortions.
>
> (Gallagher 2003, 2)

Yet, this claim that the model is a descriptive abstraction of time-consciousness does not meet Dainton's objection. Dainton's objection is that retentions and protentions are not part of any description of time-consciousness, concrete or abstract. Despite Gallagher's claim, retention theory *does* introduce distortions into the account of time-consciousness.

Perceptual Experience and Retention Theory

Dainton's objection comes from a general problem with how the protention-primary-impression-retention structure relates to the experience of change. It does not capture the simplicity of experienced change, especially not perceived change. Such changes do not seem to have the structure given by Husserl's model.

For example, take the experience of seeing a waving arm. I see the arm's position change. Let the arm's change be a movement from the left, to the middle, to the right.

Let:

- Primary impression (x) be a primary impression of x.
- Protention (x) be a protention of x.
- Retention (x) be a retention of x.

Husserl's model posits the following phenomenology of that change. The description of each structure for experience at a time is as follows, and in the following order:

1. A *primary impression* (A)—the appearance of the arm on the left
   A *protention* (B)—the appearance of the arm in the middle
   A *protention (protention* (C)—the appearance of the arm on the right

Followed by:

2. A *retention* (A)
   A *primary impression* (B)
   A *protention* (C)

Followed by:

3. A *retention* (retention (A))
   A *retention* (B)
   A *primary impression* (C)

These stages are depicted in Figure 6.2. The highlighted line is stage 2. This structure of protention-primary-impression-retention is what is experienced at each moment of a subject's experience.

Yet, this change is not all that retention theory includes in the experience. We are also aware of each of the stages *in each* stage; for example, in 2, we are aware of 1 and 3. As such, in 2, along with being aware of a primary impression of A, we are aware of a retention of A (as in 3) and a protention of A (as in 1). Thus, for A, we are also aware of the vertical line in Figure 6.3.

Thus, we have multiple experiences of the same particular event—of it as it is in the future (a protention), the present (a primary impression), and the past (a retention). We have these multiples for all events in time—including the ones before and after it.

Yet, at each moment, we can somehow tell which tripartite structure is the correct one for us: which is the correct primary impression, which the correct

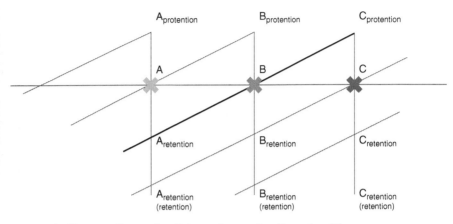

Figure 6.2 Change as Protention-Primary Impression-Retention (1)

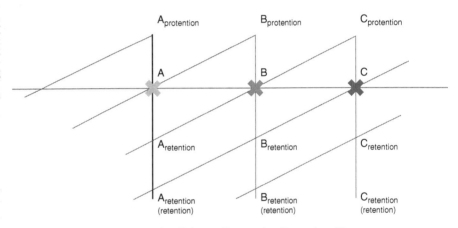

Figure 6.3 Change as Protention-Primary Impression-Retention (2)

retention, and which the correct protention. For example, if we are in stage 2 above, we can somehow tell that we are in stage 2 (where, say, B is the primary impression), and not in stage 1 or 3 (where B is not the primary impression, but a protention and retention, respectively). We can do this even though, given retention theory, we are also aware of the structure of stages 1 (where the primary impression is A) and 3 (where the primary impression is C).

So, how do we tell apart the stage we are actually at from the other stages? Here is one way we might be able to do it: Through our experience, the stage we are actually in is apparent because our position in *physical time* is apparent to us. That is, our positions on the horizontal line on which the primary impressions of A, B, and C lie is part of our phenomenology. This is highlighted in Figure 6.4.

For example, I know where I am on the horizontal line of physical time. Thus, I know that I am having a primary impression of B (stage 2). However, this requires an awareness of our point in physical time, and not just the phenomenological

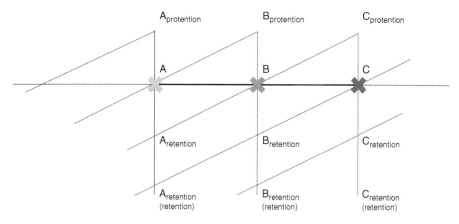

Figure 6.4 Change as Successive Events ABC

time. Yet, if we are aware of physical time, physical time becomes part of phenomenological time. For a metaphysician, this is not a problem. However, for a phenomenologist, it involves a commitment to the reality of such physical time—and, also, an awareness of that time.

Furthermore, if we can be aware of physical time, then this weakens the need for the other, more complex structure. If I am aware of my position in physical time, and aware of the positions of A, B, and C in physical time, then why do I also need retentions and protentions in my awareness? If I am only aware of myself in physical time, but not A, B, and C, then how does my awareness of physical time help me?

For example, say that I am at B. I am aware which events are earlier than my position (such as A) and which are later (such as C). But, by being aware that A is earlier than now, I also know that it was present and is past. What else is there to retention? And knowing that C is later than now, I also know that it will be present and is future. What else is there to protention?

As such, the tripartite structure seems to be at least partially metaphysical, unnecessarily complex, and if we are aware of our physical time, just unnecessary. Let us consider an alternative: extensionalism.

Extensionalism

If we are aware of our position in physical time, then there is a different possible account: experience of events over physical time is explained by our experience itself being over that time. This is *extensionalism*. In the retention theory diagrams, if the horizontal line gives everything needed to explain observing the changing position of your arm, then we just have the following:

1. A, the appearance of the arm's position on the left, is as a primary impression.
2. B, the appearance of the arm's position in the middle, is as a primary impression.

3. C, the appearance of the arm's position on the right, is as a primary
    impression.

Dainton refers to the view that we can just experience primary impressions in
order as *extensionalism*.

Extensionalism is the position that we experience a succession of events, such
as the stages of a change, by having an experience itself with successive parts.
For example, to experience a hand on the left, then the hand in the middle, then
the hand on the right, we have an experience with three parts that matches those
stages of change: one part is for the hand on the left, one part is for the hand in
the middle, and one part is for the hand on the right.

Extensionalism seems to be the simplest description. Perhaps, however, it is *too*
simple. Surely the explanation of experiencing a change cannot simply be a case of
experiencing one event, then another, and finally another? What is missing here?

Objection 1: No Succession

The above sequence is just the same as a sequence of primary impressions. One
might think it has the problem raised against this account of experienced time
in the retention theory section. It lacks an appearance of succession, that is, of
time. It is a succession of impressions or parts of an experience. However, those
alone cannot give us a sense of the succession between them.

This worry gives rise to a common objection to simple accounts of experienced
discussion. In the following extended quote, James expresses this objection well:

> The mental stream, feeling itself, must feel the time-relations of its own states.
> But as these are copies of the outward time-relations, so must it know them
> too. That is to say, these latter time-relations arouse their own cognition; or,
> in other words, the mere existence of time in those changes out of the mind
> which affect the mind is a sufficient cause why time is perceived by the mind.

However, James continues, this answer "is too crude":

> [B]etween the mind's own changes being successive, and knowing their own
> succession, lies as broad a chasm as between the object and subject of any
> case of cognition in the world. A succession of feelings, in and of itself, is
> not a feeling of succession. And since, to our successive feelings, a feeling
> of their own succession is added, that must be treated as an additional fact
> requiring its own special elucidation, which this talk about outer time-
> relations stamping copies of themselves within, leaves all untouched.
>
> [...] what is past, to be known as past, must be known with what is pre-
> sent, and during the "present" spot of time.
>
> (James 1918, 628–629)

Here, we only have the succession of experiences. We do not have what joins them together so that they result in an experience *of* succession. That is, an account of how these experiences or impressions are *connected* is wanting. Stating that we have an experience with parts, each for each experienced event, is not enough: why are these parts of *that* single experience?

Response: Diachronic Co-Consciousness

Dainton posits an irreducible feature of consciousness to explain it. These are parts related by *diachronic co-consciousness*.

Co-consciousness is a relation posited to distinguish elements of a single complex experience from elements separated across multiple experiences. An element of your experience, an element of St Augustine's experience, and an element of some drifting extraterrestrial; these are not co-conscious. However, when you see a tall plant in a short pot, the consciousness of the plant and the consciousness of the pot *are* co-conscious (Brooks 1994, Dainton 2000).

The other aspect of this account is *diachronic*. Co-consciousness of a plant and pot *at the same time* is *synchronic* co-consciousness. Co-consciousness events spread over multiple times is *diachronic* co-consciousness (Dainton 2000, Power 2010). As such, the different primary impressions are part of the same consciousness; they are co-conscious. This co-consciousness is diachronic: it extends over multiple times. This is how they are experienced as succeeding each other in time.

One might ask how this diachronic co-consciousness comes about. One might also ask for some explanation of what exactly it is. Despite the somewhat esoteric terminology, an example of diachronic co-consciousness is easy to show. It is any perceptual experience of a change. It is the order of the stages of that change. It is seeing my hand on the left, then in front of me, and then to the right. So long as I am aware of such a unified sequence of stages, then I have diachronic co-consciousness.

How the change comes about is, much like how temporal passage comes about, a separate issue. The only point here is that, if the change comes about because it is an experience of physical time, then it is extensionalism.

Objection 2: Diachronic Co-Consciousness Does Not Connect Different Experiences

However, even using diachronic co-consciousness, some experiences are not connected to each other. These include my experiences yesterday and today, or my experience in this moment and one a few minutes ago. Given James's reference in the quote to past and present experience, these seem to be the kind he thinks challenge any simple identification of experienced succession with successive experiences.

An experience now and a few moments ago are not diachronically co-conscious. Yet, they appear to be in some way connected, to be experienced as part of the same sequence of events in time. So, how do I explain how that previous experience is connected to this current one?

Response: Overlap Theory

Dainton proposes what is called *overlap theory*. Overlap theory is the position that the contents of one experience, such as stages of a change, overlap the contents of a previous experience. For example, the earlier stages of my current experience of change overlap the later stages of a previous experience of change.

For Dainton, overlap theory satisfies two conditions:

- No nesting (or as he sometimes calls it doubling): by overlapping, multiple separate experiences have the numerically identical contents as parts. For example, an early stage in my current experience can overlap a later stage in my previous experience.
- Connection: the contents of the experiences are shared, and this sharing connects them.

Furthermore, overlap theory is a phenomenological theory that draws on the physical time of experience. It "is robustly realist: not only do we have a direct experience of temporal relations and temporally extended phenomena, but successive phases of a stream are welded together by nothing other than direct experience" (Dainton 2000, 165).

Objection 3: The Overlap Is Not Explained

The content may be *shared* by overlapping experiences, but how is that captured by the phenomenology? How is it apparent to me that these experiences are shared? This is explained by retentionalism by my being aware of having had the previous experiences (and forthcoming experiences).

I may argue that the other stage is experienced as being part of the earlier experience. But how do I know that the earlier experience is the earlier experience—and my current experience is not a future experience? What seems to explain it here is simply stipulated: there is an ordered relation between the experiences, we are aware of it, and that is all.

In response, why must extensionalists in particular explain this relation? Other theorists do not explain similar relations. For what joins protentions, retentions, and primary impressions together? Stating that this structure is a fundamental part of the phenomenological experience of time does not explain this structure. We might as well stipulate that overlapping and diachronic co-consciousness are a fundamental part of the structure.

In any case, for phenomenology, an explanation of a feature of experience is not necessary. What is required is a description of experienced time, not an account of how it comes about.

Finally, one may ask what is the point of this alternative to retention theory? The main point is that extensionalism is a theory of time-consciousness that does not involve the complex structure of Husserl's model. The account is simpler and more phenomenologically accurate. Unlike Husserl's model, it only involves awareness of the stages shared with previous experiences, not awareness of everything else.

Objection 4: Time-Consciousness Must Have a Tripartite Structure

Retention theory must be true because experience must have a tripartite structure. We must have it because our experience, even of change, cannot be *over a time*. Experience can only be *at a time*. As such, our experience *at that time* must have retentions—for some stages of the change—and have protentions for other stages.

In response, why must experience be at a time? One argument is that this is how it appears. However, if there is perceptual experience of change, it is *not* how it appears—at least, not with respect to the phenomenology of perceived change.

Here is one response: a tripartite structure is how it *must* be. It does not matter how it appears. Such a response is a move beyond the appearances. It is not obviously in the spirit of phenomenology. Yet, it is still a means of explaining experience. It just requires a different approach. For example, an approach to time from cognitive science.

Study Questions

1. Is time mind-dependent or mind-independent?
2. Is change mind-dependent or mind-independent?
3. If you answer differently for 1 and 2, what is the best explanation for how one of these (time or change) can be mind-dependent and the other mind-independent?
4. The author (me) confesses scepticism about the experience of temporal passage. Do you agree? What is the best evidence of such an experience?
5. Can presentism be true and yet we experience real change?
6. Evaluate and compare retention theory and extensionalism as phenomenological models. As phenomenological models, check each against your experience of time.

Notes

1 See Chapter 2.
2 This does not mean clock time. Clock time may not depend on your mind alone; you cannot decide by yourself the length of a minute. However, the grouping or division of moments into minutes is something minded individuals decide upon together, and only to some degree of shared convenience.
3 See Chapter 1.

Suggested Readings

Augustine 1961 is an excellent accessible writer; his chapter on time (chapter 11) is worth reading in full; the parts in this chapter are in §14. There are many different commentaries on this work; Le Poidevin 2003 is a good start.

Similarly, James 1918 is worth reading for his thinking about the experience of time. Dainton 2001 and Prosser 2016 are recent texts on the subject. For anthologies on the philosophy of time with papers on temporal experience, almost all 21st-century anthologies have some papers. For example, Bardon 2012, Callender 2012, and Dyke and Bardon 2013. For another classic take on the matter, one not discussed in this chapter, see Bergson 1889. For discussion on time-lag and hidden time, see chapters 6–8 in Power 2018.

Husserl 1991 outlines his phenomenological concerns with time, the thinking that leads to his model, and to the model itself. (Husserl's writing can feel dense, but he revisits the same ideas repeatedly. I recommend you read it quickly and a few times, rather than once and slowly.) For discussion of retention theory, see chapter 7 of Gallagher 2012; for a deeper and longer study, see De Warren 2009. For a defence of extensionalism, see Dainton 2001 (also, chapter 9 of Power 2018).

7   Philosophy of Cognitive Science and Time

Overview

Time is of increasing interest in cognitive science and the philosophy of cognitive science. The philosophy of time impacts the role time can play in cognitive science research in a number of ways. One is the phenomenology of time, discussed in Chapter 6. Another is the relationship between phenomenology of time and related cognitive processes. And lastly, the philosophy of time plays a role in how to correctly describe such processes in time. This chapter investigates the latter two kinds of impact philosophy of time can have on cognitive science.

First, we look at the relationship between the timing of consciousness and the neural correlates of consciousness (NCC). We look at the relationship between the *timing* of consciousness and its NCCs. It is proposed that the best model of their timing is that consciousness and NCCs are simultaneous. That is, when consciousness happens, NCCs happen, and vice versa. A consequence of this proposal is that the temporal structure of NCCs and consciousness may be isomorphic—it is the same structure—rather than heteromorphic—it is different structure.

Second, we apply the ideas of timing to a well-known and controversial experiment purported to show that there is no free will. Although the experiment itself has recently been shown to have a methodological issue, the idea of such an experiment is still important. The concept of free will is outlined and contrasted to other kinds of events in the world, such as determined events and random events. The experiment is described, focusing on when different important parts of it occur and the consequences of this timing for when an act of free will occurs. Lastly, it is argued that the standard interpretation of this experiment mistakenly assumes that our judgements of the timing of our own will is self-evident.

Third, we apply the philosophy of time to examine the consequences of temporal *illusions*. The main examples from the literature are the cutaneous rabbit, the flash-lag effect, and the phi phenomenon. The consequences of these illusions for the accuracy of one's experience of time is outlined, and then critically examined.

Lastly, the chapter turns to focus on the evidence of cognitive science and its impact on the philosophy of time. Some philosophical theories of time fare better with the evidence than others; those that do better are not the ones typically claimed to be intuitive.

Introduction

Cognitive science is the interdisciplinary, scientific study of the mind. It embraces "philosophy, psychology, artificial intelligence, neuroscience, linguistics, and anthropology" (Thagard 2019, online). Although a cognitive scientist can vary in their disciplinary focus and expertise, all have a scientific component to their research. They pursue answers to questions about the mind through scientific experiment, seeking empirical evidence. However, cognitive science can include some non-scientific disciplines as well—notably, philosophy.

Time is a growing subject of interest in cognitive science. The publications and discussions on the subject are varied and extensive. The role philosophy plays in such cognitive science work on time also varies. Some areas of philosophy, such as phenomenology, have played a role since the beginning. Most cognitive scientists studying time are familiar with Husserl's phenomenological account of time. Some have even adapted and developed it. For example, the late Francis Varela adapts phenomenology into his neuroscientific work on time, giving rise to what he calls *neurophenomenology*. Other researchers in cognitive science use the cognition of time to explain central ideas of their theories. The philosopher of cognitive science Dennett uses the perception of time to illustrate his heterophenomenological model of consciousness. And, as briefly discussed in Chapter 5, an influential linguistic theory uses time to illustrate metaphorical speech.

Yet, although time plays a role in the deliberations of cognitive science, it is not obvious that the *philosophy* of time plays a role. Works where philosophy of time is explicitly discussed are rare and brief. For example, Dennett briefly describes Mellor's work on perception only to contrast it with his own view. This chapter corrects that. It examines how the philosophy of time can impact cognitive science. Three subjects in cognitive science which may be impacted are:

- The neural correlates of consciousness (NCCs)
- Interpretations of free will experiments
- Temporal illusions

The Neural Correlate of Consciousness (NCC)

We have a complex experience of time. We have experiences with different co-conscious elements (or parts). We experience things happening now, including changes. We also have other kinds of temporal experiences, such as episodic memory of particular events in our lives. At least, this is how it appears to us. This is our *phenomenology*.

We are creatures with phenomenology; we are also creatures with physical bodies. At the very least, through us, phenomenology has some relationship to the physical world. In some theories, some of the phenomenology represents the physical world and some of it does not; the part that does not is *intrinsic phenomenal character*. In other theories, all phenomenology represents the world. It is transparent or *diaphanous* (Crane 2011). As we are aware of a garden through a transparent window, or a lecture through the intricate technology behind a webcam, we are aware of the world *through* the phenomenology; we are not aware of the phenomenology itself.

Some parts of the physical world are more directly or intimately related to the phenomenology than are other parts. These are the parts of the physical world immediately correlated with it. Consciousness supervenes on it or is even identical to it. And this is not necessarily the part that is the content, that the phenomenology represents. It is the part of the physical world that is composed of the neural correlates of phenomenology—or, as they are usually known, the *neural correlates of consciousness* (NCCs).

NCCs are the neurological structures most linked to experience in the physical world. They are correlated with experience in a way other physical events are not: "A fundamental assumption is that for every mental state there is an associated neural state" write Portas et al., "We also assume that mental states are completely determined by neural states. In other words, it is impossible for there to be a change of mental state without a corresponding change in neural state" (Portas et al. 2004, 270). NCCs are "the minimal neuronal mechanisms jointly sufficient for any one specific conscious percept" (Mormann and Koch 2007).

For many physicalists, NCCs are important to understanding how consciousness is possible in a physical world. And, in most *physical* theories of consciousness, NCCs are enough for experience: if you have NCCs, then you have consciousness. For humans, some theories also consider them *necessary* for consciousness; if you lack NCCs, then you lack consciousness.

Reasons for NCCs

One obvious reason for holding that NCCs exist is empirical. Some physical events are found to correlate with consciousness in a way that other physical events are not. In almost all cases, these physical events are neural events. If I have a pain in my arm due to an injury there, then there are typically three events: the feeling of pain, some particular neural activity, and the actual physical damage in my arm. To stop the feeling of pain, I might heal the damage to my arm. However, even if I do not heal it, I can stop the pain by stopping the neural activity being stimulated by the damaged arm. Indeed, even if I heal my arm, but that particular neural activity continues, I will feel (phantom) pain. This may be taken to show that, if there is a certain kind of neural activity, then there is the feeling of pain, no matter whether my arm is healed or injured; but if there is no such neural activity, then there is no feeling of pain. This neural activity is an NCC.

NCCs also play an important philosophical role for physicalists. They hold to a physicalist view of the world. One principle of such a physicalist worldview is that the world, along with being physical, is *causally closed*. The world is *causally closed* if and only if every physical event is caused by another physical event. No physical event is caused by something non-physical, such as an ectoplasmic spirit. If an egg rolls off a table, it is because something physical made it roll. If physicalism is true, and there is causal closure, it is never the case that an egg rolls because it was pushed by a ghost.

However, some theorists argue that consciousness is not fully explicable in terms of physical and biological laws, including neural activity. In particular, there is the *Hard Problem* of consciousness, the problem with reconciling the subjective, phenomenal feeling of consciousness with physical events correlated with it. This problem motivates some theorists to hold that physicalism must either be false or expanded to include conscious states (e.g., Freeman 2006).

NCCs and Causation

Conscious events seem to be causes of physical events. For example, I *feel* pain and flinch. The feeling of pain seems to cause my flinching. But the pain does not seem to be a physical event. If it is not physical yet is a cause, then it violates causal closure of the physical world.

NCCs are alleged to help solve that problem. A reason to think some event A causes another event B is because A precedes B. So, a reason to think a conscious event, such as a pain, causes some physical event, such as a flinch, is because the pain precedes the flinch. NCCs accompany their correlating conscious events. If the conscious event—pain—precedes the physical event, Y, then (one assumes) the NCCs also precede Y. And, being physical, NCCs can cause other physical events, without violating causal closure. As such, a pain's NCCs can cause the flinch; the pain need not. The conscious event need not cause anything.

Alternatively, NCCs have a different relationship to conscious events. They are not just correlated with conscious events but *identical* to them (e.g., Blackmore 2003). Pain just is its NCC. This allows consciousness to cause things in the world. Pain is physical (neural activity); it can cause the flinch. In that case, the conscious pain's causal power is no problem for physicalism.

This gloss on NCCs ignores many issues and controversies over the relationship between NCCs and consciousness. For this chapter, it is unnecessary to discuss them all. What matters is this: in the preceding description, it was assumed that, if some neural events are NCCs of consciousness, and consciousness precedes an event, then the NCCs precede the event as well. But why? One answer is that time is relevant to identity and causation between NCCs, consciousness, and even the physical events that NCCs and consciousness may cause.

NCCs and consciousness have a particular temporal relationship. So, how might philosophical thinking about time affect our understanding of that relationship?

The Relationship between the Temporal Structure of Consciousness and NCCs

One view of the relationship between conscious experience and any correlating physical structure is *isomorphism*. Another is heteromorphism or representationalism.

Isomorphism

If two things are isomorphic, then they have the *same* structure. The isomorphic view (or isomorphism) is the position that, in consciousness, the apparent or experienced structure is isomorphic to the NCCs' structure. When we think about this in terms of time, this view is that, for experiences of time, the apparent temporal structure is the same as the real temporal structure, for example, of the correlating NCCs.

We see an example in Chapter 6 with the phenomenological models of time-consciousness, retention theory, and extensionalism. In extensionalism, the phenomenology of time is a succession of events, such as stages of a change. This succession is a real succession (being along "physical time"). That is, the phenomenology of time—the experience of time—is the same as something physical in the world. If that "something physical" is the experience's NCCs, then the experienced time is isomorphic with the NCCs.

Similarly, some early psychological researchers, such as some Gestalt theorists in the 1920s, considered it a general feature of experience that it is isomorphic on neural activity. For example, Koffka argued that what we immediately experience, what he called *phenomenal objects*, are neurological structures (Koffka 1935). One way to understand this is isomorphism between what we experience (phenomenal objects) and NCCs (the neurological structure).

Heteromorphism

However, many consider this a naïve view of consciousness (e.g., Blackmore 2003): it assumes that how things seem is identical to how things are. An alternative to isomorphism is heteromorphism.[1] Instead, one might be heteromorphic about conscious experience and NCCs.

Experience is *heteromorphic* to NCCs if they have different structures to one another. A motivation for heteromorphism is that the structure we attribute to experience is part of the represented *content*. However, the NCC structure is part of the representing *vehicles*. The content's structure need not match the vehicle's structure. For example, a heteromorphic representation of a cat (the content) is by the word "cat" (vehicle). But the animal and the word for it do not have similar structure.

This is a common rule of representation: representational content need not be isomorphic to the representational vehicle. And it is conceivable that the rule applies to time. "We must be careful to distinguish between the time of representing and the temporal content represented" (Grush 2005, 198; for discussion, see also Arstila 2019).

If the representational concept of their relationship holds, then nothing needs to follow from how things temporally appear (content) to the temporal structure of consciousness itself. The temporal content is merely represented content. The temporal structure of consciousness is the vehicle. Again, such vehicle and content need no more be isomorphic than the word "cat" and a cat be isomorphic.

To work out if temporal experience and NCCs must be isomorphic or heteromorphic, we could start by answering what kind of structure both must have. The structure of temporal experience has already been explored in Chapter 6. There are two competing models of phenomenological time. It was argued that one, extensionalism, matches the phenomenology of time better, i.e., the conscious experience of time. And even though it is an analysis in terms of physical time, perhaps that is merely part of the phenomenology as well. The structure of actual physical time, that of NCCs, of vehicle of consciousness, is something else entirely.

Given representationalism, appearances are not enough. They settle one half of the relationship, the phenomenology. What we need is to settle the other half of the relationship, the physical structure of the NCCs.

How do we work that out? Part of it depends on our thinking about physical events in time. This thinking can be impacted by commitments in the philosophy of time; we defer it to the next section. However, there is an important temporal relationship that requires no obvious thinking about the philosophy of time. This is the relationship between the timing of experience and its NCCs.

Timing

NCCs are physical events in the sense that shaking leaves, changing clouds, and clacking pebbles are physical events. They are neural events that *happen* in the brain. They have a where and they have a when. They exist in a time and in a place.

It is not as clear that conscious experiences exist in a place. Some theorists think consciousness is just not something physical, with a spatial location.[2] A reason for this thinking is that consciousness does not obviously have a location (e.g., Heil 2004; for a separate discussion, see Allen 2006).

However, as discussed in Chapter 6, consciousness is in time. It may not have a where, but it certainly seems to have a when. Notably, conscious experiences appear to happen around the time when some physical things happen. For example, we are awake *when* it rains outside.

Furthermore, conscious experiences are temporary. There are times when conscious experiences happen and times when they do not. I shift from being asleep and non-conscious to being awake and conscious—then, several hours later, I return to non-conscious sleep. And lastly, I have all my conscious experiences after I am born and before I die (one assumes).

With these considerations in mind, we can talk about two cases of *timing*:

1. The NCC's *timing*—the time or *moment* when NCCs happen.
2. Consciousness's *timing*—the time or *moment* when consciousness happens.

Note that consciousness's timing here does not concern a consciousness of *time*, such as hearing a sequence of notes; that is the *phenomenology* of time. This concerns the timing of consciousness itself, i.e., when it happens, not what it shows. For example, in both of the phenomenological models in Chapter 6, the moment is that of physical time.

This is important. It is possible that someone may have a conscious experience that appears to lack temporality. Yet it is, in fact, in time. You might have an apparently non-temporal mystical experience of a timeless void. Yet, possibly, you had this experience in time, for example, just after lunch and some time before dinner. In that case, the *timing* of your mystical experience is between lunch and dinner.

Thus, there are the moments, the timings, of conscious experience and of the NCC. What is the relationship between these two moments? How are experience and NCCs related in time? Here are three possibilities:

A. The NCC has no relation in time to the experience.
B. The NCC is *earlier* or *later* than the experience.
C. The NCC is at the same time as the experience. NCC and experience are *simultaneous*.

Which of these is the most plausible?

The NCC Has No Relation in Time to the Experience

There is no temporal relationship between NCC and the experience. Consciousness happens in one time series; NCCs happen in another time series. They

- Are not part of the same temporal series.
- Are not simultaneous.

- Are neither earlier nor later than the other.
- Might be past, present, or future. However, neither is past, present, or future to the *other*; they are not part of the same *series* of past, presents, or futures.

Call the time series in which the experience happens *conscious time* and the series in which NCCs happen *physical time* (taken from Power 2010).

We might hold this view of their relationship because we want to hold phenomenological time to be separate to physical time, and we hold conscious time to be such phenomenological time. Why want this? One reason is we are cautious because of the Hard Problem. We do not yet know how to understand consciousness's relationship to the physical world. As such, we defer identifying a common time between the physical and consciousness. And so we do not identify conscious time with physical time. However convincing such a position might be, there are objections to it.

Objection 1: Causation Is Not Possible across Different Time Series

Assume that a cause comes before its effects. Any event that is before another event is in the same time series. If conscious events are not in the same time series as physical events, then conscious events do not cause physical events and physical events do not cause conscious events.

If I throw a ball, causing a window to break, then the ball-throw is before the window-break; the ball-throw and window-break are in the same time series. Similarly, if a pain I feel causes me to flinch, then the pain is before my flinch. My flinch and the pain are in the time series. If they are not in the time-series, then the pain does not come before the flinch, and the pain does not cause it.

One might object that consciousness does not cause anything physical to happen. One may even argue from causal closure that it must not cause anything physical to happen. However, if consciousness and the physical are not in the same time series, then not only does consciousness not cause physical things to happen, but no physical thing can cause consciousness either.

Physical things cause things to happen *in time*. If a physical thing and something else do not share time, then the physical thing cannot affect it or cause it. For example, physical injury causes pain: the injury is physical; for it to cause pain, it must come before the pain; thus, injury and pain are in the same time series. This is true even if injury causes pain indirectly through causing an NCC, which then causes the pain. If pain and injury are not in the same time series, then injury does not cause pain.

Objection 2: We Cannot Know from Empirical Research When Consciousness Happens

If we determine when events happen by observing physical things, then we cannot determine when consciousness happens. For example, if we judge the timing of events by looking at a clock, then we judge it by looking at something physical. Conscious events are not in the time series containing that clock; we cannot use clocks to determine when the conscious events happen.

In response, we might use *conscious* events to determine when things happen. We may appeal to some kind of *phenomenal clock* to judge the time. For example, we might count changes or repetitions in sensation, such as throbs of pain or changes from pain to relief.

However, this raises an almost identical problem, except that the physical and conscious change places. If we use conscious events to time things, we cannot say when physical things happen. There could be any duration between the conscious event and whatever physical events I pick out connected to it, be it NCCs or other physical events related to them.

For example, say I become conscious when I wake up and stop being conscious when I fall asleep. If I judge when things happen by NCCs, I can say when dawn happens or dusk happens. But if I judge when things happen based on when I am conscious or unconscious, then, because it is a different time series, I cannot say that I wake up (a conscious event) at dawn (a physical event) or fall asleep at dusk.

The NCC is Earlier or Later than the Experience

The NCC happens earlier than the conscious event. For example, the neurons fire, then there is a conscious experience. Here is one possible reason that the NCC is earlier than the experience: a standard conception of physical causation has causes happening before their effects. NCCs happen before experience because they *cause* the experience with which they are correlated.

This has some intuitive appeal. For example, you eat an ice cream; the ice touches a sensitive tooth; a physical nerve signal travels from the tooth into your brain, firing neurons; these neural firings then *cause* a rush of feeling—a rush of pain.

Objection 1: Denies the Possibility of Mind-Brain Identity Theory

However, that the NCC is earlier is problematic given a specific form of physicalism: mind-brain identity theory (Blackmore 2003; Heil 2004). Mind-brain identity theory is the position that the NCCs are *identical* to the correlating experience; "correlation" is not the correct word for what holds between them; what holds between them is *identity*.

If NCCs are identical to experience, then they happen *when* experience happens. This is the *indiscernibility of identicals* (Leibniz' law): if A is identical to B, then any property that A has B has too, and any property that B has, A has (for more on this law, see Chapter 3).

If NCCs happen *before* consciousness, they do not happen when consciousness happens. The NCCs do not have the same temporal properties as the experience.

As such, NCCs that happen before consciousness are not identical to consciousness. Mind-brain identity theory is false.

Furthermore, this difference in time between NCC and the experience means that the experience cannot itself be physical. Recall that NCCs are the most immediately relevant physical events. There are no closer physical events to experience; otherwise, *they* would be the correlates of consciousness. But, if the NCC and experience are separated in time, then experience happens at a time when nothing physical happens; otherwise, it would be the NCC.

For the NCC to be at a different time, the experience must happen at its own time. This suggests dualism in this model of consciousness. And, of course, unless consciousness and NCCs are self-causing, causation alone prevents their identity; "to hold that [NCCs] are the causes of states of consciousness [...] is misguided. It implicitly involves an undesirable dualism of matter and mind" (Polák and Marvan 2018, abstract).

One might simply insist that NCCs are before conscious events, or vice versa, and not bring causation into it at all. However, this still leaves the issue of non-identity between them. There is no obvious gain in doing this.

Again, like possibility A, what applies to NCCs being earlier than conscious events also applies to conscious events being earlier than NCCs. For example, consciousness causes NCCs: consciousness happens and is followed by the neurons firing. The separation of cause and effect, and the separation in time, means that consciousness and NCC are not identical.

Objection 2: It Is Difficult to Know from Empirical Research When Consciousness Happens

There is also a secondary issue. We may ask what is the duration that separates the NCC and conscious event? If we do not know, then this raises a problem similar to the second objection against possibility A. We do know when the conscious event happens by looking at the NCC (or vice versa); there could be any duration between them.

This problem is relevant to a well-known experiment on the timing of free will. The scientific methodology has recently been discredited. However, the philosophical thought underneath it is useful for illustrating the problems of timing, as well as more general issues around simultaneity and consciousness.

The NCC Is Simultaneous with the Experience

There is no duration between NCCs and conscious events. Consciousness is at *the same time* as NCCs. It is *simultaneous* with them. The duration between NCC and conscious events is *zero*. There is no duration between them. When the NCC happens is when the related conscious event happens. The NCC moment is the conscious event's moment.

If causes are before their effects, then one cannot cause the other. Causes and their effects are not simultaneous (unless they are self-causing). What can be simultaneous are entities standing in relations of *supervenience*. Supervenience is a form of correlation. A subvening physical entity correlates with a supervening mental entity if the following holds: for any change in the mental entity, then there is a change in the physical entity; "it is not an *explanatory theory*: it merely states a pattern of property covariation between the mental and the physical" (Kim 2000, 14).

One of Kim's definitions of such supervenience uses simultaneity:

> *Supervenience:* Mental properties *supervene* on physical properties, in that necessarily, for any mental property M, if anything has M at time t, there exists a physical base (or subvenient) property P such that it has P at t, and necessarily anything that has P at a time has M at that time.
>
> (Kim 2000, 10)

Finally, simultaneous conscious events and NCCs can be identical. By definition, if A is identical with B, then A has the same timing as B, i.e., A is simultaneous with B.[3] This possibility suits mind-brain identity theory.

These are the possible temporal relations between consciousness, or conscious events, and their NCCs. Which of them should we accept?

Given these objections, possibility C, that NCCs is simultaneous with conscious events, is the best. There are epistemological reasons to resist possibility A: we have no idea when consciousness happens from observing the physical world, or vice versa. Possibility B allows causation; however, we do not know the exact time between the physical cause and the conscious effects (or vice versa); as such, there remains an epistemological worry here.

The remaining option is that NCCs and conscious events are simultaneous. We may resist accepting simultaneity because, although it allows for mind-brain identity, it denies physical causation. But we can at least know when it happens.

Still, given we do not know how consciousness is related to the physical world (especially with the Hard Problem in the background), none of these possibilities is forced on us. The preference for simultaneity is methodological, not metaphysical. It involves making a rule rather than discovering a law. It is a matter of preference which rule we use to understand time in cognition. Other factors play a part here.

With that in mind, let us apply thinking about timing to the following issues around time and cognitive science:

- The timing of free will
- Temporal illusions

The Timing of Free Will

Free will is undetermined by other things. For an agent, free will or the decision to act seems to be a *first cause* of voluntary action (Steward 2009). They do not feel it as caused by other events—at least, not in the way that physical events cause each other, by force or by chance. Nothing else wholly determines it. Yet—in the sense that indeterminacy is random or merely probabilistic—neither is free will indeterminate (Taylor 1958, 227–230). Free will is self-determining or self-causing.

One holds one's own will to be a source of action because it is how one's own will *feels*; it is "a wind blowing from nowhere toward the world" (Sartre 1947, 31). Other events can of course influence our decisions. We may be persuaded, discouraged, or even bullied to act. However, we are always free to do something else.

At least, so it is claimed that it seems to us. We may ignore these claims, especially if we think everything about a human being is physical.[4] Yet, it is difficult to dispense with free will in understanding human life. It is difficult to praise or blame the actions of ourselves or others if we understand that they must happen or are merely random. For a will that is in some way physical, it seems it can only be either unfree or without purpose. As such, for moral reasons, we may accept that the will is neither. It is free and it is purposeful.

Theorists about the will that resist this account typically fall under one of two kinds: *compatibilists* and *non-cognitivists*. Compatibilists insist that free will can be determined or probabilistic. They argue that some form of free will is compatible with either classical determinism, non-classical indeterminism, or both. *Non-cognitivists* deny that there is ethical or moral action; as such, we do not require free will.

However, another group of theorists, even if they accept free will is important, argue that free will is an illusion. There is no free will; there only *appears* to be free will. Wegner writes that "we each have a profound sense that we consciously will much of what we do, and we experience ourselves willing our actions many times a day" (Wegner 2002, 2; also, see Wegner 2003). Despite that, he argues that this is only an illusion.

It is beyond the scope of this chapter to evaluate these philosophical positions. The focus here is on the empirical basis for the last claim—that free will is an illusion. The most well-known and discussed empirical work is Libet's experiments. These experiments are on the *timing* of both the will and its associated neural activity. This evidence is alleged to show that free will is illusory. It is not self-determining; it is determined by something else, a neurological event called the *readiness potential* (RP).

Recently, this experiment has been discredited for methodological reasons. The RP seems not to be evidence of a physical cause. However, the background thinking in the experiment illustrates a particular philosophical attitude about the relationship between consciousness and neural activity, although the philosophy of time gives reasons to doubt this attitude. Again, it concerns assumptions about timing.

Measuring the Timing of the Will

What follows is adapted from Power 2010. There are three important elements in Libet's experiment: the *voluntary act*, the *experience of volition*, and the *readiness potential*.

The voluntary act is the action we identify as being under the agent's own will or *volition*, such as shouting or pressing a button. The agent decides to voluntarily act; they do not decide to involuntarily act.

The experience of volition is the feeling of free action experienced that the subject experiences. In the experiment, the subject was the judge of the act's freedom or volition; if it seemed to them to be a free action, it was treated as such. This was contrasted with bodily acts which subjects do not experience as voluntary (e.g., movements of limbs due to clinical conditions such as Tourette's or Parkinson's etc.: Libet 2004, 129). In other words, the subject experiences the action as caused by their own (at least, apparent) "free will".

The readiness potential (RP) is neurological activity associated with the other elements. The RP is "a recordable electrical charge in brain activity" that "regularly and specifically" precedes the resulting voluntary act by about 800ms (Libet 2004, 124). Many supposed then that, because it always accompanies voluntary acts, RP is caused by our will to act (Libet 2004, 124).

What matters in the experiment is the *timing* of these three elements. It was known by the time of the experiment that both RP and the experience of volition preceded the voluntary act. In addition, it was known that the RP preceded the voluntary act by 800ms. But Libet wanted to measure two further values:

1. The *duration* between a decision to act and the voluntary act that follows it.
2. The *duration* between the decision to act and the RP.

However, there was a difficulty. You can read a RP in brain activity and you can observe a voluntary act, for example, you observe a subject press the button on a whim. However, the *decision to act* is not obviously public. It is either something private but only accessible to the deciding subject; it is hidden from everyone else. Or it is hidden from *everyone*, something unconscious or forgotten, including the subject. In both cases, the moment when a subject decides is more difficult than the other elements to detect or measure.

To measure the moment of this decision, which he called *W-time*, Libet took the following steps:

1. In the experiment, a clock was placed in the room with the subjects. This clock had a spot that rotated around the clock's face, like a seconds hand on a clock.
2. In each trial, subjects were asked to note the position, when they decided to act, over which the clock's spot passed as it rotated around the face. This position, Libet reasoned, gave W-time.
3. The experimenters also measured where the spot was when the RP occurred (called *RP-time*).

Thus, two times were recorded:

- *W-time:* for subjects, the clock time that seemed to be when they *decided* to act (again, not when they acted).
- *RP-time:* for the experiments, the clock time that seemed to be when the RP happened.

Again, for the subject, the decision seems to be part of the *first cause* of a voluntary action, and also seems uncaused. This apparent freedom is what makes actions arising from it voluntary (or seem to be).

However, if the subject's will is the first cause of one's action, it comes before anything else that causes the action. This includes the RP. Again, the RP occurs regularly before voluntary acts, suggesting that it is a cause. As such, if the will is the first cause, the RP is an *intermediary* cause: the will causes the RP; the RP causes the act.

Under this hypothesis, the *W-time*, when we decide to act, is earlier than the RP-time, when the RP happens.

However, this is not what Libet found. He found that the RP-time is earlier than the W-time. Thus, Libet concluded that the RP occurs before the will, the conscious decision, to act. As the RP is one of the causes of the voluntary act, the conscious decision can only be an intermediate cause between the RP and the voluntary act. If the conscious decision causes the voluntary act, then it is itself caused by the RP.

Therefore, the will is not a first cause of the given voluntary act, despite how it seems. If this is for a voluntary act that we consider relevant to free will, such as a moral act, then this is evidence that moral acts do not have free will as a first cause.

Objections

Many objections have been raised against this experiment over the years; for discussion of many of them, see Libet et al. 1999. Here, let us consider two.

First, Schurger et al. (2012) deny the RP is a genuine cause. If right, the empirical work does not provide evidence against free will as a first cause because the RP is not an earlier cause. Second, Midgley notes that the kind of act here seems unlikely to be evidence of a merely spontaneous act:

> It has always struck me as extraordinary that, in these experiments, nobody seems to have taken the trouble to ask the subjects what they had been thinking about before they made their movements. Had they done so, the subjects would surely have had answers to give. They might have said something like, "Well, I was thinking, that's probably about five minutes, is that enough?", or "My elbow was itching", or "I'd finished counting up to 100", or simply, "I was getting bored".

(Midgley 2014, 106)

Even so, it is possible that someone might redesign the experiment, addressing the above challenges. Given a new approach, they may discover what seems to be empirical evidence. Given the interpretation of this evidence, to show the lack of free will, we could show something else specifically sits in the causal history of the will and the resulting act. As such, one might think, the question of free will is only an empirical question. We just need the right experiment.

However, there is another problem with the experiment, or any like it. This is not an empirical problem. It is not based on a misunderstanding of the kind of act. It is problem about the philosophical assumptions underpinning the design.

The design of the experiment assumes that we experience one event "while" or "when" we experience another. That is, we experience one event simultaneously with experiencing another event. Yet, notice why we think we do experience these simultaneously: these events *appear* to be simultaneous. That is, apparent simultaneity is evidence of *actual* simultaneity.

This view is found in some influential views on consciousness and its NCCs. For example, Singer (2016, 11 and 23) offers the following constraint on NCCs and conscious experience:

> The state of being aware of something has a number of distinct proper-ties that constrain the underlying neuronal mechanisms. One important fea-ture of this state is unity or relatedness: Contents of which one is aware are experienced as simultaneously present and related to each other.
>
> [O]ne might consider consciousness, or the state of conscious processing, as a state where distributed computational results can be bound together into a coherent whole, establishing multiple, simultaneous relations between the various distributed items.

In these quotations, the contents of consciousness are experienced as simul-taneous. This experience constrains the underlying neuronal mechanisms, requiring them to be simultaneously related. That is, there is both apparent simultaneity and actual simultaneity in consciousness, and the latter is shown through the former. If this is right, if actual and apparent simultaneity are identified with each other, then apparent simultaneity is enough to justify actual simultaneity.

With this in mind, let us return to W-time, the timing of the decision to act. The evidence for W-time is that, for the subject, the decision to act and the wall clock's position appear simultaneous. This is then taken by Libet as evidence that the two events *are* simultaneous.

However, there is another response here: apparent simultaneity is mistaken. It is possible that the decision to act happens earlier than external events that seem simultaneous with it. The subject's experience of their decision to act precedes what seems to happen simultaneously on the clock. Even though they are unaware of this precedence, it cannot be concluded that the dur-ation between will and voluntary act is the same as between the clock and the voluntary act.

In that case, we cannot conclude that RP, or anything else physical we find, is earlier than the will. We do not have evidence from such an experiment that free will is an illusion. Instead, the *simultaneity* is the illusion.

Response: We Should Assume that Apparent Simultaneity Is Actual Simultaneity

If such apparent simultaneity is merely apparent, and not actually because of simultaneity between events, this requires an explanation. We cannot simply assume that the appearance of simultaneity is false. We may be forced into denying the appearance. But to be so forced, we need a reason.

This is especially the case if denying apparent simultaneity is simultaneity means that we do not know which physical events happen when consciousness happens. This ignorance raises the problem of relating the timing of experience to the timing of NCCs.

Rejoinder 1: Phenomenology Is Not a Theoretical Constraint

Appearances are unimportant. The phenomenology is no constraint on theories about the nature of the mind or consciousness. Such a position on phenomenology is found in important related theories of consciousness and cognitive science (e.g., Dennett 1991, Blackmore 2003). Eliminativism about consciousness is the view that the common or standard folk conception of consciousness is not one that theorists need hold on to; it can and indeed will be eliminated given more rigorous, typically scientific, theories. Heterophenomenology is a view of the phenomenology of consciousness: it is that third-person, scientific theories are sufficient to explain such phenomenology; there is no need to bring in the first-person, traditional phenomenological view.

Such scepticism arises in response to theories of consciousness that hold phenomenological states to have non-public or non-physical characteristics—often referred to as *qualia* or *phenomenal properties*, the kinds of properties that drive the Hard Problem of consciousness. These properties are only open to the first-person subject of a conscious state. They are not found in the public properties of physical theory; there is an *explanatory gap* between physical explanations of consciousness and sufficient explanations of consciousness. Subjects learn about fundamental aspects of their consciousness through what might be called "introspection"—careful attention to what is immediately apparent to them.

Sceptics argue that there is no convincing reason to hold that there are such properties. One reason for this scepticism is that such properties are not public. As such, they cannot play a role in a public or shared theory of consciousness. Any theory of consciousness is such a shared theory. If that is right, these phenomenal properties cannot play a role in any theory of consciousness.

Another reason to be sceptical is that, as well as being private, reports of the phenomenal data are inconsistent and unreliable. Even if everyone is certain of their own phenomenal properties, their own private *autophenomenology* (as Dennett has called it), they are inconsistent in their reports. They cannot agree with others' reports of others' supposedly similar phenomenology. Here's Dennett:

> It is just astonishing to see how often "academic" discussions of phenom-enological controversies degenerate into desk-thumping cacophony, with everybody talking past everybody else. This is all the more surprising, in a way, because according to long-standing philosophical tradition, we all agree on what we find when we "look inside" at our own phenomenology.
>
> (Dennett 1991, 66)

For example, I deny that there is a phenomenology of immediate temporal passage but assert that there is a perceptual phenomenology of tenseless change. Others disagree. We also have different models of time-consciousness, each of which seems consistent with our own views, but not with others' views.

We may continue to debate which side is correct, nodding along with those who agree with us, and scorning those who do not. However, perhaps a better response is to simply take our irrevocable differences as evidence that neither side has any force. The public evidence cannot come down on either side; there is no consistent phenomenology of time.

However, if we wish to take phenomenology seriously, we may not want to reject appeals to phenomenology of time in general. Perhaps we can do this: we reject appeals to *some* phenomenology, justifying our rejection by issues around the specifics of that phenomenology. For example, we reject the phenomenology of simultaneity because of issues around the appearance of simultaneity. Yet how can we pick out simultaneity like this? Why would simultaneity be particu-larly susceptible to rejection?

Rejoinder 2: Apparent Simultaneity and Absent Duration

Power 2010 argues that it is a mistake to treat apparent simultaneity as some property or entity that is apparent. Apparent simultaneity is merely the non-appearance of something else: duration.

There are two ways perceptual experience—or cognition generally—can fail:

1. A perceptual experience fails because it perceptually appears as if there is more than there is.
2. A perceptual experience fails because it perceptually appears as if there is less than there is.

The difference is significant. 1 is a genuine illusion: for the subject, there appears to be something, such as a property, which is not there. However, 2 gives no reason to think there is a genuine illusion. The error is only because the experience is limited: it is only some of what is there. It does not include every-thing that is there.

Limited Experience in Time

If I peer into a dark shop from the street, and only see a few dim objects in the shop, my perceptual experience misses some of what is in the shop. This does not mean that I am under an illusion of something in the shop. It only means that I have a limited perception.

Even in the brightest, clearest act of perception, we have limitations like this: in bright sunlight, we look at the surface of a stone and see a mustard stain of lichen; we cannot see the gaps between the patches of lichen.

There are also limits to our detection of the *timing* of what we perceive. As discussed in Chapter 6, there are time-lags in our perception: the distant objects that we seem to perceive are at different times to the moment when we perceive. This duration is absent from the phenomenology or appearances of this percep-tion. We do not perceive it or seem to perceive it. Yet, the duration is still there.

There are multiple ways to understand this point. If one is a representa-tionalist about experience, then there is no representation going on. We are not representing this hidden duration, such as the time-lag. We are not even representing an absence of this duration. We simply do not represent it at all.

If we apply this thinking to simultaneity, an appearance of simultaneity is misleadingly described. Simultaneity can be also thought of as an absence of something. It is an absence of duration, for example, between events. When we look at a multitude of different distant stars, they appear to shine simultan-eously. However, all there is to this apparent simultaneity is that we cannot detect the (often significant) durations between them.

Again, denying the appearance of something that is an absence is not a problem for any theory. It is not the sort of phenomenology that must be saved—in part because it is not really an appearance at all.

Along with removing background assumptions in Libet's work, this point about simultaneity generalizes to any experiment which times a subject's intro-spective judgements by the subject's observations of some external timer, such as a clock. We need not assume that the subject's report of simultaneity between the timer (clock) and their own cognition is evidence of their own cognition's timing. It only means that they do not detect an actual duration between clock and cognition. They may very well be unable to detect such a thing, and it may very well be there.

Simultaneity Thresholds

Furthermore, there are other cases of perceptual error that seem to involve merely apparent simultaneity like this. These are cases in which there is a *coin-cidence* or *simultaneity threshold*. A simultaneity threshold is a lower limit to perceptual awareness, beneath which a difference in time between stimuli cannot be detected.

For example, in visual perception, the simultaneity threshold is 20ms; in auditory perception, it is 2–3ms (Dainton 2000, 170; see also Elliott et al. 2006). If we visually perceive stimuli separated by less than 20ms, we do not perceive them as separated by *any* duration. If we auditorily perceive stimuli separated by 2–3ms, again, we do not perceive them as separated by any duration. In these cases, they seem to happen at the same time and, thus, appear to be simultaneous.

We need not posit illusions to explain simultaneity thresholds (or spatial thresholds, for that matter). We need only posit a perceptual incapacity to detect such fine distinctions. We need only posit a *limit* to perception. Where there is only such a limit, there is no illusion. Otherwise, again, we are under illusions whenever we cannot see.

This is evident with cases of blurred motion: the stages in the position of a fast-moving object seem to be simultaneous; as a result, the object seems spread over a space all at one time; however, it is not spread out in the space, at least not *all at one time*; it passes through the space, being at different locations at different times. As such, this is a case of apparent simultaneity between things that are not actually simultaneous (for more on motion blurs and the philosophy of time, see Power 2015).

This need not be an illusion. It can be due to the limits of perception. We cannot detect the difference in times of the different events. With this analysis of apparent simultaneity on hand, as something akin to simultaneity thresholds, we turn to consider illusions—and, in particular, temporal illusions.

Temporal Illusions

A common understanding of illusion is as an error in how things seem. Typically, this concerns the phenomenology of perception (Calabi 2012), although there are other kinds such as memory illusions (Power 2018). Philosophers commonly add that it is an error in the appearance of a *property,* such as a colour, shape, sound, or texture. This is to distinguish it from hallucinations, which are taken to be mistaken appearances of *objects,* such as aliens, angels, and ghosts.[5] In an illusion, then, there appears to be a property but there is no such property. For example, if I see what seems to be a red banana, and the banana is not red, then I may be under an illusion of the banana's redness.

However, illusions are not just any mistaken belief about a perceived property.[6] I can have a mistaken belief about a property yet how it appears to me is, in fact, correct. This is illustrated in Figure 7.1. I think that I see a red banana (A). However, my friend informs me that this is impossible: bananas can only be yellow. Trusting my friend, I believe that I am under a colour illusion of a banana: I believe it is yellow (C) but this one has an illusory red colour (D). However, my friend and I are wrong. Our belief that the fruit in front of me cannot be red is mistaken. I am looking at a red banana—a plantain (A).

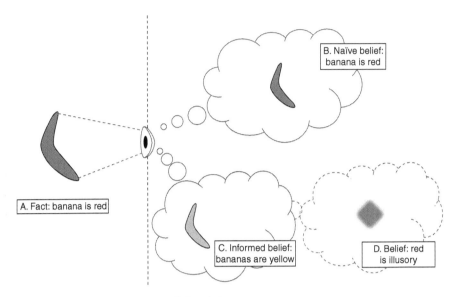

Figure 7.1 Conflicts between Belief and Appearances

There are sometimes alternative *psychological* definitions of illusions. For example, Reynolds suggests defining illusions in terms, not of truth and error, but in terms of "a discrepancy between one's perceptions of an object or event observed under different conditions" (Reynolds 1988, abstract). Hoffman suggests we avoid defining illusions as untrue because perceptions "that we would not want to call illusions or hallucinations, are, in the normal case, untrue". He proposes an alternative definition of an illusion as a perception that is not an "adaptive guide to behaviour" (Hoffman 2013, 85). However, most people across most disciplines understand it involves error. (As such, I keep it here.)

So, a temporal illusion, an illusion of time, is any case of experience in which there appears to be time but there is no time—that is, an illusion of some temporal property or relation. "Time" here is not independent time (we do not experience that) but some property or relation between things. As such, a temporal illusion is a case in which (a) there appears to be some temporal property *T* and (b) there is no such temporal property *T*.

Before discussing temporal illusions, a word of caution: a temporal illusion is not an illusion of something that is *not* temporal. It is not, for example, an illusion of colour. Nor is it merely an illusion of something that depends on time but is not itself time. For example, a temporal illusion is not just any illusion of motion. We may have an illusion of motion because we see a sequence of illuminated dots in a digital display; yet, the apparent temporal order of this change in illuminated dots may be correct; what is incorrect is *what* changes (for discussion of an example of such a change, see Chapter 9).

Furthermore, given what an illusion is, a temporal illusion is not merely an error about time. It is not merely a mistaken belief about time, or a misinterpretation of something temporal. I may wrongly believe what time it is on the other side of the world. This does not mean I am under a temporal illusion.

Examples of Temporal Illusion

Illusions undermine arguments from experience as evidence of certain features of the world. As such, temporal illusions undermine arguments from experience as evidence of temporal features of the world. For example, you argue from the experience of temporal passage that there is, in fact, temporal passage.[7] If your opponent knows illusions of temporal passage are common, then they can argue that experienced passage is only an illusion; being only an illusion, the experience is not evidence of actual passage.

For the purposes of this chapter, we discuss how thinking about time and timing can impact our understanding of their illusory nature. We then discuss how this might apply to philosophical thinking about time. Through this, we can show how cognitive science, threaded through philosophical thinking, might draw conclusions from such illusions to using experience in the philosophy of time.

There are multiple examples of temporal illusions. We look at three typical and commonly discussed examples: the cutaneous "rabbit", the flash-lag effect, and the phi phenomenon.

The Cutaneous "Rabbit"

The cutaneous "rabbit" experiment is discussed in Dennett 1991 and Grush 2005. Subjects are stimulated by two series of taps on a limb, such as along the length of their arm. The taps are delivered fast enough that they are felt as perceptible changes. They are taps separated by fractions of seconds, not separated by, say, minutes or hours. This is depicted in Figure 7.2.

The taps are delivered along two parallel lines (x and y). Initially, the taps are irregular. For example, in the figure, before time t_1, there is a tap along:

1. Line x (A) *then*
2. Line y (B) *then*
3. Line y again *then*
4. Line x …

After t_1, the taps are like little hops (as if by a rabbit). These are *regular taps*:

5. A tap on X and a tap on Y *then*
6. A tap on X and a tap on Y *then* …

The puzzling experience is this:

- At or before t_1, if subjects are asked are taps 1–4 irregular or regular, then subjects report that these taps *are irregular*. They are not like little paired

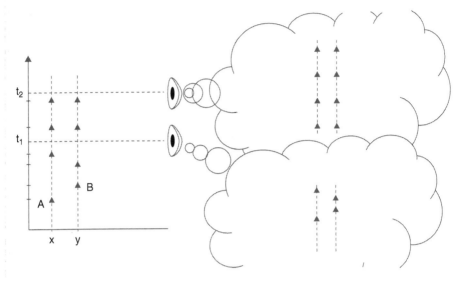

Figure 7.2 The "Cutaneous" Rabbit

hops along both x and y. For example, according to the subjects, A and B appear to happen at different times. This is a correct judgement.

- However, at t_2, after the regular taps have also happened, if subjects are asked are taps 1–4 irregular or regular, then subjects report that 1–4 are *regular*. They *are* like little hops. For example, according to the subjects, A and B happen simultaneously. However, these taps are not regular (A and B happened at different times). There is an incorrect judgement. It is an error in the feeling of *when* these taps happened. This, it seems, is a temporal illusion.

The Flash-Lag Effect

The flash-lag effect is shown in Figure 7.3. Each of a series of spots around a circle's circumference is illuminated in turn. Every so often, a spot separate to that circle (D) appears and disappears. At the time that D appears, one of the circle's spots (C_1) is illuminated. Also, subjects report seeing a spot at a particular location while D is illuminated.

However, the spot they report seeing (C_2) when D appears is not the one that is, in fact, illuminated (C_1). C_2 is a *later* spot in the circle. C_1, the spot that is actually illuminated simultaneous with D, seems to be illuminated *before* D. Again, this change appears to be a perceptible change. It is not one that takes longer than can be perceived, e.g., C_1 is illuminated and then, some minutes later, C_2 is illuminated. That two spots appear to be illuminated simultaneously but are not illuminated simultaneously looks, again, to be a temporal illusion—in this case,

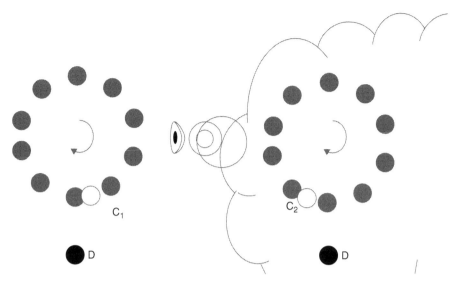

Figure 7.3 The Flash-Lag Effect

of relative timing, i.e., the illusion is that they both seem to happen at the same time, but do not.

There is another mistaken appearance in the flash-lag. A *single illuminated spot* seems to move around the circumference of the circle. In fact, there is no single spot. There are just the individual spots illuminated, of which C_1 and C_2 are examples, one after another. This appearance of a single spot is an example of another mistaken experience, the phi phenomenon.

The Phi Phenomenon

The phi phenomenon is an appearance of continuous motion of a single object from one location to another. This appearance is mistaken; there is no single spot in motion. Instead, there are at least the following stages of the visible change:

1. A spot in the first location that appears and then disappears
2. A spot in the next location that appears

These appearances give the overall effect of a single spot that moves continuously from the first location to the second. But no such single spot exists. Indeed, no spot *moves*, and certainly not continuously. It is only spots at each location appearing and disappearing in sequence, discretely, with a gap in time between them.

Furthermore, when the apparent motion includes spots of different colours, it appears as if the illusory moving spot also *changes colour* in between its passage between the two actual spots. What makes this particularly puzzling is that, if

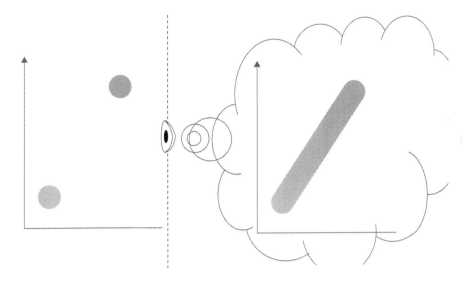

Figure 7.4 The Phi Phenomenon

there is no later appearance of the spot, there is no apparent colour change (Kölers 1972; discussed in Dennett 1991). However, there is nothing there to change during the apparent motion.

Furthermore, the apparent colour change seems to depend on what happens *after* it occurs. If the later spot does not appear, the colour change does not happen. It is as if the later event *causes* the earlier event. If causation matches temporal order, then this implies either an illusion of temporal order (or backwards causation—we ignore this).

Each of the above phenomena—the cutaneous rabbit, the flash-lag effect, phi—are typically claimed to involve the appearance of something that is not the case, and thus are illusory. Furthermore, these phenomena are often taken to be illusions of *temporal* properties. If this is right, these temporal illusions can be taken to undermine claims that the experiences associated with them give reasons to believe in the relevant temporal characteristics. They also undermine ideas such as *isomorphism* for time-consciousness and models such as extensionalism. These show the apparent time (the phenomenological time) is different to the physical time in terms of simultaneity, continuity, and temporal order.

Illusions of Simultaneity and Temporal Order

As said earlier, many philosophers of time deny that temporal passage is anything more than an illusion. That is a good for tenseless theorists, who deny there is temporal passage. However, these phenomena here, if temporal illusions, are not good for tenseless theorists; they are illusions of properties otherwise accepted by tenseless theorists.

For example, Paul 2010 proposes a solution that purportedly defends tense-less theory against claims that experience favours tense theory. Paul argues that the phi phenomenon shows that temporal passage can be illusory because perceptual experiences of motion can be illusory. However, Paul's solution is not so helpful to tenseless theorists as it might initially appear. As discussed in Chapter 6, tenseless theorists have no problem with perceptual experiences of motion. Paul may be right that phi shows illusions of motion. But it is an argument that undermines both tense theory and tenseless theory arguments from experience.

This is because these phenomena are of the order and simultaneity of things. Such temporal order and simultaneity, as typically described, are tenseless:

- *Cutaneous rabbit:* At t_1, apparently, taps A and B are at different times. At t_2, apparently, taps A and B are simultaneous. The taps A and B are not simultaneous.
- *Flash-lag:* D seems to be illuminated when C_2 is illuminated. However, it is not the case that D is illuminated simultaneously with C_2.

Described this way, both of these phenomena are illusions of simultaneity.

In addition, D appears to be illuminated later than C_1. However, it is not the case that D is illuminated *later* than C_1. This is an illusion of temporal order.

- *Phi phenomenon:* Through a period of time, a single spot seems to move through a space. However, no spot moves through that space—or, indeed, through *any* space over *any* time. There is one spot at one end of that space and another spot at the other end.

This is an illusion of a spot's movement through the space. Furthermore, there is an illusory colour change midway, that is, *during* the apparent motion. The appearance of motion in this experience is something *merely* apparent. There is nothing in the world that has these properties; or, if there is something that has these properties, it is not something we detect in having these experiences.

Illusions Are Evidence of Heteromorphic Representation

Dennett discusses these illusions in a number of places (Dennett 1991; Dennett and Kinsbourne 1992). In seeking to understand them, he considers Mellor's account of perceived temporal order (see Chapter 4). Then he responds as follows:

> [T]he top sentence of a written description of a standing man need not describe his head, nor the bottom sentence his feet. This principle also applies, less obviously, to time … [t]he representing by the brain of A before B does not have to be accomplished by:

first:

a representing of A,

followed by:

a representing of B.

(Dennett 1991, 148; see Roache 1999 for comment)

Dennett does not think that the conscious representation of time is anything special. For Dennett, the apparent order of events is *represented*. This analysis is representationalist. There may be temporal order, but the appearance of temporal order, being represented temporal order, does not require actual temporal order.

This analysis requires a heteromorphic account of representation. As such, it requires denying the isomorphic view of representation. However, saying they are represented is not a full answer. It does not say what kind of representation there is or what such representation means for the relationship between the phenomenology and the physical world. When we look more deeply at it, must we accept that the representation of time is heteromorphic?

Objection: Hidden Time

There is a time-lag between distal objects and local perceptual stimuli (Power 2013, 97–98). There are also a variety of lags within the perceptual process in the brain itself. These lags are hidden durations, that is, durations that are not apparent to the subject themselves. They are not the only hidden durations. There are also durations between events too short for us to detect, such as the duration in motion blur or in the display of an old cathode-ray TV.

Such hidden durations require a difference between the appearance of time and actual time. However, they do not undermine the isomorphic view. They show that temporal experience is isomorphic to only *some* of the temporal structure in the world. In these cases, we have limited experience of the temporal structure. But, as discussed above about conditions of illusions, a limit to experience is both a common feature of experience and not one involving illusion.

So, if we can provide an isomorphic relationship between the apparent temporal structure and some actual temporal structure in the world, then there is no need to appeal to illusion—or, indeed, heteromorphic representation. Furthermore, although we have incomplete experiences of the world, they need not be representations of the world. Instead, they can occur because our experience merely fails to represent some of what is in the world. It fails to represent the lag between long-past starshine and our perception, for example. This is not a representation of *absent* starshine. That is, all there is to such experiences is that they are silent about some of the physical world.

So, can hidden duration explain the cutaneous rabbit, flash-lag, and the phi phenomenon?

Illusions of Simultaneity

The cutaneous rabbit and some of the flash-lag have relatively straightforward explanations. To show how there is no need for illusions to explain these phenomena, we replace any reference to non-simultaneity with duration between things, and illusory simultaneity with *hidden duration*. Or, if that sounds too conspiratorial, *non-apparent duration*):

> *Cutaneous rabbit:* At t_1, apparently, taps C and D are at different times. At t_2, apparently, taps C and D are simultaneous. Taps C and D have duration between them.
> This is a hidden (non-apparent) duration.
> *Flash-lag (1):* Apparently, spot A's being at location 1 is simultaneous with spot B's being at location 2. However, it is not the case that spot A is at location 1 simultaneously with spot B at location 2.
> There is a hidden (non-apparent) duration between spot A at location 1 and spot B at location 2.

Illusions of Temporal Order and Duration

The apparent motion in the flash-lag and the phi phenomenon is more complex and involved. It is not merely an error around apparent simultaneity. It involves errors around apparent temporal order, for flash-lag and phi, and, further for phi, *continuous* motion. How can we explain them?

> *Flash-lag (2):* Apparently, spot A's being at location 2 is earlier than spot B's being at location 2. However, it is not the case that spot A is at location 2 *earlier* than spot B at location 2.

This is an illusion of temporal order.

> *Phi phenomenon:* Through period P, a spot that seems to be spot A appears to move through location C. However, spot A does not move through location C through period P—or, indeed, through *any* time. Spot A, if it persists beyond the moment it is illuminated, remains in its original location.
> Furthermore, there is an illusory colour change midway, that is, *during* the apparent motion. There is no colour change because there is nothing during the apparent motion.

How can we explain these illusions of temporal order and change? It seems we cannot appeal to mere limits to our perception, to something hidden that is not apparent to us:

- The mistaken appearance of events' temporal order is, at best, a hidden dis-order or reorder of events.
- The mistaken appearance of duration is, at best, a hidden lack of duration, i.e., a hidden simultaneity.

Positing something hidden to explain these is problematic because the hidden thing is less than what is apparent. A lack of duration is no duration, that is, less than any duration at all. It is like looking into a dark shop and seeming to see someone there, when no one is there; then, insisting there is no hallucination—it is just a limited visual perception of *no one*.

However, even in these situations, there might be a way to appeal to hidden properties to explain the illusions. Power proposes a solution turning on there being more to perception than what we perceive. There are also perceptual processes resulting from such objects impinging on our senses. Along with the unperceived time-lags between external objects and our perceptions (discussed earlier), there are also unperceived internal time-lags in perception.

For example, we see a constellation of stars appearing to shine simultan-eously, forming a figure in the sky. However, they shine at different times, with the differences in those times hidden; as such, there is no figure there; it is a trick of limited sight from a particular point on the Earth. Similarly, our experience comes from proximal stimuli, such as light hitting our retina, that appear to be simultaneous or to have a particular order. Yet, some of the temporal proper-ties between these stimuli are hidden. This hidden time explains why the stimuli appear to be simultaneous or to have their particular order (Power 2018).

This is not just an appeal to the perceived objects and their properties, including hidden properties. It appeals to properties of perceptual experience itself. For this reason, even if this works for reinterpreting illusions, one may reject it. It is no longer merely limited experience of external objects in the world, along with their properties. It is limited experience of stages leading to experi-ence, such as sensory stimuli and the NCCs.

Whether this kind of answer is acceptable depends on the following question: must a subject's inability to detect the structure of the sensory stimuli and NCCs in their experience be explained by illusion? I think it is plausible to say no; that is, it is no illusion to be unaware of the structure of experience itself. If that is right, then we can appeal to this limit to deny there are temporal illusions in the flash-lag and phi phenomenon.

Philosophical Positions on Time

Finally, let us draw current debates in the philosophy of time into thinking about temporal illusions. Are the answers that appeal to hidden duration available to any philosopher of time? There are reasons to think their availability varies by philosophical position on time.

Dennett argues that, when we model how consciousness works, we ought not totake empirical evidence at face value. Many empirical researchers, investigating the physical material of cognition, base their investigations and interpretation on mistaken assumptions about the mind. "Cognitive scientists themselves are often just as much in the grip of the sorts of misapprehensions and confusions as outsiders succumb to, and being down in the trenches sometimes makes them even more susceptible" (Dennett 2009, 231).

Dennett's best-known example is the *Cartesian Theatre*: humans have conscious experience through a theatre-like central area in their brain, in which consciousness runs like a film on a cinema screen. This model interferes with research into consciousness: it imposes unnecessary limits, affects interpretation of evidence, and impacts the apparent plausibility of theories that conflict with it (Dennett 1991; also, see Blackmore 2003).

Similarly, research into the cognitive science of time may be based on mistaken assumptions about time. In Chapter 6, we discuss such assumptions in thinking about the phenomenology of time-consciousness. However, there can also be similar assumptions in thinking about the underlying cognitive structure of time-consciousness, and evidence for it.

The most significant example in this chapter is that the appearance of simultaneity is, in fact, a limited experience of duration. Different theories about time have different commitments to the possibility of such a hidden duration and of failing to experience it as merely a *limit*.

Presentism and the Growing Block Theory

Presentism has the most straightforward and dramatic impact on interpreting time-consciousness as illusions. If presentism is true, then there is only one real moment in time—the present. Any duration is only a past or future duration, and thus something unreal. Thus, what is hidden—a duration—is something unreal.

This makes an explanation of the illusion through a hidden duration an example of appealing to there being less there than there seems to be. That is, it is no more a limited perception of what is there than a hallucination of a person is a limited perception of no one.

Similarly, for the growing block, where it concerns a *future* duration, the growing block theory is the same as presentism. Where the duration is past, the growing block theory is the same as eternalism.

Eternalism

Eternalism can have real duration. Thus, it can have hidden duration. However, whether that is all there is to it depends on further commitments to the philosophy of time.

Tense Theory

If tense theory is true, then there is only one real present. Any duration is partly past or future. Thus, what is hidden—a duration—is partly past or future. If what is perceived seems to be present, yet is separated by this past or future duration, then there is still an illusion here. At least one of the things that is perceived as present is not: it is at a different time to the other things that are present. Thus, given tense theory, it is either past or future. It only *appears* to be present.

Furthermore, according to Power 2018, given the conception of the present in eternalist tense theories, this is an illusion. Presentness is something special in tense theory. It is not merely an absence, for example, an absence of pastness or futurity. As such, a mistaken appearance of presentness is an illusion of *presentness*. What that means depends on further commitments in one's tense theory. For example, for a "moving spotlight" theory, there is an illusion of a "spotlight" on the event—an event that is, in fact, not present.

There is, however, a different possible response for tense theorists. Some theorists hold to tense logic or Prior's idea of the present (see Chapter 5). They might respond as follows: the present is the same as unmodified existence or reality. In Austin's terms, a real duck is just a duck—similarly, for tense logic, a present duck is just a duck; a present event is just an event.

In that case, this can be merely a limited experience—a failure to notice anything temporal in the duration other than it happens. As tense theorists, there is more here: some of these events must be past or future; any duration must be at least partly past, future, or both. Thus, what is hidden is both duration *and* tense.

Tenseless Theory

For tenseless theory, the hidden duration can be present. What is separated by it, and perceived, can also be present. However, there is still the tenseless duration that is hidden. Unlike presentism, this is something real and not apparent to us. Our perceptual experience can, like simultaneity thresholds, be merely because of a perceptual limit.

As such, unlike the tense theories, there is no further issue for tenseless theory in explaining the alleged temporal illusions as cases of limited experience.

Study Questions

1. Say that there is a fixed duration of 1 millisecond between NCCs and consciousness. How would you know that there is *this* duration, rather than 2 milliseconds or 10 minutes?

2. What experimental evidence would show there is no free will? (And what experimental evidence would show that there IS free will?)

3. This chapter proposes that illusions of simultaneity are only failures to experience duration. Can you think of an experience of simultaneity that would be more than this? That is, a) an experience of two things happening at the same time that is not merely b) failing to experience a duration between them.

4. This chapter describes some of the evidence from cognitive science, from the perspective of the philosophy of time. It does not describe this evidence as it is commonly described or understood in the cognitive science literature. Is there a theory of time that best matches the common descriptions of these phenomena? If so, which philosophical theories of time do you think this supports?

Notes

1 There is also homomorphism (Le Poidevin 2007). For the purposes here, we can treat this as identical to isomorphism.

2 What other kind of object could it be? Perhaps a phenomenal object, to borrow a term from Köhler 1929 or a sense-datum (although both are particular to various theories not considered here).

3 However, a final cautionary point: Mind-brain identity theory is, strictly, not a theory involving NCCs. NCCs and conscious events are correlates. Correlates are not identical with each other. In this case, NCCs of conscious episodes are not correlates at all. It might be better to call them neural aspects or identities (NIC) of conscious episodes (for more, see Blackmore 2003).

4 Chapter 4.

5 Because we talk about time, hallucinations are irrelevant. Time that appears to us is not an object. It is a property of something or a relation between things. This is why arguments that may be for a conception of time as an object—substantivalism—do not turn on experience (for more on hallucinations of time, see Power 2018).

6 A mistaken belief may sometimes be commonly called an illusion, e.g., I might have illusions about the importance of my job. However, I take this to be metaphorical in the spirit of "seeing someone's argument" or "grasping a difficult theory".

7 Chapter 6.

Suggested Readings

Dennett's *Consciousness Explained* is the modern classic on consciousness and cognitive science; an extended section is on time and cognitive science. Prosser's *Experiencing Time* is a philosophical text on the experience of time that brings in a lot of cognitive science and evolutionary theory.

Wittmann's *Felt Time* is an accessible book on the psychology of time by a cognitive scientist aware of the philosophy of time. On temporal illusions and other mistaken experiences of time, see Power 2018. Also worth looking at, if again outside philosophy, is Libet 2004; his explanation of why and how he carried out his famous experiment is useful to thinking about time and the mind.

There are several philosophy and psychology anthologies on time, as well as sections of more recent philosophy of time anthologies. Many are in the bibliography. For temporal illusions, Arstila et al.'s *Illusions of Time: Philosophical and Psychological Essays on Timing and Time Perception* (2019) contains new papers from both philosophers and psychologists.

8 Rationality of Time

Overview

There are various attitudes one can have about time: desires, fears, and beliefs about when something happens, how long it takes, whether it is future, present, or past. Which of these attitudes about time are rational beliefs, based on reason, that can change through argument and evidence? And which are irrational, originating without reason and immune to argument and evidence? Of the irrational attitudes, must we have them, no matter their irrationality?

Most theorists agree that some attitudes toward time are irrational. But which and why can be a matter of dispute. Here are three types of attitude toward time discussed in the literature:

- *Near-bias (N-bias)*: We care more about what happens sooner rather than what happens later.
- *Future-bias (F-bias)*: We care more about what happens in the future than the past.
- *Temporal neutrality*: We care equally about what happens at any and all times.

N-bias is commonly thought to be irrational. It conflicts with the rational requirements of prudence. For example, caring about one's retirement might necessitate not satisfying one's own impending desire. Many theorists discuss F-bias as if it is rational. For example, it is seen as rational to prefer past pain to future pain. However, more recently, questions have been raised about F-bias's rationality. When considered in light of one's life overall, it seems to not be based on either reason or argument.

Finally, there is temporal neutrality. If N-bias, F-bias, or any form of temporal bias, is irrational, then it seems reasonable to hold that lacking such bias is rational. This lack is temporal neutrality. However, neutrality faces a challenge from what seems to be the rational position to take on the *symmetry argument*. The symmetry argument is that, from a position of temporal neutrality, one's birth is as significant a limit to one's life as one's death. Yet, the rational position here is that death is far worse than one's birth. How can temporal neutrality account for this?

Rational and Irrational

One of the ways rationality is important is that it enables us to pick out attitudes that are not rational. It does so by providing systematic ways in which we fall short of standards of rationality (Yudkowsky 2015). For example, an attitude can be irrational by being *epistemically irrational*. The attitude is "either not supported by the available evidence or not updated in the light of new evidence" (Bortolotti 2014, 127). "A clear violation of epistemic rationality is hanging on to a belief that has been repeatedly challenged by reliable evidence" (Bortolloti and Mameli 2012).

As an example, Gendler describes how people behave around the Skywalk, a transparent platform over the Grand Canyon. It is common for people walking out onto the Skywalk to hesitate and even feel intense fear. Their fear, they say, is that there nothing is supporting them, and so they will fall to their deaths. It seems they believe the floor is dangerous despite three other beliefs that conflict with such a belief: the belief that other people are casually walking on it; the belief that the believer is just like those other people (they do not think the other people are wizards, for example); the belief that the surface they walk on is a transparent solid surface.

Yet, this apparent belief in danger persists. Even as the subjects walk safely across it, they are afraid, fighting a conviction that they will fall. The conviction is an irrational attitude: it is not based on the evidence nor does it change given further evidence.

Furthermore, this attitude does not force them to act in a certain way. People who walk out onto the Skywalk hesitate and feel fear yet, nonetheless, continue to walk out on to the platform. Yet, if their fear is because they believe that there is nothing there, then a belief driving the fear requires they believe that stepping out on to the platform is stepping into nothing, into empty space. They should not believe they can walk on it precisely because they *do* believe they will fall through it.

In such a case, there seem to be two conflicting beliefs:

- The fearful belief that one is in danger because stepping forward is to step into empty space.

- The belief that one is safe because stepping forward is to step onto a transparent platform.

These beliefs are incompatible; to believe one is to disbelieve the other. If one believes *both,* one is holding two incompatible beliefs. The rational response is either to hold only one belief or *epoché*: suspend belief in both—accept that both are equally plausible, and neither can be accepted (see Chapter 1). Yet, subjects report and act as if they, in some sense, believe and act on *both.* They tremble with fear and walk out anyway:

> Surely they believe that the walkway will hold: no one would willingly step onto a mile-high platform if they had even a scintilla of doubt concerning its stability. But alongside that belief there is something else going on. Although the venturesome souls wholeheartedly believe that the walkway is completely safe, they also alieve something very different. The alief has roughly the following content: "Really high up, long long way down. Not a safe place to be! Get off!!"
>
> (Gendler 2008, 635)

For Gendler, the irrational fearful attitude is so significantly different that it is better not to call it a *belief.* It is something else, something he calls an *alief.*

As evident from the example, aliefs are like beliefs. They have meaning; they are about something; they are propositional or semantic. Such aliefs are evident in various ways: they influence your behaviour, reactions, feelings, and tendencies toward unexamined thought.

However, no matter how compelling an alief is, and no matter what compels it, it is not a *rational* attitude. The alief that I will die if I stay on the glass surface of the Skywalk is not justified. No evidence is forthcoming to support this belief. The only evidence is that you are standing on the glass, and this *undermines* the alief that I am in danger.

Aliefs are also not explained merely by ignorance. They do not merely arise in the absence of argument or evidence, dissipating in their presence. I fear spiders because I believe a spider running over me is a terribly dangerous thing to happen. Yet, I have no evidence to think spiders are dangerous. I have plenty of evidence to the contrary; I live in Ireland where no poisonous spiders live. Still, no matter what I am told, no matter how trustworthy the teller, no matter my own experience, I do not change my conviction that spiders are dangerous. I have an alief about the danger of spiders.

Furthermore, we can continue to have an alief while also understanding how it came about; it does not disappear just because we understand it. In grasping the reasons for the alief—e.g., that the fear of the Skywalk or spiders is based on evolved reactions—does not change it. An evolutionary account of how such convictions arise can be accurate and well-understood by everyone, yet fail to dissolve those convictions for anyone. We continue to fear spiders despite no spiders ever doing us any harm.

This does not mean that we cannot change aliefs. It is only that, changing aliefs does not come from sound arguments or sufficient counter-evidence. There are successful treatments for some aliefs. Controlled exposure in cognitive behavioural therapy, for example, can deal with irrational fears of spiders.

Finally, if a certain attitude about some subject is an alief, or is otherwise irrational, then a rational argument defending some position on the subject cannot use the content of the attitude as a premise in a sound argument. If I argue that the Skywalk is unsafe based on an unjustified conviction, then it is rational for others not to accept that argument. In contrast, I can draw on rational arguments: if I argue that the Skywalk is not safe because pieces of it visibly break off and drop into the canyon, then it is rational to accept that argument.

Turning, then, to time: knowing which temporal attitudes are rational and which temporal attitudes are irrational matters to the philosophy of time. If we assert that some position on time is true, and that we are justified in having that belief, then we assert that it is rational. If we argue from a conviction which, it turns out, is unjustified, then it is rational for others not to accept that argument.

So, which attitudes might be rational or irrational about time? Here are two conflicting sets of attitudes about time: *temporally biased attitudes* and *temporally neutral attitudes*. These attitudes conflict because, if one is temporally biased about something, one cannot be temporally neutral about it, and vice versa. The further question is which of these attitudes is rational, and thus may support a theory of time?

Temporal Bias

Last year, I had a terrible toothache. It hurt a great deal, keeping me awake for several nights. When the pain finally passed, the relief lasted a long time. I have not thought about it since; I have not even thought about the relief. Yet, I can barely think about anything other than my present backache. It hurts a great deal, keeps me awake all night. Similarly, sitting in my empty penthouse after a long day at the office, I remember a childhood trip to the beach. It pleases me a little as I think about it, but not as much as it pleased me as a child.

A great deal of psychological research shows that most people place different amounts of importance on activities based on *when* they happen in time (e.g., Persson 2005; Green and Sullivan 2015). "Some people care not only about what things happen, but also about *when* things happen" (Hare 2007, 358). The differentiation in importance based only on when it happens is *temporal bias*:

Temporal bias: Events have different levels of importance only because they have different positions in time.

Temporal bias is based only on differences in time. It is not based on differences in anything else. For example:

- I place a different level of importance on an event because it happens to my cousin rather than myself. It is a bias based on a difference in *who* events happen to (Hare (2007) calls this *egocentric bias* or *agent* bias).
- I prefer the heat of a ghost pepper to that of a jalapeno pepper. This is bias based on a difference in the Scovile scale of capsaicin concentration.
- I prefer ice cream to hot chili, and hot chili to a toothache. This is (or can be) a bias based on a difference in *mouth-feel*.

These three examples are of bias with respect to people, chili heat, and "mouth feels" (if you can include a toothache in that). The events in them can be at different times and I can prefer the pleasurable event at one of those times over the painful event at another time. However, this does not make me temporally biased.

Say, on Tuesday, I have some hot chili; on Wednesday, I have ice cream; finally, on Thursday, I have a toothache. Because of a mouth-feel bias, I prefer what happens on Wednesday over what happens on Tuesday or Thursday. However, there is no temporal bias here. The days do not matter to my preference; what matters is what happens on the days.

Yet, temporal bias can be mixed with such differences and biases based on those differences. How temporal bias can show itself when mixed with such other biases is that my other biases do not sufficiently explain why I consider one more significant than another. Instead, we must consider when they *happen* to explain the difference.

For example, if I only place more importance on what happens on Wednesday to what happens on Thursday or Tuesday *because* it happens on Wednesday, and not on Thursday or Tuesday, I am temporally biased. Say, then, I have chili on Tuesday and ice cream on Wednesday. Despite my usual preference for chili, I prefer the ice cream over the chili. On other days when I have ice cream, I do not show this preference for it. If, in such cases, the *only* difference my preference consistently matches is a difference between Wednesday and any other day, then the evidence is that my preference is based only on a difference in day. This is a form of temporal bias.

Note that bias is not merely preference. Bias concerns significance or importance. Whatever it is that one is biased about is more *significant* than its alternatives. If something good happens at a locus of bias, then being there intensifies your preference for the good thing. But if something bad happens there, then the location intensifies your desire to *avoid* it. You resist it more than you would if it happened somewhere else. If you dislike chili, and you are biased toward Wednesday events, you avoid eating chili on Wednesday more than you avoid eating it on any other day.

No one is likely to be biased towards Wednesday events over Tuesday events. However, other kinds of temporal bias are more plausible. Here are two kinds that Persson describes:

- *Future bias (F-bias)*: The future has a greater importance than the past (2005, 211–221).
- *Near bias (N-bias)*: Times closer to us have greater importance than time far from us (2005, 205–210).

We return to N-bias further in this chapter. For now, consider F-bias. F-bias is a special kind of temporal bias. This is *tense* bias.

Tense Bias

The difference beneath F-bias is not difference in dates or days, such as Wednesday and Thursday. It is difference in an A-series position, *tenses*.[1] It is difference between the past and future. Call this kind of bias *tense bias:*

> **Tense bias:** Events have different levels of importance because they have different positions in the tense series (or A-series).

Are there other tense biases? As Persson describes it, there is only future bias. There is no past bias or present bias. However, another bias he describes fits a present bias in many respects. This is perception-bias (or *P-bias*).

Present Bias (P-Bias)

According to Persson, because of *bias toward the perceived* (P-bias), subjects "are episodically thinking more about some event—for example, their feeling pain—when it is perceived than when it is not perceived". In addition, there is "a stronger desire with respect to some event when it is perceived than when it is not perceived". This begins a spiral of reinforcement. The desire "further amplifies the tendency to think more about the sensibly present, and what to do about it, producing thoughts which in turn strengthen the desire connected with the event perceived, and so on" (Persson 2005, 183).

Persson denies this is merely a bias toward the present. It is, instead, a bias toward "what each one of us perceives" of the present (2005, 196). However, when thinking of it in relation to the future or past, P-bias is a sufficient surrogate for present bias. We can consider P-bias in comparison to future and past perceptions, and ask: are we biased toward the present perception over future and past perceptions? Intuitively, we are: past and future perceptions, such as a past warm day and future toothaches, do not have the kind of hold or reinforcement had by present perceptions, such as the present taste of ice cream.

For the sake of this chapter, let us constrain ourselves to experience, be it that of ourselves or others, and be it past, present, and future experience. In that case, we can treat P-bias as a surrogate for present bias.

That we have present bias is uncontroversial for other philosophers. For example, Prior's paper on tense beliefs is based around *relief*, on the phrase "thank goodness that's over" (Prior 1959). That paper is primarily an analysis of language and of meaning. However, it is driven by how the present feels as if it matters more than other times: the tooth pain is worse when present than when past; we feel relief when the pain is no longer *present*, rather than when it is no longer future; we fear and avoid a present pain more than we do a future pain.

Future Bias (F-Bias)

With future bias (or F-bias), the thought of events affect us more when the events are future than when they are past. Persson defines future bias (of F-bias) as:

> [T]he propensity to prefer, hope, or wish that negative states of affairs, such as feeling pain, be in the past rather than in the future, while positive states of affairs, like feeling pleasure, be in the future rather than in the past (or a propensity to fear the reverse)
>
> (Persson 2005, 212)

Green and Sullivan break such bias in two—for pleasure and pain:

> An agent S is biased toward the future with respect to pleasure iff for two exclusive experiences, E1 and E2, where E1 is at least as pleasurable as E2, S prefers E2 because it is a present or future pleasure rather than a past one. [...]
>
> An agent S is biased toward the future with respect to pain iff for two exclusive experiences, E1 and E2, where E2 is at most as painful as E1, S prefers E1 because it is a past pain rather than a present or future one.
>
> (Green and Sullivan 2015, 949)

Like present bias, F-bias seems uncontroversial. I might say: obviously, I prefer future pleasures to past pleasures; and, as obviously, I dislike future pains more than past pains. Future things are *more significant or important* than past things. Future ice cream is *better* than past ice cream. Future pains *are worse* than past pains:

> If we prefer to have our pleasures ahead of us, and our pains in the past, it seems to be because the contents of our futures matter more to us than that of our past. So we want the better to be in the future and the worse in the past.
>
> (Persson 2005, 211)

Parfit's Surgery

Parfit 1984 provides a thought experiment to illustrate the intuitive appeal of F-bias. Say that you undergo some invasive surgery, and are told that the safest way to undergo it is as follows:

- You undergo a very painful operation that takes either (a) ten hours to complete or (b) given something discovered early in the surgery, only one hour to complete.
- You are not anaesthetized. You are awake throughout the procedure, feeling the pain.
- However, to relieve your suffering overall, the doctors give you a pill before the procedure that wipes all your memories of it. As a result, after the surgery, despite the pain during it, you remember nothing. Post-operation, it seems to you as if you have just had a deep sleep.

Here is what seems right: despite the fact that you do not remember the procedure, however it goes, you would prefer the hour-long version over the ten-hour long version. It involves less pain. If pain is bad, and to be avoided, then it is rational to prefer to less pain—and so prefer the hour-long version over the ten-hour-long version.

However, this preference changes when the *tense* of the procedure changes:

- You enter the patient's ward. The ward has another patient in your situation. You take the pill and fall asleep.
- Sometime later, you wake up and the other patient is gone. You ask a nurse if you have been through the operation.

The nurse tells you that they do not know if you have. All they know is that you are either:

1. The patient who already had surgery and experienced the long, ten-hour agonizing operation.
2. The patient who has yet to complete surgery and is due soon to go through the hour-long operation.

Parfit states that, intuitively, we prefer 1 over 2. We prefer to already have had the ten-hour operation, even though this means, given the entire episode, we experience more pain than the future hour-long operation. However, it is the more preferable pain just because it is the *past pain*. Presumably, this is because we prefer to have a lesser pain over a worse pain (Parfit 1984).

That is, for some reason, the past pain is not worse than a future pain. Yet, the future pain is not worse in terms of length or in its effect on our memory. It is only its futurity that could make it worse than the past pain. This is F-bias.

The Rationality of Tense Bias

It is generally agreed that this bias is intuitive. To anyone you may ask, it is obvious that it is much better to have "a more painful surgery in one's past rather than a less painful surgery in one's future" (Green and Sullivan 2015, 964). Indeed, if waking up, we are unsure whether we had the operation or not, "the desire to be after the operation seems to be completely justified" (Zuradzki 2016, 159). And people frequently do not treat the bias as error (Zuradzki 2016, 168). We treat this as a reasonable judgement, an obviously true belief. It is markedly unlike *aliefs*, such as fearing the Skywalk platform.

Such temporal biases may seem justified, and even rational. Yet, are they rational?

Sometimes, Parfit seems to intend his thought experiment to show that F-bias is rational. He introduces it to challenge the idea that "it is irrational to care less merely because of a difference in *when* some pain is felt by oneself" (Parfit 1984, 164). If it is a challenge to this view, then it must be because this bias is rational. In that case, there are valid arguments or empirical evidence for the preference.

So, what are the arguments and evidence for F-bias being rational? Might it be some philosophical theories of time. For example, could tense theory justify F-bias?

Reality Is More Important than Unreality

Take it that the following is trivial: it is rational to be more threatened by a Komodo dragon's bite than that a dragon's flame. Komodo dragons are real; fire-breathing dragons are not. Even if we have only an image of both—having never encountered an actual Komodo dragon—still, there is more to fear from the lizard than the mythological beast. However irrational I am to fear either (I am unlikely to meet a Komodo dragon), at least wariness of Komodo dragons is *more* justified than wariness of fire-breathing dragons.

But why? Dragon burns are presumably much worse than Komodo bites (however poisonous the latter). So why are we more wary of the Komodo bite? Here is an intuitive reason: Komodo dragons are real. Fire-breathing dragons are unreal. A Komodo *could bite us*. A medieval dragon could not burn us.

The reason for thinking of one thing as more significant than another is that the former is real, and the latter is not. In the philosophy of time, there are different views as to the reality of things in time. So, perhaps we can explain F-bias by thinking about the reality of things in time.

For example, according to presentism, only the present is real, and not the past or future. If past and future things are as unreal as dragons, and present things as real as Komodo dragons, then it is rational to place greater significance on present events than on either past or future events.

This works for presentism and P-bias. The present is real, other times are not, and we consider the present more significant. Yet, what of other theories of time and of other biases, such as F-bias?

Objection: This Only Works for Presentism and Present Bias

It does not work for a combination of all biases and theories of time. Hare notes appealing to reality to justify P-bias cannot work if one is an eternalist. For eternalists, the past and future are as real as the present. So, P-bias cannot be based on a difference in reality (Hare 2007).

Again, given eternalism, both past and future are real, and so cannot be distinguished that way. Yet, presentism cannot justify F-bias either. Given presentism, both the past and future are unreal. Although the present may be more significant than both, there is no reason based on reality for the future to be more significant than the past.

One theory does distinguish the past and future in terms of reality—the *growing block theory*. However, the appeal to reality cannot work with growing block theory. For growing block theory, it is the future that is *unreal*; a future pain is unreal whereas a past pain is real. As such, our greater fear of future pain over past pain runs directly against any growing block theory distinction between the past and future. If the reality of these events in time is what makes them important, then, given growing block theory, we should place more importance on past events than future events.

As such, one can appeal to reality for justification of P-bias if presentism is true, but not if other theories are true. As such, presentism can justify P-bias (although, again, not F-bias).

Does this benefit presentism? Only if we wish for P-bias to be rational or we can prove that P-bias is rational. For this to work for presentism, we must be independently motivated to hold that P-bias is rational. A rational P-bias may be compatible with presentism and no other theory. But if P-bias is not rational, then it cannot support any theory (any more than alief about the Skywalk can support the theory that the Skywalk cannot support people). However intuitive P-bias may be, we must either accept it as rational just on grounds of intuition or, alternatively, have independent reasons for holding it is rational.

We Have Control Over the Future

Perhaps we care more about the future because we care more about what we can act to bring about; we care more about what we can cause to happen. We consider more significant what we can cause to happen or can control.

In that case, we prefer the present to the future, and the future to the past, because of the degree of control we have over each of these times. We can control the present more than we can control the future. We can control the future and the present. However, we cannot control the past.

If that is right, our bias *against* past events is because we cannot control such events. As such, no matter when events happen, if we cannot control those events, we would be as biased against them as we are against past events.

Objection: There Are Significant Uncontrollable Future Events

Yet, there are many uncontrollable future events that we are not so biased against. They involve pains that we still prefer to avoid over similar past pains. As an example, we fear death. Death is in everyone's future. Yet, it is also out of our control. We cannot avoid it (ultimately). Still, unlike past events beyond our control, our inability to control death does not make death less significant.

It might be answered that, although death is fearful, it is an ineligible counter-example. We cannot compare the relative significance of past and future deaths. A past death is not one we can have any attitude towards. Assuming there is no afterlife (if there is, then we do not strictly die), then there is no position from which we can measure the important of our own past death. We never survive our own deaths to carry out that evaluation.

As a rejoinder, if we could be in such a position, it is difficult to imagine that death would be more significant—for example, more fearful—if we had *more* control over it. Death's significance is precisely in our inability to control it; it is not diminished by that. As such, the relative *control* we have over events in time does not match the relative *significance* of those events for us.

Biases Give an Evolutionary Advantage

We might clarify the control answer. We are P-biased and F-biased because of some evolutionary advantage these temporal biases give us. These biases provide us benefits in competition with organisms that are not P-biased or F-biased. Here is Hare:

> It is not an accident that we are future-biased with respect to pain. That fea-
> ture of ourselves has been selected-for by evolution. In light of the direction
> of causation, ancestral creatures that focused their practical attention on the
> future did better than their peers that focused their attention on the past.
> And a cognitively efficient way to focus a creature' s practical attention on
> the future is to have the creature care a great deal about its future pains and
> not at all about its past pains.
>
> (Hare 2013, 512)

Why does F-bias mean a creature does better than its peers? According to Green and Sullivan, the evidence shows that our F-biases are due to evolved *control heuristics*. A heuristic is a useful evolutionary shortcut that allows us to respond cheaply and quickly. It can involve instinctive or automatic judgements that, in general, reliably provide evolutionary advantages. In the case of F-bias:

> [F]uture-biased emotions and preferences evolved to track asymmetries in
> control. A policy of not caring very much about the past is part of a good

strategy for focusing on what is within our control, since future events are sometimes under our control while past events never are.

(Green and Sullivan 2015, 968)

We can tell a similar story for P-bias. Since, like future events, present events are sometimes under our control, and past events never are, we tend to focus on the future and present over the past.

This evolutionary explanation of why we have these biases may be correct. But does it make biases rational?

Objection: Evolutionary Explanations Are Neutral with Respect to the Rationality of Beliefs

If aliefs are promoted for evolutionary reasons, evolution is insufficient for an attitude's rationality. It can be more useful to believe something that is false, or to act on emotions that are not mediated by reason. For example, dangerous jealousy can be selected for by evolution; it can be selected even if it is delusional or does not benefit the jealous individual themselves (Buss 2011). An organism's beliefs and thoughts do not need to be accurate to improve the survival changes of that organism or their descendants:

> Improvements in sensorimotor control confer an evolutionary advantage: a fancier style of representing is advantageous so long as it is geared to the organism's way of life and enhances the organism's chances of survival. Truth, whatever that is, definitely takes the hindmost.

(Churchland 1987, 548)

Evolution does not demand reasonability; it demands suitability for evolutionary success. Although a tense attitude such as F-bias is evolutionary advantageous, this advantage explains why they come about and persist, not how rational it is to have them—or, indeed, its usefulness in modern society. That is, it explains attitudes such as aliefs. But, alone, it is not enough to explain rational beliefs.

That is, an evolutionary explanation does not require tensed attitudes to accurately match how things really are. The present need not be significant in any way. The future need not be more important than the past. Such bias is neutral with respect to arguments about the reality of tense. All it does is provide an explanation for why tensed biases occur. A tenseless theorist can accept this kind of explanation.

Tense theorists may respond that an appeal to tense bias as irrational is biased toward tenseless theorists. Can making these attitudes irrational, and thus dispensing with any challenges they raise for tenseless theory, be justified as a dialectic approach? What is being explained, a tense theorist might insist, is basic to human thinking and challenges tenseless theory itself. Surely that means *something* in the debate about time.

Yet, there is another kind of temporal bias which it is generally agreed is irrational. Furthermore, this other kind of bias has similar flaws to F-bias.

Near Bias (N-bias)

Parfit thought F-bias was rational. However, he held that another kind of temporal bias was irrational. This is what he called *bias toward the near*. Persson calls it *N-bias*. The following is a definition (adapted from Green and Sullivan 2015):

> An agent S is biased toward the near with respect to pain/pleasure iff for two exclusive future experiences, E1 and E2, where E2 is at least as painful/pleasurable as E1, S avoids/prefers E1 because it would occur nearer to the present.

> (Green and Sullivan 2015, 948)

We ascribe more significance to events based on how far, how temporally "distant", they are from us. Say that there are two events that are identical save in one respect—one, N, happens nearer in time than the other, F. Based only on that temporal proximity, N is significant in comparison to F.

For example, say that I promise you the following:

- If you do the washing up, you will receive ice cream now.
- If you do the cooking, you will not receive ice cream now; instead, you will receive more ice cream—tomorrow *and* the day after.

Presuming that ice cream is good, more ice cream is better, and washing up is as good as cooking, then you are N-biased if the above promise motivates you to do the washing up.

Are people N-biased? The psychological evidence suggests that there is such N-bias in the general population (Zuradzki 2016). And we can prime intuitions about it through adapt Parfit's thought experiment.

Say that you wake up and, instead of learning you have either already had the operation, or not, you learn that you have not had the operation. However, the operation will either be:

a)   A ten-hour operation three months from now
b)   An hour-long operation three hours from now

If it is intuitive that you prefer to be in the scenario a) over the scenario b), then you are N-biased. This is to prefer undergoing the worse operation, in terms of pain, because it is farther off in time; that is, the nearer the operation is, the worse you feel about the pain.

However, the "near" in this needs some qualification. It could mean two things: near in the future and near in the recent past. We could also have N-bias toward past events. For example, you wake and learn you already had the operation. However, the operation was either:

a)   A ten-hour operation three days ago
b)   An hour-long operation three hours ago

Intuitively, the difference in past durations seems far less significant than the analogous difference in future durations. It seems that, so long as the operation is past, I just do not care how long ago it happened. All that might distinguish the two operations is the relative vivacity of my memory of each. But this is not about near and far-off past events themselves.

We will return to this kind of response later on in this chapter. For now, assume that we are N-biased about future events, and not N-biased about past events. Is such N-bias rational or irrational?

Reality of the Near Over the Far

Unlike F-bias, the "reality" of the events that are near and far does not explain why we prefer one over the other. This is apparent where the near and far time have the same tense, e.g., it is the near future and far future.

Whether or not the past and future are unreal, as held by presentists, or only the future is unreal, as held by growing block theorists, or all are real, as eternalists contend—both near and far future times are future. The reality or unreality of one means the reality or unreality of the other. As such, like F-bias for eternalists, the reality or unreality of the different events makes no difference to their significance—and so cannot explain the presence of this difference.

Objection: We Often Want Unpleasant Things Sooner Rather than Later, and Pleasant Things Later Rather than Sooner

Unlike F-bias, we are not always N-biased. We sometimes want the bad thing sooner rather than later, and the good thing later rather than sooner. For example, I may wish to lance a boil now, even if it brings pain. Or I might save up for a holiday, even though I could go now.

However, one reason to prefer pain now is to "get it over with". This is in part because we want to manage our irrational feelings. We need to remove the pain of anticipation, or of fear and even of desire. As Persson writes:

> If one cannot reduce the intensity of the fear and of the feelings of the unfulfilled desire to avoid the pain [...] one shifts tactic to wanting to reduce their duration.
>
> (Persson 2005, 208)

I may believe that a pain is going to happen, for example, I must go to the dentist for an operation. I dread this pain and would avoid it if I could. But I also know I cannot avoid it. However, I also know the pain is temporary; it will be quick. As such, the feeling of dread is so terrible that I want to also end it. Because the pain is quick, I move to have the operation done sooner—so that the dread will dissipate sooner, along with the pain.

This is still a case of N-bias. I am acting to have less pain—reduced suffering from anticipation—sooner rather than later.

Similarly, Persson writes, we tend to sustain the anticipation of pleasure. Future pleasure can generate two emotions:

(a) Pleased the future has this pleasure in store
(b) Strong desire, long for pleasure, and discomfort of unfulfilled desire

If we do not feel (b), then postponing pleasure "prolongs the positive state of gladness or joy". But if one's predominant emotion is of frustration, "one will naturally try to enjoy it as soon as possible". Again, one is N-biased—one wants the pleasure sooner rather than later.

So, how might we explain this bias? Is it based on something rational? Unlike F-bias, theorists generally agree that N-bias is not rational. Treating a temporally near event and a temporally far event as different just because one is near and the other far is unjustified, especially where it comes to events in our own lives that we will experience.

For example, even selfish people rationally prefer something that benefits them even if it farther off in time than something else near. For example, in a famine, they will put off eating food and hoard it for themselves at a later date.

N-bias is imprudent and "prudent people make choices that result in their leading better lives (featuring, inter alia, cushy retirements, better health, and extra marshmallows)" (Green and Sullivan 2015, 951). So, even selfish people might agree we should eliminate these irrational biases "when determining the scope of moral or prudential obligations" (Zuradzki 2016, 150).

However, Zuradzki suggests a possible rationale for such bias. This concerns personal identity. A subject may more closely identify with themselves at a nearer time than a farther time. The "psychological link that is guaranteed by memory and other processes, between me now and me in 30 years time is much weaker" than the link guaranteed between me now and me tomorrow (Zuradzki 2016, 163).

One reason that N-bias is more readily thought irrational than F-bias is because F-bias cannot make us act in a way that is contrary to our own long-term good. F-bias will not make us arrange things in a way that we will later regret. It is not *bad* for us (Green and Sullivan 2015). But N-bias can be bad for us. Aiming to satisfy desires sooner rather than later, for example, or avoid pain tonight than avoid greater pain tomorrow, we risk creating greater suffering for ourselves overall.

Persson's Explanation of Temporal Bias

Persson attempts to account for the irrationality of both N-bias, F-bias, and P-bias. He also recommends a way of countering these biases so that one can more easily make rational judgements. As it is a more detailed account than merely pointing at evolution, and offers a rational approach to these attitudes, it is worth briefly outlining.

The account is based on other, non-temporal concepts developed by Persson. These are perceptual bias, the *mechanism of spontaneous induction* (MSI), and what he calls *para-cognitive attitudes*. For the purposes of this discussion, we can consider para-cognitive attitudes to be identical to aliefs.

Perceptual Bias

According to Persson, perceptual bias plays a part in explaining temporal biases. As discussed, perceptual bias is bias toward what is *perceived and present*, over what is imagined or thought. We consider what we perceive in the present to be more important or significant than other experiences or attitudes, such as imaginative experience or thought. For example, a perceived present taste of a cake is better than an imagined taste of cake or the thought of a cake as tasty. A perceived pain is worse than an imagined pain or the thought of pain.

We have already discussed perceptual bias; it is the basis of present bias (P-bias). But why is this preference for the perceptual an irrational bias, a something in us, rather than in the world? Isn't what is perceived more significant than other things, e.g., what is imagined or thought?

In some cases, the content of an imagining or thought can be better or worse than the equivalent content of a perception. To use an example by Persson, I might prefer not to feel the social awkwardness of helping someone who is homeless; in doing so, I also imagine the suffering they continue to endure without my help. For me, only imagining it, a homeless person's suffering may feel a less significant pain than my present social discomfort. Yet, according to Persson, this is a false sense of significance: homelessness is much worse a pain than social discomfort.

The Mechanism of Spontaneous Induction (MSI)

The mechanism of spontaneous induction (MSI) is a cognitive mechanism that, as the name suggests, gives rise to inductive judgements apparently instantly, without the apparent need of reflection or deliberation. From past experience, we observe A followed by B. A typical view of induction is that is requires multiple observations and recollections of A following B.

However, Persson argues that not all forms of induction require us to reflect on a multitude of observations to be activated. Some forms of induction are *instinctual* or *spontaneous*. We observe A followed by B; observing A again, we spontaneously anticipate that B will happen. This is because induction also happens instantly upon our first observing a sequence of A then B.

Furthermore, although MSI is spontaneous, it can draw on previous experience to fill out the contents. If we experienced event A before, and also that B followed A, then, when we next experience A, we will spontaneously induce that *B follows A* (Persson 2005, 3).

Imagining Sequences from the Present into the Future

Why do P-bias and MSI generate F-bias? Persson argues that, because of P-bias and MSI, we more frequently and vividly experience sequences of future events than we do past events. The difference in the power of these experiences explains the biases we have toward the relevant times.

Because of P-bias, when I imagine a temporal sequence, I tend to imagine events extending from the perceived present. The P-bias is the origin, where the sequence begins, with other events extending away from that origin. So, for example, if I imagine the steps in constructing a building, I tend to imagine the first step in the construction as being present. I do *not* tend to imagine the first event as being in the past, such as the credit crunch, or in the future, such as the death of the sun.

Because of MSI, when I imagine the first event as present, I also spontaneously imagine the event that follows it. That is, I spontaneously imagine an event that is later than a present event. Any other events I imagine follow on this sequence—giving a sequence of later and later events. An event that is later than a present event is a future event, and each one is later again. As such, I imagine the events extending into the future. Thus, MSI:

> [E]xemplifies our tendency to imagine things rolling on from the present into the future in the kind of order we have experienced them, for it consists in roughly imagining that the future will be that which, in the past, followed upon what was like what is now the perceived present.
>
> (Persson 2005, 213)

Note that this is a tendency. It is possible for us to look backward from the present and imagine a sequence into the past. However, we do not look backward *from* the present to the past. If we imagine a sequence involving a present and past event, we imagine the sequence as going from a past event to events after it—i.e., into its future, and perhaps to the present event.

As such, the experience of a remembered past event is weaker than the experience of an imagined future event. In imagining the future events that follow perceived events, because of MSI, our representations of them are more forceful or vivid than any comparable past events.

This, then, is why there is F-bias. We vividly imagine some future events because of our tendency to imagine temporal sequences with the present as the origin and the future as spontaneously induced from that origin. We do not have such a mechanism for past events. As such, we are biased toward the future over the past. In addition, as a condition of this analysis, we are biased toward the present over the future. Assuming that significance is transitive, we are also biased toward the present over the past.

Finally, why do P-bias and MSI generate N-bias? Given MSI, the experience of the imagined events that most closely follow the perceived event is stronger than the imagined events that occur further along the imagined temporal sequence. Whatever the strength of an imagined future event, it is not as strong as the experience of a perceived event. Then, with respect to different imagined futures, the nearer imagined futures are more intimately linked to the perception than the farther imagined futures. As such, the nearer representations are stronger than the farther representations.

By itself, Persson's account is not an explanation of such biases' utility—at least, not its utility in the modern world. Instead, his suggestion is that we evolved such tendencies, and they are built into how we represent the world to ourselves. What makes it more than simply "it benefits us"—and thus the common evolutionary answer—is that Persson tries to identify the *specific* reason for this in us, and also what brings it about. It is a product how we represent, through imagination and perception, the past and future to ourselves.

Persson's Proposal to Overcome Temporal Bias

Again, this answer does not save the biases from being irrational. It is irrational to treat a relative under-representation of the past as meaning it has lesser importance. This is what happens in this model. However, Persson uses his model of these biases to propose a way we can overcome them.

Persson recommends that, to be as rational as possible when making judgements about time, we should represent different scenarios as vividly as possible. This brings the force of these scenarios as close as possible to competing with the force of perception. It offsets the irrational tendency to take what is perceived, and what is imagined as following what is perceived, as having greater significance than what is otherwise imagined (Persson 2005, 215–221).

For example, imagine Parfit's past ten-hour operation as vividly as one imagines one's future operation—that is, with as much accuracy as one imagines the future pain. When you do that, Persson argues, you judge a ten-hour operation in the past as worse than a one-hour operation in the future. As such, "we are as distressed by our own past pains when we recall having them" (Persson 2005, 221). You form a rational judgement. Your judgement is not F-biased.

Temporal Neutrality

If we have no temporal biases, then are we not temporally neutral? To close, let us consider what this involves. And ask whether it is rational to be temporally neutral?

We can define temporal neutrality as follows:

Temporal neutrality: There is no difference in anything's significance because of different positions in time.

It might seem that, if temporal bias is irrational, then temporal neutrality, as the only alternative, must be rational. However, there are many ways to be temporally neutral. Some may strike one as too much to accept as a rational attitude to adopt.

I prefer what happens on Wednesday—I eat ice cream—to what happens on Tuesday—I have a toothache. It is not because it happens on Wednesday. It is because I prefer the actual events that happen. I prefer eating ice cream (which happens on Wednesday) over toothaches (on Tuesday). The day of the week does not matter. I am indifferent, disinterested, or neutral about the day of the week—that is, about the temporal character of the event.

Such an attitude is to be *temporally neutral* about the days of the week. In the case that *when* means the day of the week, when does not matter to me. Such temporal neutrality seems obvious. It is intuitive. What could there be about a weekday that makes any difference to our preferences?

However, there are other ways neutrality may seem less obvious. Some of them are familiar: they involve F-biases and P-biases. If F-bias is intuitive—something Parfit believes, for example—then neutrality with respect to the past and future is counter-intuitive. Still, however intuitive F-bias seems to be, if F-bias is irrational, then neutrality about the future is, as its contrary, rational.

We can make further discriminations in temporal neutrality. Some of these do not appear so rational. We might ask if this is because of further temporal biases beyond those toward the future, the present, or the near:

- *Cosmic temporal neutrality:* You have no preference for any time at all, be it a time during your life, before your life began, or after it has ended. The moment of the Big Bang is as significant to you as the moment you are born, the moment you read this, when you must next open the window, or a particular piece of asteroid crumbles to dust.
- *Selfless temporal neutrality*: You have no preference for any time in your own life or times of others' lives. You treat a day in some other human's life as significant as a day in your own life, and vice versa, even if those people live far away, many years ago, or many years in the future.
- *Lifetime temporal neutrality*: You have no preference for any time in the whole of your life, from birth to death. You consider the time of your birth as no more or less important than the time of your death, or of your reading this now.

The most obviously rational of these three is *lifetime* temporal neutrality. These events fall within one's own life, from one's birth to one's death. These events are distributed over several times. At each time you read this, your birth is in the past and your death is in the future. For you reading this, there are many other events in your life as well (unless you are remarkably bright and remarkably unfortunate).

If you are temporally neutral about your life, then the times of these experiences and participations are equally important. No matter which event is happening to you now, all of these events hold their value before they occur and after they are done.

Again, if we are temporally neutral about our lifetime, then we are also neutral about tense. Much of anyone's life is past or future; only some of it is present. If an individual is indifferent to different times in their life, they are indifferent to which is present, which is past, or which is future. As such, a lifetime temporal neutrality is incompatible with *tense bias*.

Event Neutrality

Note, again, that an important aspect of temporal neutrality is that it concerns times. Again, it does not concern events. Grasping this distinction is central to clarifying the stakes about rationality of bias or neutrality.

I may believe you are not temporally neutral because you prefer your twelfth birthday to your two-billionth birthday. These look like *times* and so your preference is between times. However, it may be that you do not prefer one of these birthdays over the other because of the *time*. When you were twelve, you floated in the sea while, when you were two billion, you were very thirsty while the sun died out above you.

To make this difference clear, let us refer to *temporal neutrality* and *event neutrality*:

* *Temporal neutrality*: No time is any better or worse than any other time.
* *Event neutrality*: No event is any better or worse than any other event.

Here, we assume that event neutrality is neither rational nor a neutrality anyone holds. For various reasons with respect to their characteristics, and how they compose and impact our lives, we *do* prefer some events over others; furthermore, it is *rational* to have this preference. Even if we decide to attempt indifference to our own impulses, to care nothing for cultivating or satisfying our needs and longings, we do so to have a different attitude towards life. This is preferring one way of being—one kind of happening in the world—to another. We desire a desireless, impulse-less life to one filled with desire and impulse.

This is one reason that we may be biased, say, toward the events of our youth over our old age. It is not because we are tense biased—this time, toward the past. It is because we are what we might call *activity-biased*. We are biased toward situations we can participate in actively—for example, situations we can control, change, avoid, plan for, or find meaning in. Or we are biased toward events that can most significantly impact the longest period of our lives. Again, this makes us youth-biased: what happens to us in our youth is more likely to impact more of our life than what happens to us in our old age—simply because there is more life after youth to be impacted than there is after old age.

Similar analyses can be made of differences in the significance of most events. In all these cases, we can be temporally neutral while lacking event neutrality. Yet, there is one kind of event that seems to undermine this distinction between temporal neutrality and event neutrality—and indeed to undermine temporal neutrality entirely. This is death.

Death

Are we rationally permitted to be temporally neutral and yet fear death? To do this, we must find a non-temporal reason for why death is fearful. Yet, unlike pain, injury, or grief, the non-temporal bad-making features of death are difficult to pin down.

First, we do not suffer death the way we suffer pain, injury, or grief. If I have a broken leg, I have a bad experience of being more limited than normal in my activities. If a loved one is gone, I feel the pain of separation. If I have a toothache, it is bad because toothache is bad (presumably). We must experience and live through these bad things.

But death by definition is not lived through, and so neither can it be suffered through. As Lucretius writes:

> [I]f by chance there is to be grief and pain for a man, he must needs himself too exist at that time, that ill may befall him. Since death forestalls this, and prevents the being of him, on whom these misfortunes might crowd, we may know that we have naught to fear in death, and that he who is no more cannot be wretched [...]
>
> (Lucretius 3.867–896, trans. Bailey 1910)

The Symmetry Argument

Furthermore, much of what can be said of death can be said of birth. Both death and birth are edges or boundaries on life; within both of them, we are alive; outside both of them, we are not. This has led to the *symmetry* argument for the view that we should fear death as much as we should fear birth. Both are boundaries on our life.

We might say that, for life, there is the following difference: death is the end and birth the beginning. This assumes an order in events that gives different significance to each boundary. Because death is the *later* boundary, it is worse than birth. This is a temporal bias, one based on when each boundary occurs. If this bias is rational, it seems to be the rejection of temporal neutrality.

However, perhaps the fear of death is event bias. We fear the kind of event death is, not when it happens.

In the 1990s science fiction comic *Zenith*, the narrator begins in middle age but is cursed by his enemies to become younger as the years go on. He changes from middle age to a young man (going out running again in the morning), to a teenager, to a child, to eventually a baby, a new-born, and then he vanishes (Morrison and Yeowell 1992). One might call this end of his life his *birth*. It resembles many aspects of birth. It is just that it comes at the *end* of his life. However, precisely because it comes at the end, it seems more accurate to call it his death. True, how it ends resembles how it began. However, this does not mean it is not death. It is only that it is a death that, in all other ways, resembles birth.

Similarly, the BBC series *Doctor Who* frequently has characters come into existence resembling humans of quite advanced age, the age of natural demise (for example, an early doctor was in his sixties). The fourth season of the TV series *Mork and Mindy* (1981) reveals that Mork's alien species start their infant life resembling older men. However, they are born and are infants because they are at the start of life; these events are not deaths just because they resemble others' ends.

Another suggestion comes from Yehezkel 2016. Birth is necessary for life, but death is unnecessary for life. This difference explains why we fear death and not birth. However, Deng objects to this answer. If the necessity of one and the contingency of the other is their only difference, then this modal difference, typically, reverses the significance:

> [S]uppose the main relevant respect in which [birth and death] differ is that past nonexistence has to happen, while future nonexistence just happens. It's not clear what bearing this, by itself, has on how comparatively fear-worthy they are. If there is a connection, why not think that what has to happen, and is "unavoidable", is rather more fear-worthy than what just happens and is "avoidable"? Suppose two tigers run towards you, and only one looks avoidable; shouldn't the other one scare you more?
>
> (Deng 2016, online)

Only the timing of these events marks them out as birth and death, along with the difference in what is fearful about them. It is not some other quality of them. It is not a person's pain or pleasure at the time (we can die in less pain than we had at birth), the knowledge they possess (The Doctor is born with a great deal of knowledge), or the shape and size (Mork's son looks nothing like a human infant). Neither is it is their comparative modality: if death were genuinely avoidable, it is not obvious it would be more fearful than birth, which is necessary.

If one of these boundaries is preferred over the other, then the only reason seems to be temporal. If that is right, then it is not compatible with temporal neutrality. We ascribe different significance, at least, to the later boundary than we do the earlier boundary of our lives.

Tense and Death

Suppose that this fear of death is rational. Is such a rational fear a reason to prefer one philosophical theory of time over another?

Green and Sullivan note that some theorists do argue that fear of death supports the tense theory (Green and Sullivan 2015; also, Hare 2013). However, when looking at the specific views of time endorsed by tense theorists, this support is not so clear.

Presentism does not seem to offer any explanation of death's significance. The future and past are unreal under presentism. Our deaths are not present at a time when we are also present. As such, given presentism, for us, our deaths are always unreal. Given the general presentist view that what is present and real is significant, our deaths should never be *comparatively* significant for us; they are never present for us. Similarly, the growing block holds the future to be unreal. Like presentism, this gives no special significance to death.

As for tense theorists who are eternalists, such as moving spotlight theorists, again, although death will be present, it will be present when the person is not. As long as the person is alive, death remains future, and so outside the spotlight's window. If the spotlight provides significance, it never provides it to death for the deceased.

Does this leave tenseless theory with an advantage? Temporal neutrality often seems more compatible with tenseless theory than it does tense theory. Like temporal neutrality, all times are equal: they are equally real and equally past, present, and future. As such, if a fear of death (and no fear of birth) is incompatible with temporal neutrality, perhaps it is also incompatible with tenseless theory. Here is one reason: what neutrality and tenseless theory have in common is that they are both incompatible with fear of death (and not fear of birth).

For example, some forms of tenseless theory make no temporal distinction between the boundary of birth and the boundary of death. As discussed in Chapter 4, there are tenseless theories that hold temporal order to be merely local and not global. That one event is earlier than the other, one past when the other is present or future, is not a fundamental, absolute, or universal difference in things. In that case, the difference between birth and death is not a fundamental, absolute, or universal difference in things. What explains the difference is something else.

Similar to the future's unreality in presentism or growing block, or its lesser significance in eternalist tense theory, this kind of tenseless theory's conception of the future is supposedly less significant than other aspects of time. The problem with this conception of the future is not that death itself is not more significant than birth. It is that this conception of the future gives no reason for that significance. They are both future and past to this moment; it just depends on how we pick the direction in time.

However, some kinds of tenseless theory do have a fundamental difference based on temporal order. For example, B-theorists who hold that temporal order is absolute and fundamental can define an absolute and fundamental difference between birth and death. Birth is the *early* boundary of life while death is the *later* boundary. Whatever the significance of this difference, B-theorists can use this temporal difference in their explanation of the difference between death and birth.

Yet, there is still a problem: death's being later than birth provides no obvious reason why the order of these events makes one more significant. I can have a particularly good day, one I will remember for the rest of my life, followed by a day that is comparatively bland or even bad. That the latter day is a *later* day does not increase its significance.

As such, none of these theories of time seem to provide much towards explaining death's fearful significance. Fear of death, rational or irrational, is independent of whether we believe time is tensed or untensed.

Death and F-Bias

Returning to F-bias, could it be that it is rational to fear death under some philosophical theories of time because F-bias is rational under those theories? Green and Sullivan argue that, whatever justifies F-bias, it is not a philosophical theory of time. Just like fear of death, for presentism "the past and future are metaphysically very similar in that neither exists. Presentism does not give us a metaphysical reason to favor future experiences over past ones" (Green and Sullivan 2015, 953). Similarly, for tenseless theory, distinguishing the past and future can seem arbitrary.

However, there is one important feature of death that it does not share with F-bias towards events in our life: we never compare our attitude to this event when it is future and our attitude to it when it is present (or perceived as present). Unlike events we live through, such as pain, we never get to have an attitude to present or past death. We never get to compare the significance of future death with presently perceived death, and so check the comparative significance of it being future.

Instead, our attitude toward our life's future boundary (our death) is only comparable to similar events in the past—that, to our life's past boundary of birth. But that event is also one we do not live through, because it was never future for us. We never get to say, "Thank goodness death is over!" nor dread our own future birth.

Neither tense theory nor tenseless theory can explain why fear comes from death's futurity or being later than any event in our lives. We must seek the answer elsewhere. The work discussed in this chapter proposes some options; most conclude that there is an aspect to it that is not fully rational. Thinking about it under different philosophical theories of time makes it no more rational.

Study Questions

1. I have the irrational belief that a future pain is worse than past pains. Can I use that to justify the statement that future pains are worse than past pains? If a belief about time arises from natural selection, is that sufficient justification for its content?
2. According to theorists in this chapter, F-bias is part of human attitudes toward time. Could it be a contingent part of our attitudes, that is, just as some people may lack empathy or pain, it is possible to lack F-bias? For example, could there be a past-bias, analogous to F-bias, but toward the past instead of the future?
3. An unreal future is purported to be intuitive. Yet, intuitively, we do not long for or fear things we believe to be unreal, no matter what they are or what properties they might have. How, then, can it be intuitive to long for or fear the future?

Note

1 See Chapters 2 and 5.

Suggested Readings

Parfit's original discussion is found in his classic 1984 *Reasons and Persons*. Sullivan's 2018 *Time Biases* is a focused philosophical discussion on temporal rationality. Persson's 2005 *Retreat from Reason* has a long discussion on temporal bias and neutrality.

9 Philosophy of Art and Time

Overview

Lessing divided art into Arts of Space and Art of Time—or spatial art and temporal art. We define temporal art as separate from other forms of art, considering some common objections. We then move on to how art represents time, focusing on the most-discussed artistic medium, cinema. Is cinema the best form of art for representing time? It does seem better than some other forms, such as painting. Yet, what of ephemeral art? Some such art seems to directly represent time or represent time with itself. The proposed answer is that cinema is best because, while being able to represent temporal properties directly, it is also the freest form of art to represent time.

We examine the claim that art can be used to decide between different theories of time. One objection is that any kind of structure, for example strange temporal but also strange spatial structure, may be represented by art, but that does not mean we must believe there is such structure.

We consider two specific objections to philosophical theories of time. One is that the nature of music purports to undermine *four-dimensionalism*, a contemporary philosophical view of time. The other is based on Bergson's philosophy of time, which inspired some filmmakers in their thinking about cinema. Bergson's theory of time is often claimed to conflict with the common philosophical interpretation of relativistic physics.

Temporal Art

The art theorist Lessing (2005) classically divides art into two kinds—an *art of space* and an *art of time*. Lessing gathers classic sculpture and painting under the art of space; he gathers music and poetry under the art of time. An art of time "employs wholly different signs or means of imitation" from an art of time, such as poetry. The difference is in how each kind of sign exists in time or space. Painting uses "forms and colors in space" and poetry uses "articulate sounds in time". As such, painting is an art of space because its signs lie beside each other; "signs arranged side by side can represent only objects existing side by side". Poetry is an art of time because its signs succeed each other; "consecutive signs can express only objects which succeed each other, or whose parts succeed each other, in time" (Lessing 2005, section xvi, 91).

Later, cinema was also drawn under the art of time. For example, Eisenstein and Tarkovsky are both influential filmmakers and theorists about time in cinema. For Eisenstein, cinema is an art of time because of its capacity for montage; for Tarkovsky, cinema is an art of time because of its capacity to depict the time of filmed objects (e.g., Tarkovsky 1989, 124; Totaro 1992, 22).[1]

Depiction here is not merely representation. We discuss the nature of representation in more depth later in this chapter. For now, the difference is this: many things may be represented by many other things, and there is nothing particular that the representation need share with what it represents. However, depiction is different. A depiction is in some sense like its object, that is, there is some kind of necessary resemblance between the depiction and what is depicted. For example, a picture depicts some things it represents because it looks in some way *like* what it represents. Looking "at a depiction of a cow is somewhat like looking at a cow"—even though, of course, a picture is intrinsically different to a cow (Le Poidevin 2007, 135).

Call art of space *spatial art* and art of time *temporal art*. The table develops Lessing's distinction.

	Spatial Art	Temporal Art
(a) What it must have	The artwork has space as a necessary component. It uses *space* in its representation or other artistic aspects, such as its aesthetics. For spatial artwork, if there is no space, then there is no artwork. For example, if painting is an art of space, then, if there is no space, there is no painting.	The artwork has time as a necessary component. It uses *space* in its representation or other artistic aspects, such as its aesthetics. For temporal artwork, if there is no time, then there is no artwork. For example, if music is an art of time, then, if there is no time, there is no music.
(b) What it can only do	The artwork can only represent space—in Lessing's terms, objects or their parts arranged in space (e.g., side by side).	The artwork can only represent time—in Lessing's terms, objects or their parts succeeding each other in time.

Given these distinctions, we can ask: Are there actual cases of temporal art-work? Why wouldn't there be cases of temporal artwork? We have already listed a few. It seems that we easily find work that falls into both categories. We need only find instances of painting, sculpture, poetry, music, or cinema.

Objections

According to Mitchell, "the whole notion of 'spatial' and 'temporal' arts is misconceived" if employed to generically differentiate works of art. Artists often make works that fall into both types of art. Not just often, but fundamentally in their practice:

> [The] tendency of artists to breach the supposed boundaries between tem-poral and spatial arts is not a marginal or exceptional practice, but a fun-damental impulse in both the theory and practice of the arts, one which is not confined to any particular genre or period. Indeed, so central is this impulse that it finds expression even in the writings of theorists like Kant and Lessing who establish the tradition of denying it.
>
> (Mitchell 1985, 100)

Instead, Mitchell argues, the distinction between temporal artworks and spatial artworks is not artistic or categorical. It is political. Whatever might raise the distinction, one might object that many, perhaps all, artworks meet conditions (a) and (b). If this is right, labelling a work as being either temporal or spatial art, or one and not the other, may be a pointless exercise.

Contrary to (a), all artwork needs both space *and* time. No matter what they represent, works alleged to be spatial artworks, such as painting, exist in time. Sculpture and paintings are not atemporal; they have moments in which they begin to exist. They also have moments when they cease to exist: A wooden sculpture decays; a painting fades in sunlight or mildews in storage. Furthermore, works alleged to be temporal artworks, such as poetry and music, occupy a limited amount of space. They are performed or broadcast from *somewhere* and are not performed or broadcast in other places.

Lastly, aside from the artworks themselves, we, as artists or observers, require both space and time to engage with such artwork. If I observe a sculpture, I must at least walk around it, an activity that takes space and time. I also need time to reflect upon it. If I listen to a piece of music, I must be somewhere to hear it. If I am in a different location, I will not hear it. Appreciating a picture, reading it, happens in time:

> [I]n fact it needs a very long time. There are examples in psychological lit-erature of the weird descriptions given by people of identical paintings flashed on to a screen for as long as two seconds. It takes more time to sort a painting out. We do it, it seems, more or less as we read a page, by scanning it with our eyes.
>
> (Gombrich 1964, 301)

Contrary to (b), all artwork can represent *both* space *and* time. For example, the way a piece of music is produced can invoke space—I hear the drums to my left, the violins in front of me, the choir to my right. Or a painting can represent a sequence of events. For example, the Bayeux tapestry represents the defeat of the Saxon King Harold; more explicitly, comic strips represent sequences of events, and even in quite complex ways (McCloud 2001).

Painted artwork can even represent *independent time*, that is, time as independent of other things. At least, painting can do so allegorically. For example, in Poussin's *The Dance to the Music of Time,* time is represented independent of the other features in the work, as an old man with a musical instrument.

As such, many if not all artworks are both spatial and temporal artworks. Lessing's distinction cannot be made to sort them.

Rejoinder: What Defines an Artwork in Only Some Cases Requires Time (or Space)

All artworks require space and time to exist and to be observed. However, this concerns only the physical properties of an artwork. An artwork is not just a physical object, exhausted by its physical nature. It also has artistic properties. These properties are necessary for its identity as an artwork. And these properties are just the kind we use to decide whether a work is a spatial artwork or a temporal artwork.

For example, an artwork has representational and aesthetic properties. Whatever those properties are, these determine that some object is an art object. And, when we ask if a work is spatial or temporal, we decide based on these artistic properties. If we put aside merely physical characteristics, we observe that some art has time necessarily in what it represents or in its aesthetic affects, while others do not. The former are temporal artworks. (One can have a similar distinction for space.)

Sauvage's Concepts of Temporal Artwork

Sauvage (1968) distinguishes four concepts of a temporal artwork. Some of these concepts may be useful in working out what makes a temporal artwork, His first and second concepts are not useful: the work is *in* time; the work requires time to be appreciated. These concepts apply to all artwork. They are based only on the work's physical properties.

Sauvage's third concept is that a work *represents* time indirectly; time is represented through the things it represents. For example, a film evokes a year passing through a series of changing objects: leaves change colour; streets become covered in snow which then melts away; the sun speeds across the sky. A painting of a horse with its legs curled beneath it in the air represents a horse in time: it represents a horse in motion and motion requires time. To use Sauvage's terminology, the work *evokes time* or involves a *temporal sign*.

Sauvage's fourth concept is that a work represents time directly; time *itself* is represented. It is not merely evoked. Time is a subject in the work. Time is described in Poe's poem *Nevermore*. And, as already mentioned, Poussin's *A Dance to the Music of Time* represents time as an old man playing music (Sauvage 1968).

Could temporal art be art that satisfies the third and fourth senses of the temporal in art, while non-temporal art (such as spatial art) does not?

That is, temporal art (a) represents things, and through that indirectly represents time or (b) represents time *itself*. Spatial artworks do not do this: they do not indirectly represent time through representing other things, and they do not represent time itself.

The answer seems to be no.

Objection: We Can Infer Time through All Artworks

The above concepts of temporal art assume that it is clear that something *represents* time and not something else. This sounds right for art that directly represents time, such as Poe or Poussin. But for art that represents time indirectly, the distinction is muddier. Second, contrary to Lessing, that a work represents time does not mean that it requires time to do so. There can be art that uses only space to represent time.

For example, in the 19th century, Muybridge created photographs of horses suspended in mid-gallop, their legs curled in the air beneath them; before these photographs, many thought that horses moved very differently (their legs splayed out, as seen in older paintings of moving horses).

Anyone familiar with stills of horses in movement knows to interpret what they see as pictorial representation—indeed, a depiction—of a horse in motion. Motion needs time. At the very least, it needs the duration the motion requires. Through that depiction of horse in motion, we have a depiction of a horse in time. By the third sense, this is a temporal artwork.

Yet, once we include this example as a temporal artwork, it is hard not to include any work that represents things occupying space. Most everything represented as being in space shares the following with the horse's mid-gallop: it is a temporary state of affairs. A castle, a figure in repose, a garden, a barren cliff, or the sun—these are all temporary things, existing in space and also in time. Once we understand this, we can infer its temporal nature. This is the same as, once we understand an airborne horse in a photograph, we can infer time from it.

We might reply that a horse's gallop requires time; so, a depiction of its gallop indirectly represents time. However, the other things occupying space do not require time; as such, their depictions do not indirectly represent time. A garden, or a landscape, as it is depicted in a pastoral scene, maintains its apparent structure *permanently*. They look like that eternally, unmoving, unchanging, forever. "Just as the very basic theme of poetry is that of time passing, the very basic theme of painting is that of the moment made permanent" (Berger 2019, 92).

We might then say such scenes are *timeless;* they do not indirectly represent time. But a horse's suspension is not timeless; it cannot maintain its apparent suspension permanently. It is mid-air in motion, and the motion eventually carries it to the ground.

Yet, again, this distinction disappears when we think a little more thoroughly about things in time. A pastoral scene can persist in the timescale of humans, or at least the timescale of a human driving by in a car. But it does not really persist. It changes. When we see a mountain shrouded in mist, we see things fall just as much as a horse touching down. The mist falls by mid-morning. The mountain falls after several million years.

Temporal Artwork as Constraining Imagination

Perhaps what differentiates temporal artwork from spatial artwork is not the reality of what they represent. It is the possibility or imaginability of what they represent. According to Kant, aesthetic judgement involves the "free play" of the imagination (e.g., Kant 1787/1987, 112–113). Perhaps spatial and temporal artworks can be distinguished by how they constrain or define the imagination. If the imagination is temporally constrained, then it is a temporal artwork. If it is spatially constrained, then it is a spatial work.

For example, the difference between the horse's gallop and the landscape is that, when we observe the depicted landscape, we can imagine it as unchanging or timeless. It seems as if it can be that way forever, nothing moving, nothing changing. It is irrelevant that no actual physical landscape can be unchanging or timeless. However, we cannot imagine the horse hanging in mid-air as timeless. As we look at the depicted horse, we cannot help but imagine that in a moment it will land. So, with temporal artwork, even the merely imaginary or possible in the depiction needs time. With non-temporal artwork, the merely imaginary or possible does not need time.

Yet again, this may be a difficult generalization to work with. It is unclear if a galloping horse must be imagined as happening in time. Perhaps one cannot imagine a timeless world filled with frozen horses frozen mid-gallop. Perhaps one can imagine such a thing.

One response here is to reject this suggestion; that a work is a temporal artwork should not depend on something so possibly subjective as how imaginable the temporality of what it depicts can be. Still, it is not obviously fatal to subjectively distinguish temporal and spatial artworks; unlike features of the objective world, art typically involves subjects—both as creator and audience.

For now, let us leave this discussion and consider another condition.

Formal Properties of Temporal Artwork

I am playing all the right notes. But not necessarily in the right order.

Eric Morecombe (1971)

Perhaps there is another way to draw the distinction between temporal artworks and spatial artworks. Alperson states that temporal artworks have time in their *formal properties*. In music or cinema, the creator "exploits time as a formal element". A composer "controls certain features of the temporal ordering of tones" (Alperson 1980, 408). According to Souriau, "The three chief classifications of aesthetic facts relative to musical time concern (a) its dimensional extent (b) its structure, notably in the form of rhythm, (c) its agogic (tempo or speed) variations" (Souriau 1949, 300). Similarly, a cinematic artist (for example, a director or editor) controls the duration, order, and pacing of scenes in a film.

This order has a particular artistic result—for example, it leads to a representation or an aesthetic effect. The work is pleasurable, strident, anxious, frightening. The result depends on time through the work's formal properties. This is what makes the artwork temporal.

What is meant by controlling the temporal order of an artwork? For Alperson, the ordering of music elements in time changes the nature of the artwork. The order of the elements is part of an artwork's identity. Change the temporal order and the nature of the music changes. This suggests that temporal order—and so time—*must be* part of the music, and not just as a physical thing. It is part of the artistic properties—of the representational or aesthetic aspects of the work.

Notably, for music, this order is not only in our engagement with the work. It is needed for the work of art to exist, even if it is unobserved. The jingle of an empty ice cream van on an abandoned beach still has temporal order in its elements. If the notes are in a different order, then the van plays a different tune. Furthermore, the work cannot be appreciated as a work of art unless at least some of the notes can be appreciated as separated over time. This distinguishes it, as a temporal artwork, from a spatial artwork.

Instant God

Say that, in some possible world, there is an almost omniscient and omnipresent being. Call it an *Instant God*. This being has the capacity to know and experience all things, except that it has one constraint: it only exists for an instant and can only experience what happens in that instant. As such, it can experience any artwork that can be experienced in an instant. With this constraint, it can see the whole of a painting—the arrangement of paint on it, the shapes, and what it represents. For example, it can see a painting of a landscape or a galloping horse. It can also see the whole of a sculpture, from all sides: its curves, its balance, and also what it represents, for example, a weeping figure.

However, because Instant God is constrained to an instant, it cannot observe a piece of music. The notes of the piece happen at different times. The Instant God only experiences what happens at an instant, i.e., at one time. Even if all the notes are played simultaneously, and the godlike observer can distinguish them, they do not hear the notes played in the intended order. For example, in a musical piece, they cannot distinguish the sequence of notes A-D-G from the sequence of notes G-D-A. They cannot watch even the briefest filmic scene; they experience a movie as paused. These works require more than an instant of time; the Instant God has no more than an instant of time.

The works such a God is blind to are temporal artworks. Their properties as artworks require time to do their artistic work, and to do so uniquely to that work of art. To be a particular piece of music, a work's notes must have a particular temporal order; to be a particular film, a work's elements must have a particular order to their scenes.

We can, of course, create something otherwise identical to such a work but omit the temporal ordering of elements. We can play all the notes of the ice cream van's jingle all at once. We can show all the frames of a film in one instant. Instant God can observe all these works. Furthermore, for us, the result still exists in time. We can still engage with them in time. We can hear the ice cream cacophony in an instant on the empty beach. The frames can lie simultaneously around us, like a gigantic zoetrope.

However, time is not necessary for these artworks. As such, they are not temporal artworks. But they are also different to an actual jingle or film. That such works are non-temporal works of art does not make the original they come from non-temporal. The original and these new instant pieces are different particular works of art.

So, we have two possible ways of defining or picking out temporal artworks. Temporal artworks are defined:

- By how time defines the imaginability of their content
- By how time constrains their form

Art's Representation of Time

Say one wishes to represent time in a work of art. Is there any form or medium of art that one should prefer over another? For example, should one prefer cinema over landscape painting or static sculpture? Or are they all equally preferable?

There are reasons to prefer one form over another that are not about representation. I might be unable to afford the materials for sculpture or film, but I can afford the materials for drawing or poetry. I might have more experience working in one form than in another, e.g., I prefer 3D online art because I have been programming since childhood and am comfortable with complex graphic coding. I might emotionally or psychologically prefer one form to another, e.g., I work in dance because a local community group runs free dance classes; it does not run land art classes. And, of course, I have no interest in representing anything when I make art.

However, for representation, is any form of art preferable to others? Many artists consider film or cinema to be a preferable form of art for time. For example, the artist Grace Weir writes that, working in video and photography, she "became interested in the specific nature of the media itself. Time and light are both intrinsic to film-making and photography." She prefers film because it "addresses the time in which something is being actualised, the time it takes for something to happen, it maps one time the onto another time, the viewer's time" (Weir 2016). Perhaps what is special about film in representing time is that it connects the audience's time to the time of its content.

To arrive at how cinema may be a preferable form of temporal art, consider an analogy with another kind of art: realist painting.

Realist Painting

Much of classical painting requires some resemblance between the vehicle and content. The representing vehicle *depicts* the content, rather than merely representing it. Depiction involves a work resembling its subject in some way, and this resemblance doing the work of representing. With respect to its depictive aspect, the work only represents if it has some of the content's properties or relations. As such, given the work must exist to represent, the content also exists.

For example, Caravaggio's The *Taking of Christ*, a painting of Judas' betrayal of Jesus, represents a dark night of compulsive fear and bitter resignation. It is composed of dark colours around human faces, and lines within the faces. These dark colours depict a dark night; the lines form the shape of faces seen from some distance. The lines are arranged so that they resemble, on Judas' face, fear as he embraces his teacher, and, on Jesus' face, resignation as he turns his cheek.

In this depiction, the parts of the painting representing these people's faces do resemble human faces. They do not simply *indirectly* represent those faces the way the word "face" does. Furthermore, this resemblance is part of the form by which the content is portrayed. Because parts of the painting in some way *resemble* the content, the painting represents.

Of course, such paintings do not *fully* resemble what they represent; their composition is from materials that their subject matters rarely are. The bright red cloth represented in Vermeer's paintings is not made of crushed beetle shell (unlike the paint he uses to depict it). These works resemble linguistic representation in this way at least: they are not the things represented by them.

However, this difference does not matter to *how* the work represents. A work needs material to compose it. But not all of this material is what represents. The crushed beetle shell is needed for the representation to be possible, but its crushed-beetle-shell-ness does not represent anything. What represents the red objects in Vermeer's paintings are areas of the picture that have *redness*. This is also what is *represented*. Again, the representation is by resemblance.

We may call this kind of work *realist* or *realistic* in the sense that it *depicts*. It is "a platitude that depiction is mediated by resemblance, it's a platitude that a picture is realistic to the degree to which it resembles what it represents (in relevant respects)" (Blumson 2014, 24).

A complication for simply calling such work *realist* is that it does not *only* represent through resemblance. Through the resemblance, non-existent things can be represented. All that exists is the representation; actual existence is not represented by resemblance. Non-existent things cannot be wholly represented by what exists.

Despite its power, Caravaggio's *painting* is all that is in the gallery. There is no actual betrayal, fear, or resignation on the gallery wall. There are only representations of these emotions. There are only inanimate things—arrangements of oil on canvas—that look like the expressions of people undergoing such emotions. There are still similar colours and shapes in the painting, such as the lines that resemble the worry lines on Judas' brow. But the painting does not contain feelings as people do. No actual emotions are depicted by resemblance in the painting.

Painting and Time

A painting can depict space through resemblance. A painting of a door on a wall can be exactly the same size as a door. It can also represent space without resemblance. A painting of an open door through which corridors and other doors are visible can be on a thick outer wall of a gallery, with no further corridors or doors beyond it.

However, other than one exception, painting cannot represent time through *resemblance*. It must represent the world through arrangements of material in space. Nothing more is available to this form of art (and there are similar restrictions to, at least, classic sculpture). This is not enough to depict time, even if it is enough for representation (Le Poidevin 2007).

Consider the following temporal properties and time-dependent features. Painting cannot depict any of them by resemblance.

- *Temporal order:* In a painting, nothing that it represents is happening at a different time or before anything else that represents. For example, one part of a painting—call it the background—depicts a prehistoric landscape and another part—call it the foreground—depicts a present scene. However, there is no temporal order between these different scenes. There is only spatial order between them.
- *Duration:* A painting of an ice cube in the heat can last a hundred years; the ice cube does not. A painting of a house contemporary with the work's creation may exist hundreds of years after the house has burnt down. Vermeer's work has lasted longer than its subjects. But even if the work lasted as long the subjects—e.g., created when they were, and destroyed when they were gone—this fact has nothing to do with what it represents of its subject.
- *Movement:* Nothing that represents moves in a painting. A painter can represent movement but not through movement. For example, they can paint a blurred figure—the kind of blur suggesting the figure is rushing by.

However, whatever is there is not really rushing by. So long as the painting lasts, it rests in that location of the painting.

Abell writes:

> A painting or drawing might depict a moment in time. It may even be possible to infer from the moment depicted either what events have led up to it or what events will follow. However, such pictures are incapable of depicting events as occurring in a temporal sequence.
>
> (Abell 2010, 278)

Movement

We need to discuss movement in a little more detail. Some objects blurred by movement—such as spinning fan blades—can move so fast they appear to be something else that is at rest—such as a transparent blurred disc. In the case of the painting, such a blur is not an apparently resting object that is actually in motion. It is what appears to be something at rest that is, indeed, something at rest. However, because of our prior understanding of blurs, we interpret it as an object in motion.[2]

Again, this does not mean that painting cannot represent time. There are many cases of non-temporal work that represent time. It just cannot depict time by *resemblance*.

And again, we may engage with such work *in time*—reading one word after another, viewing one panel after another—but this is about how we must work. That is about how an observer engages with the work, not about the artwork itself.

Temporal Art and Time

According to Abell, "cinematic representation is a distinctive form of depiction, unique in its capacity to depict temporal properties" (Abell 2010, 278). Yet is it so unique? Is cinema the most perfect form of temporal art? Might some more effectively represent time than cinema?

Cinema can represent time by resemblance. For example, in her 2003 film *Dust Defying Gravity*, the artist Weir represents the duration of her camera drifting through Dunsink Observatory in Ireland. This is resemblance: the duration of the vehicle (the film's length) is the duration of the content (the time of the drift through the rooms).

Time is represented in Sauvage's third sense of temporal art—time as it appears in the changing of things. Cinema can show the order of events by an order of events; a film can present a scene of a bird flying through the air after showing a scene of it sitting on a branch about to fly. A film can depict a duration: we can watch real-time footage of traffic in city. It can show the movement of objects on the screen.

Deleuze's Direct Cinema

Yet, according to Deleuze, modern cinema does something more. Classical cinema depicted the movement of things—their actions. But later cinema moved beyond that. The aim of later, direct cinema, *cinéma vérité*, is to "achieve the direct presentation of time" (Deleuze 1989, 38). Such cinema creates what Deleuze calls a *time-image*, an image primarily representing time, rather than a *movement-image*, an image that primarily represents movement. This is a representation of time in Sauvage's fourth sense of temporal art.

But how does direct cinema represent time directly rather than through something else, such as movement? It disrupts the depiction of movement or other kinds of change. It creates (in Deleuze's terms) false forms of movement, an appearance of movement that is dependent on the appearance of time. By watching a sequence of scenes over a duration, we gain a sense of movement. But the movement comes from the sense of time, not the other way around. "We no longer have an indirect image of time which derives from movement, but a direct time-image from which movement derives" (Deleuze 1989, 129).

Furthermore, some filmmakers think time can self-represent in cinema; time or some aspect of time—such as a particular duration or temporal order—may also represent *itself* in cinema, and not merely something that resembles it. For example, according to Tarkovsky, time is necessary to what cinema represents. "One cannot conceive of a cinematic work with no sense of time passing through the shot, but one can easily imagine a film with no actors, music, decor or even editing" (Tarkovsky 1989, 114). Cinema is not merely a "montage", an editing of scenes together. Editing only "brings together shots which are already filled with time, and organises the unified, living structure inherent in the film" (Tarkovsky 1989, 114). Time is in the shot itself, in cinema's method of representation. Cinema is "sculpture in time".

In Tarkovsky's films, there are scenes in which the camera barely moves but there is movement. The filmed objects move: waves of grass suddenly blow to the side by the wind (in *Mirror*); a cup rolls off a table (in *Stalker*). In these scenes, the time that is represented just is the time the artwork takes to represent. A man drives his son through a roadway tunnel (*Solaris*), and the scene lasts for as long as the duration of the journey.

There is no edit or montage of the time. There is just the actual time of what is being filmed, including the order and duration. In contrast, there are spatial edits. For example, in the tunnel journey, switching from the view out of the car's windshield to a view of the son in the backseat.

Yet, although films can use time to represent itself, they frequently do not. Most ninety-minute films have stories spanning days, weeks, or years, often with flashbacks and flashforwards.[3] Durations represented in these films do not represent themselves. Yet, the point remains: cinema *can* do this, unlike painting or sculpture.

Furthermore, self-representing time can play a significant role in cinema. For example, in the 1991 *Pulp Fiction*, there is a real-time conversation about fast food in different countries. It takes as long as the conversation, with no gaps. This resemblance has artistic value: in *Pulp Fiction*, it feels as if we are with these characters in a mundane, everyday, normal way; we are lulled into a comfortable pace—and shocked out of it by the violent scenes immediately following them. A scene in *Big Night* in which the brothers cook breakfast together lasts as long they take to cook; according to Weir, this pace shows the importance of this ritual for them, detailing their care and attention in carrying it out (Weir 2017).

Time Cannot Self-Represent

In cinema, time seems to self-represent. However, there is reason to deny that, in fact, time self-represents. Recall Tarkovsky's comment that the film represents the time of the object. It may *seem* to do so. The time of what is represented is the time of an object; but the time that the work uses to represent this is the time of the film performance or the audience. These resemble one another. However, even if both have the same duration (as in *Big Night*), these times are not the same.

In *Mirror*, we see what seem to be reeds blown to the side. We see what seems to be movement of the reeds. However, there are no reeds there. There may never have been reeds there. There might have been a special effect that gives the convincing appearance of there being reeds when there are no reeds. However, even if there are moving reeds when the filming occurs, the time of this movement is not the time the audiences experience.

As discussed in Chapter 1, one debate on the nature of time concerns its relationship to other things. Two main positions on this are relationalism and substantivalism.[4] Relationalism is the position that time is derived from or dependent on something else; for example, time is a relation between material objects; time is a property of changes in material object. Substantivalism is the position that time is a substance—something that can exist independent of other things. Whether we conceive of time as relationalist or substantivalist, there is reason to deny that the audience's time is the depicted object's time, no matter how it appears, or how realist the film.

If relationalism is true, then a particular time derives from a particular change. A different time derives from a different change. The reeds' movement is a particular change. If we do not see the reeds move, then the film does not self-represent the reeds' movement. Some other change is seen, such as change in a film image seen by the audience. Times are derived from these changes. One time is derived from the reeds' change; the other is derived from the image's change. These times may resemble each other; however, because they do not derive from the same change, then they cannot be the same time.

If, instead, substantivalism is true, then there is also reason to deny that the same time self-represents in cinema. It is possible for two things (for example, changes in material objects) to share the one time; the time of one change is numerically identical to the time of the other. So, we might have this: the filming of the reeds' movement is the same time as the represented reeds' movement. At the moment the represented movement begins, the filming also begins.

However, when the audience views the resulting film, some period of time has passed; there is a period of time in which the film goes through such stages as post-production, packing, transport, storage at the cinema, loading into the projector, and then projection onto the screen.

This period of time means the time when the reeds move is different to the time when the film is displayed for the audience to see. As such, the times are not the same; if the film represents a time with a time, it does not represent that time with *itself*.

This still allows film to represent a time by a time that resembles it. The duration the audience spend seeing the film can still be as long as the duration of what is depicted.

This raises a question of what other temporal features are represented by resemblance. For example, cinema represents the duration of the reeds' movement by resemblance. However, it also represents the reeds' *movement*. So, we appear to be seeing movement in the film, but are we? Is it merely an illusion of movement? If we do see movement, what is it that moves?

The Movement in the Image

Change is necessary to cinema. If the cinema is digital, a computer needs to refresh the screen on which the digital image plays. If the cinema is film stock, a reel must pass through a projector, each frame illuminated by the projector's light.

If these forms of creation require motion, then cinema requires motion. However, the motion of the frames themselves does not represent the motion. It is part of the physical structure of the artwork that enables the work to exist. It need not be part of what *represents* in the artwork. For example, in film, we do not see the rapid right–left flicker of the frames and interpret that flicker as motion represented in the film. Such frame motion is not like lines on a painting or a person's voice in a play. The movement of the frames is hidden from us: we cannot see one flick out of the light and another flick in. Instead, all we see are changes on the screen, changes that *seem* to be the motion of some objects.

Some film theorists believe that such apparent motion is illusory. Here is one reason: there is no object to move, for example, there is no car in a film representing a car; there only appears to be an object.

> Both by fabricating the images to be projected and by manipulating the speed and sequence of their projection, films can and do revel in the creation of the most elaborate illusions [...] The motion on the screen has to be

> unreal, but can and should faithfully portray a motion that really took place just so in the real.
>
> (Sparshott 1971, 13)

Yet, this does not mean there is no motion—only that what seems to move does not move. I might observe genuine motion while being under an illusion of what moves. For example, I see what seems to be a bird flapping its wings in a tree. As I look closer, I see in fact that the moving thing is a loose rag caught on a branch.

Currie denies Sparshott's claim that motion represented by film is not motion. First, if we deny seeing the motion, then we must also deny that we see an image. For example, if we deny seeing reeds moving in the wind, we deny the movement. But we do not see reeds *not* moving, standing still, instead. We cannot see an image of something that is not moving; the image "can hardly be of people *not* moving" (Currie 1995, 35). If we do not see something not moving, there are questions. If we do not see an image of either moving or *not moving*, what is the image of? At best, it is an image of nothing; nothing can be depicted that is not either moving or not moving. Yet, if the image is of *nothing*, how can it even be an image? And if there is no image, then what else can we be seeing?

Instead, Currie holds that we *do* see movement in the image. What moves is "part or parts of this image; if we are watching a shot of a man walking along a street, the part of the image which represents the man will move from one side of the screen to the other" (1995, 35). We do not see the movement of the whole cinema image, which is the entire illuminated screen. And the movement is not because of the original camera, or movement in the content (such as the represented reeds blowing in the wind). Instead, for Currie, parts of the image move, parts of the representing vehicle.

Currie's answer is that part of the image changes from being at one location to another location. For example, the part of the image on the screen that represents a human being moves from one part of the image to the other; this is movement of that part. But what is it about the part of the image that moves in its parts? It is not that an object—such as a frame—moves and so parts of the cinema image move. Parts of the image move.

In response, for Currie, the image is not a physical thing, like a frame or camera part. The image "has qualities not possessed by any of the physical things and events to which we appeal in explaining it" (1935, 40). Whatever it is that distinguishes the image from what physically causes it, it also picks out parts of the image. These parts are also images with qualities physical entities lack. But one thing they do possess is the ability to move. This is what they do when we see movement on the screen.

But what, then, is an image if it is not anything physical that lies under it? Here is, perhaps, an easier way of illustrating the difference between, on the one hand, physical things and, on the other hand, the image, its parts, and its properties. Consider other images than those found in cinema. In the 1960s, the late computer scientist Conway designed a game called *Life*. When the rules are implemented and run in a computer program, it seems to reproduce life and motion. Different pixels are illuminated at separate times and in different arrangements, like a miniaturized array of traffic lights in a city (Bosch 1999).

The change beneath the motion is complex. It is difficult to predict, with many unexpected patterns. However, although the different pixels change, none of them move. They light up and go dark; that is all. In doing this, they move as much as a flashing light on a buoy moves. As such, nothing real (such as pixels) must move for there to be motion in the image. But parts of the image move. For example, a distinct shape may form at the top-left of the screen, then, through a sequence of pixels illuminating and darkening, the shape migrates down and to the right of the screen. This migration is motion of the *shape*. However, the shape is not part of the physical elements, such as the pixels. It is part of the image.

If we accept Currie's response, then cinema can represent motion *with* motion, the motion of the image. That is, it can depict motion through resemblance. And, given how the image is formed out of the physical objects that make it, this motion is not found in physical things themselves.

So, how far does this resemblance go? Cinema requires time and can represent a time with another time, even by resemblance. Can it be considered, then, the best artistic medium for depicting time itself? It still has a limit: it cannot depict time with itself, that is, time cannot self-represent in cinema. Yet, can any artwork represent time that way?

Ephemeral Art

Here is one possibility: the time of some contemporary art pieces does not merely resemble a represented time but just is that time; that is, the time self-represents. For example, there are works of *ephemeral art*. These works only last a certain amount of time; in so doing, they represent that time.

Andy Goldsworthy is the founder of *ephemeral* art. He gathers together naturally found objects—for example, stones, ice, or twigs—and assembles them into sculptures at specific locations. Then he leaves them to the impact of the environment. He intends the work to fall apart. He neither plans nor predicts the exact way the work progresses, leaving it intentionally open to changes from the environment in which it is embedded. By necessity, time is part of these works; it is deliberately depicted in it by time itself (Goldsworthy 2008, 2015).

In interview with Jessica Harris, he says how time plays a role in this:

> [O]ne day, I just went out and made a couple of things on the beach and the tide came in and washed them away. I suddenly realised that I wasn't in control and time was dictating what I should make, how I could make it, and many of the earlier works were made for the moment in which they were made.
>
> (Goldsworthy 2014, 6:33–6:51)

Maher's *Nettle Coat* is a work of art that, over time, disintegrates. Although not part of the work's original intention, "the completed work began immediately to embody temporality as it withers and shrivels in the Arts Council collection" (Maher 2020). It represents disintegration by the work's own disintegration. It also represents the time of the decay by the exact time of the decay. The work can only exist from the time it is made to when its materials rot away—and the time of this rot is also part of the content.

How these allow the representation of time by resemblance is that they are pieces in the world, using what they represent as part of their structure. In one sense, they are constructed pieces. Maher makes her coat. Goldsworthy's artworks are constructed; he assembles stones while the tide is out. However, with respect to time, they are more like *found objects*.

Found objects or readymades are often a "fragment of an object, that is found (or sometimes bought) by an artist and kept" (Tate). They are indiscernible from non-artistic objects, such as snow shovels (Duchamp) or coffee-mugs (July 2005). However, they have been appropriated or placed by the artist for some, potentially disputable, artistic reason (see Carroll 2012, 27–30, 220).

Artworks like Goldsworthy's work self-represent time. To make the work, the artist may construct the object, but does not construct the representation of time. They exploit the time of the objects in the work. A time represented by a collapsing sculpture in the tide is the time it takes for the sculpture to collapse.

Yet, here is a reason that cinema is a temporal artwork in a way that others are not. Cinema needs time to represent. However, beyond that constraint, it is free to represent time in ways that ephemeral art cannot. It can use time to represent similar times, such as those of equivalent durations, but also to represent times that are entirely different.

Philosophical Theories of Time and Temporal Art

Art can represent or depict something, for example, a table or a spaceship, without needing to create such a thing, either in part or as a whole. I can draw or describe a spaceship as found in a science fiction film; I need only say or write certain things, draw a sketch, or, using special effects, make a film. I need not build an actual spaceship.

For art depicting space and time, work representing a certain space or period of time does not require that actual space or time. For example, art can represent medieval times or prehistory. Yet, it need not self-present these times. If they did need to do this, they would be impossible; the artworks are not at those earlier times. We have TV series about medieval Europe. But we do not have TV series that are recorded or played in medieval Europe.

Bourne and Caddick 2012 discuss this in the context of fictional stories in which simultaneous and temporally ordered events occur. In the examples they give, they argue that, because the worlds described are fictional, the representations in such works "do not settle questions about [...] the nature of time" (Bourne and Caddick 2012, 16).

This is especially evident in work that represents *impossible* things. For example, Escher's pictures of space are representations of impossible spaces (also discussed in Bourne and Caddick 2012). *Relativity* represents a space filled with staircases, upon which various anonymous people ascend and descend. The stairs, however, are impossible as a group. What seems to be an ascending stair when traced from one point of the image is, traced from another point, a descending stair—or even just the underside of a descending stair (Escher 1953). Similarly, we can draw a so-called Penrose triangle or tribar, an apparently three-dimensional object with edges that seem nearer and farther than each other (Penrose and Penrose 1958).

Yet, this does not mean that there must be such objects. There are no such impossible objects; there are only drawings of them.

Any equivalent to an Escher representation of time has a similar weak hold on what we must accept about the reality of time. For example, we may draw a branching time by the following steps:

• Draw a finite line.
• At one end of the line, draw two further lines that lead off it ("branches").
• Label all three lines "time".

Another example: we can draw a circle and label the circumference of the circle as "time".

It is possible that time can branch or be circular. We might infer from such drawings that time can split into branches like a tree or can be circular. Yet, all that is certainly true given such representations is the spatial structure that we use to represent time with them. These representations, on their own, do not teach us anything about the possibility of branched or circular time.

Instead, we must do more to argue for such temporal structure. We must consider the philosophical arguments for views that are represented by such work. The representations are not enough "but rather need to be supplemented by careful philosophical analysis" (Bourne and Caddick 2012).

This raises a problem for art and the philosophy of time. One of the debates in the philosophy of time concerns the reality and nature of various claimed aspects of time, for example, the reality of substantival time, the past and future, tense, and temporal passage.

These debates are about what is true of time. If art does not teach us anything, then art cannot contribute anything to these debates. Yet, some theorists do claim that art can support different positions on time.

For some art theorists and philosophers, temporal art can play a role in the philosophical debates about time. We consider two: music and four-dimensionalism; relativistic physics and art inspired by Bergson.

Music Is Inexplicable Given Four-Dimensional Space-Time

Some philosophers call the position that Minkowski space-time accurately describes the physical world *four-dimensionalism*. According to Markosian, music is a counter-example to such four-dimensionalism.

Markosian defines a possible artwork he calls *sideways music*. Sideways music has all the properties possessed by the music we ordinarily encounter. However, it differs in one significant way: the formal order properties of music, e.g., the sequence in which the notes fall, are instead spatially ordered. For example, they occur in the work left-to-right or top-to-bottom. For a piece in which a sequence of notes is played A *then* F *then* G, in its sideways counterpart, the notes may be played A *to the left of* F *to the left of* G.

Markosian uses the possibility of sideways music to argue against the physical concept of *four-dimensional* space and time. In brief, if there were no difference between space and time, then aesthetic properties of music are identical if they are laid out spatially or temporally, e.g., notes played only left to right, say, and not ordered in time, have the same properties as notes played one after another in time (Markosian 2020).

Yet, obviously, these pieces do not have the same aesthetic properties. The experience of hearing Debussy's *Clair de Lune* is very different to hearing its sideways counterpart, in which the notes are only played from the left to the right. The latter's aesthetic properties would be less pleasant (but, luckily, the playing more brief).

I assume in this chapter that a temporal artwork and its sideways counterpart are not the same artistic works. Indeed, their dissimilarity is necessary to distinguish temporal artwork from spatial artwork. A work which only draws on its spatial properties to distinguish its parts is like a painting, not a poem. And a sideways piece of music is such a spatial work. However, this difference does not count against four-dimensionalism.

First, four-dimensionalism is not four dimensions of space; even philosophers who hold that there is space-time agree that there are differences between time and the other spatial dimensions. Markosian objects that the appeal of four-dimensionalism is that time is exactly like space; if there are some differences then why not more differences? But this is not what motivates four-dimensionalism. Any similarity at all is not relevant. Particular and significant similarities are relevant, used to solve various problems, such as the reality of different times, and the composition of objects over time.[5] Four-dimensionalists also accept significant differences between the structure of something in time and in space; it is not merely the difference between it in depth, width, or height. Causation, for example, requires a difference in time (yet not so obviously in space); this is the case even in four-dimensionalism.

Second, Markosian argues that, when viewing artworks in space, the orientation of the work is irrelevant, e.g., whether the work faces north or south, or a musical instrument is upside down while being played. Yet, this is not the case. There are aesthetic differences between observing some artworks from above, to the side, and face-on. Yet, "above", "to the side", and "face-on" refer to differences in spatial perspective. As anyone stuck in the far forward corner of a packed cinema can attest, there is a different aesthetic experience to seeing a film from the bottom corner of a giant screen. As such, even *if* time were a fourth spatial dimension, it should not be surprising that observations of notes across time is different to observations of notes across other spatial dimensions.

The apparent difference between time and space in artwork depends in part on differences in how we experience time and space. It may be that four-dimensionalism means that time is no different to space, and also that analogies with spatial perspectives cannot explain music's particular aesthetic properties. However, if our idea of the difference between a piece of music and its sideways counterpart comes from our experience of them, then what is inexplicable here is how a difference in the experience of time and space is possible. Again, it should not be surprising that the experience of the music makes it aesthetically different to the experience of the sideways counterpart.

Art, Bergson, and Relativistic Physics

Many theorists and artists claim that Bergson has significantly influenced art, especially temporal art such as film and novels. Tarkovsky wanted his films to appear as if his entire film were "aspiring to an indivisible time", and so was inspired by Bergson's concept of experienced time (Totaro 1992, 25). Similarly, Bergson inspired Woolf's concept of constant flowing consciousness (although this is questionable; see Graham 1956). Furthermore, Proust claimed Bergson as an influence (Lloyd 1993, 124–128). Vuillermoz stated that cinema must be Bergsonian, and discussions "between Vuillermoz and the writer Paul Souday showed how Bergson's philosophy was considered in terms of movies, as an increasing number of viewers saw films reveal a Bergsonian notion of time" (Canales 2016, 297–298). He "influenced countless artists who were searching for ways to articulate time and memory aesthetically" (Totaro 1992, 22).

Bergson also argued against the physical concept of relative time. He argued that there is only one real time, a time evident in our experience. This time is continuous and absolute. But physical time is discrete and relative.

So, does temporal art suit Bergsonian time better than time in relativistic physics? As discussed in Chapter 4, the preference for Bergson's time is because of its continuity. Relativistic time is also continuous, and not discrete.[6] Indeed, given Bergson's view of cinema, cinema could be equally at odds with Bergson *and* relativistic physics. Bergson objected to time in cinema. Time is represented in cinema by discrete elements, the separate frames of the film. None of these frames have time in them; they are just static pictures. Nor is there any inherent order to the frames. Instead, they have time only when these discrete frames are presented in some order (Canales 2016, 284–286).

Relative Time and Temporal Art

For physics, time must be relative and, for Bergson, it must be absolute. So, perhaps temporal art matches Bergson's idea of time better because it requires absolute time? Deleuze states that, through its disruption of movement, modern cinema can depict time itself, not just time in change (Deleuze 1989). And, perhaps, this depicted time is absolute. Such a depiction of absolute time does not require there be absolute time in the world. Film is dependent on material and processes. Whether it is digital or celluloid, the film is recorded, constructed, and displayed in a physical medium. This process involves only and necessarily that there be actual change in things. It is not possible to show a film in a world in which there is time without change (such as Shoemaker's frozen world, described in Chapter 1). In addition, the change is physical; it does not obviously require absolute time. Unless, that is, physical theory is wrong about the physics of object. But then the problem has nothing to do with art as such.

Yet, what about the time that Deleuze states is *depicted*? Even here, there is reason to doubt that it requires absolute time.

First, as already discussed for cinema, what Deleuze says is depicted is more *represented*. Being a representation, it demands nothing in the world match it. When discussing how modern cinema shows time itself, Deleuze also discusses how the same form of cinema depicts strange spaces, such as "Riemanian spaces in Bresson [...] quantum spaces in Robbe-Grillet, of probabilistic and topological spaces in Resnais, of crystallized spaces in Herzog and Tarkovsky" (Deleuze 1989, 129).

None of these representations imply that the filmmakers, in fact, need such spaces to be real or that theorists ought to hold that they exist. Similarly, temporal art need not require there be absolute time to represent absolute time.

Finally, even if such artwork could represent absolute time, it is worth asking exactly what such a representation is like. Is it of time depicted as if independent of any reference frame? It is hard to imagine how to do that, to show that what is represented could not be relative to something or other. To represent something like this in a temporal artwork would require the artwork to successfully represent something both absolute and necessarily absolute. That is, it could not be relative.

This issue is similar to the question of an experience of absolute time. Other chapters (Chapter 1, 4, 6) discuss the possible knowledge or experience of absolute time. As discussed in those chapters, the experience is compatible with relativistic time. Or, it is as compatible as an experience of stillness is compatible with the Earth turning on its axis. It may seem to be of something absolute because we have no sense of what it is relative to. But this does not mean it is not relative. The work does not distinguish them.

Finally, a temporal art may be claimed to take Bergson's side because it takes the side of experienced time. In that case, the claimed conflict with relativistic physics does not arise from art itself, but from experience.

Study Questions

1. Several examples are given here of both temporal artworks (such as music and cinema) and non-temporal artworks (such as a painting). Do you agree with the different examples falling under type or artwork? Is there any kind of artwork that falls under both? Is there any that falls under neither?
2. What does this chapter suggest is the best art form for representing time? Do you agree with these reasons? Is there a better form, in your opinion? Or does the question make no sense—there is no "best" form of art for time? If that is right, then why, do you think, some artists choose certain forms to represent time?
3. Imagine the world is frozen, without any change. Can there be music?
4. Markosian argues that music conflict with some philosophical theories. If that is right, then at least one kind of temporal artwork undermines a philosophical theory of time. Do you agree?

Notes

1 For example, Tarkovsky 1989.
2 Again, the object might, in fact, be at different times. Say the work of art is created by a light moving over a canvas in a blur, such that every part of the canvas appears to be illuminated at once. It is not illuminated at once. If the top left is illuminated first, and the bottom right last, then parts of the canvas represent at different times. However, the work does not need this temporal ordering of representing parts; all parts could be at the same time. If we could instantly illuminate the whole work, it would appear the same, and have the same representational properties (see Le Poidevin 2004).
3 There are also *flashbacks*: scenes in the narrative that represent events which occur earlier in the represented timeline than events shown before in the film itself. *Flashforwards* are the reverse. They do not use the duration or temporal order of the events they are representing to represent those events in the narrative.
4 See Chapter 1.
5 See Chapters 2 and 3.
6 At least, not on the scale relevant to lived experience, which Bergson cares about. Time might be discrete on a very small scale, for example, the Planck scale, but this is not something we would experience (for discussions about experiencing continuous time, see Dainton 2001; on discrete time, see Van Bendegam 2011).

Suggested Readings

There are not many books dedicated to the philosophy of time and its relationship to art in general. Bourne and Caddick Bourne 2016 is an exception, explicitly looking at arguments about fiction and the philosophy of time. For books

262   Philosophy of Art and Time

that have chapters focused on the subject, see chapter 1 and chapter 3 in Currie 1995 and part III of Le Poidevin 2007.

Gombrich 1964 is good for outlines and criticisms of Lessing's distinction between temporal art and spatial art. Gombrich's paper is influential—there are many other papers on art elsewhere. Notably, chapter 7 of Le Poidevin 2007 discusses Gombrich's objections to Lessing's division of art into temporal forms and spatial forms. See also Lessing's relationship to relatively recent theory in McClain 1985 and Mitchell 1985.

For work on cinema and time, see Deleuze 1989. Canales 2016 is an excellent discussion on Bergson's view of time and its relationship to new art of his period, especially cinema.

10 Philosophy of Time Travel

Overview

We examine reasons for being interested in time as conceived in time travel stories over other kinds of fictional time. One reason might be that physics seems to allow it; another reason might be that it appeals to certain attitudes we have, for example, nostalgia and regret.

We define time travel and find challenges in doing so. It is not exactly analogous to space travel; in some cases, it is too broad and trivial; merely existing in time seems to fall under it. Finally, it is suggested that skipping times and reversing direction in time could be instances of it.

We consider common problems around time travel, such as causal loops and changing the past. It is argued that, although causal loops are possible, they are strange and counter-intuitive. And changing the past is impossible—it creates incompatible states of affairs, each which precludes the possibility of the others. A number of solutions are examined, such as multiple timelines. One problem with such solutions is that what may be called "time travel" is not that at all. Such forms of *pseudo*-time travel are instead other—albeit, strange—kinds of travel, for example, between parallel worlds.

However, combined with genuine time travel, such pseudo-time travel may satisfy many of the desires that draw one to time travel. A model is proposed in which there is time travel, parallel world travel, and a specific causal relationship between the original world and the parallel world. This combination does not allow one to change the past; however, it does allow one to satisfy some of the motivations for wanting to change the past.

Introduction

In 2011, an experiment near CERN briefly caused a media sensation. Experimenters claimed to have evidence of neutrinos moving faster than light. If this evidence was correct, then it showed either a violation of Einstein's theory of relativity or that particles travelled backwards in time—that is, of particles time-travelling. However, it emerged that the experiment was likely flawed in several ways—including, possibly, a loose fibre-optic cable. Once the experiment was repeated with the flaws removed, the evidence of violation or backwards travel disappeared (Major 2012).

There is still no empirical evidence of time travel on the level of neutrinos or other microscopic properties. There is also no evidence on the level popular in fiction, that of human-sized objects. Nothing and no one in the present are known to be indisputably from the future. No ancient artefacts have been shown to originate in some recent or future time (at least, no more than they are shown to originate with ancient aliens).

Philosophers do sometimes use empirical evidence in their work, but philosophy is not empirical work. Perhaps there is philosophical work to do on time travel. For example, there are questions over the coherence of the concept of time travel. Assuming it can be defined, there are questions on the possibility of time travel—or some expected consequences of it, such as backwards causation, causal loops, and changing the past.

However, as far as we know, time travel only occurs in fiction. Instances of it are found only in the realm of the imagination. As the science fiction writers Anders puts it, time travel is "a fantasy technology, no more based on real science than dragons and unicorns" (Anders 2012, online).

There are many representations of time which are fictional and are not time travel. For example, the anthropomorphic figure of time in Poussin's *The Dance to the Music of Time* is an old man playing pipes for revellers. In C.S. Lewis's fantasy series, Narnia's time is considered different to actual time. Decades and centuries go by in Narnia while only months or years go by in the human world. These allegorical and fantastical times are not considered in as much depth as time travel is in philosophy. As discussed in Chapter 9, we are not forced by art to take a position on time (for discussion on this specific to time travel, see also Bourne and Caddick 2012).

So, why does time travel acquire more interest than these other fictional times? Why care about time travel? One reason is that time travel is generally considered to be physically possible, and that physical possibility extends to human-scale travel as well. For example, the physicist Kip Thorne describes time travel through wormholes that is physically possible for humans to do. Other time only found in fiction or allegory is not physically possible like this.

Furthermore, time travel appeals to certain emotions. For example, we may have nostalgic reasons to be interested in time travel. If we are nostalgic for what we lived through, we want to live through it again; we want to revisit a perfect summer trip when we fell in love; a chance to relive an exam that we failed. Or we have what Germans sometimes call *sehnsucht*—a nostalgia for events in which we never participated. We want to see dinosaurs. We want to hear David Bowie live or see Notre Dame in its pre-2019 form. We long to visit the Australian coast when, pre-Invasion, only First Nation people were there.

Alternatively, we are curious to experience what happens in time beyond the period of time in which we expect to live. Why not grasp the chance to travel a thousand years into the future to discover what has happened to our world? Or see the world once humanity has gone the way everything goes. Like the time traveller in the Wells's *The Time Machine*, we may witness the last years of the Earth, the dome of the dying sun filling the sky. Time travel promises to show us past events when we never were.

Regret may motivate us. Regret is a universal "emotion we feel when we realize or imagine that our present situation would have been better had we made different decisions. It is a negative emotion reflecting a retrospective evaluation of a decision. It is an awful feeling, coupled with a clear sense of self-blame concerning its causes and strong wishes to undo the current situation" (Zeelenberg and Pieters 2006, 210). Something in the past occurred that we wish had not occurred. We desire to *change* it. If there are time machines, perhaps we can dissolve those regrets and change those past times.

We have *guilt*. We want to travel to a time beyond our death and repair the damage of our actions. Because of something we do now, or do not do, we want to make peace with those affected. We want to find our descendants and explain why we could not do what we should have done.

In the absence of time travel, some of these emotions, however powerful, seem irrational. To satisfy these emotional impulses, it seems we must do the impossible. Nostalgia prompts us to return to a time that is already gone. Regret demands we go back to past times and change how things went.

Time travel seems as if it can make irrational emotions rational. Yet, to explore the possibilities of time travel, or use it to satisfy certain powerful emotions, we need to understand it. So, what is time travel?

Defining Time Travel

The history of time travel is short. According to Gleick, H.G. Wells first described it in a way that we recognize it today (Gleick 2016). If that is right, the idea as we recognize it is only a little over a century old. Before that, time travel does not seem to be considered by thinkers about time, never mind a staple of fiction or of speculations about reality.

Not all descriptions or thinking about time travel are identical or consistent with one another. Nor does each require the same commitments to concepts of time. Still, we might try an initial crude definition. How about this: in fiction, time travellers typically leave one time and go to *another* time. This is just like travellers through space leaving one place and going to another place. This gives us a simple definition of time travel:

Time travel: X time travels if X travels to *other times*.

X can be anything. It can be an object, such as the restaurant in Adams's *The Restaurant at the End of the Universe*. It can be a message, such as The Company transmissions in Baker's "The Company" series. In fiction, X is often a *person*. Whatever it might be, "travel to other times" includes some problematic assumptions.

First, references to "other times" and "travel" are too weak; they include scenarios which are not typically considered to be time travel. They include scenarios to which everyone and everything ordinarily or normally belongs. If the time travelling to other times just means going from one time to the next time, then we do so by simply existing from one moment to the next, which we all usually do. "We are all time-travellers according to our ordinary way of thinking about time" (Lockwood 2005, 1).

If everyone is a time traveller just by existing in time, then this fails to catch the time travel we are interested in. Time travellers do not merely exist in time, going from one moment to the next. But, then, what do they do in time?

Time Travel and Space Travel

Perhaps time travellers do in time what space travellers do in space? As discussed in other chapters,[1] space and time have many similar features. For example, both space and time are extended: distance is spatial extension and duration is temporal extension. There are also indexical terms for both, e.g., "here" and "there" in space, "now" and "then" in time, and both have a "present".

With travel in space, you leave one place and arrive in another place. Similarly, with travel in time, you leave one *time* and arrive in another *time*. For example, in the film *Bill & Ted's Excellent Adventure*, Bill and Ted *leave* 1980s California to *arrive* in Ancient Greece.

However, there are problems with this analogy. Let x_a be the old spatial or temporal location and x_b be the new spatial or temporal location. Then, let x be s for space travel and t time travel:

- *Space travel:* O is at s_a at t_1 and s_b at t_2.

If time travel is analogous to spatial travel, we get:

- *Time travel:* O is at t_a at t_1 and t_b at t_2.

This way of being in time matches ordinary existence in time. Bill and Ted's fellow schoolmates do this, for example. When I sit and wait, or get up and look out the window, or do anything at all, I go from one time to another time. Say I begin sitting in a seat at t_1, then continue to sit in it for several moments through to t_2. In doing this, I am at one time t_1 and then at a different time t_2.

I meet the definition by "a" being "1" and "b" being "2":

- *Time travel:* O is at t_1 at t_1 and t_2 at t_2.

So, what does ordinary occupancy or existence in time lack that time travel has? What does ordinary occupancy have that time travel lacks?

Space Travel by Leaving the Previous Space

Let us continue the spatial analogy. What time travel has that ordinary temporal existence lacks is similar to what spatial travel has that ordinary spatial existence lacks.

Ordinary existence in time is like being stationary in space: in both cases, we occupy all the relevant locations *together*. We fill the region we occupy. I fill the couch I am sprawled upon and I fill the hour I spend lying on the couch.

Note, however, this "together" cannot mean *at the same time*. I do not occupy a duration at the same time. I occupy it over different times, the times that make up the duration.

In contrast, travel through a space is not filling that space altogether. When I travel from one place to another place, the place I leave ceases to have me in it. For example, I leave my house for a walk. By leaving the house, I am no longer in the house.

Time Travel by Leaving the Previous Time

Perhaps we can say something similar with time travel. That is, we travel by leaving the previous time when we travel to the next time. When you travel from one time to another time, the time you leave no longer has you in it. For example, you leave the house at 2pm (t_1) to travel to the shop for 2.30pm (t_2). By doing this, you are not in the house at 2pm (t_1) because you are in the shop at 2.30pm (t_2).

Another example: your childhood self time-travels to the future from your sixth birthday party. In doing so, you leave your sixth birthday party. Just as how leaving a house means you are no longer in the house, travelling in time means you are no longer in your childhood birthday party.

Again, given one understanding, this is the same as ordinary existence in time. If I exist from one time to the next time, then *at the next time* I am not at the previous time. I may say "I am no longer" at that previous time but "no longer" invites confusion: it suggests the previous time is, in some sense, "still around" to be unoccupied by me at the later time. However, by definition, the previous time is earlier than the later time. By definition, "still" implies a persistence of something into a later time. An earlier time does not persist into a later time. It is not still around.

For time travel, we could strengthen the analogy with space: by travelling from the previous time, I am not at the previous time. Because I travelled from that previous time, whatever happens then does not have me in it. This means, for example, your sixth birthday no longer has you in it.

But what is an event such as your sixth birthday party without you in it? Is it the exact same event, except without you? The candles are blown out, the cake is eaten, your friend's parent still frowns at an unreasonable tantrum—but now, because you travelled, you're not there to blow out the candles, eat the cake, or throw the tantrum.

Whatever sense we can make of such a description, it does not match the usual stories of time travel. Almost[2] all descriptions of time travel assume that you are at the time you travelled from. You do not disappear from it. As evident in several stories about time travel, if you travel to the same moment you left, you can even meet yourself. For example, if Bill and Ted travel from 2pm August 2020 to 3pm December 2120, visit for a little bit, then travel to 2pm August 2020, they may appear twice at 2pm 2020: once as they are about to travel and once as they have finished travelling. They do not appear after they travel to find that they are gone from that time. Instead, they appear *twice* at that time.

It seems that, even for time travel, we fill the periods of time through which we travel as one fills space, rather than travels through it. The analogy with spatial travel and non-travel fails. We need a different way of distinguishing ordinary existence in time from time travel.

Forward Time Travel

Forward time travel is travelling into a later moment than the originating time. So described, however, it continues to include ordinary existence of time. If the originating time is you reading this, and you putting this down is a future time, then it seems you forward time travel. So, what distinguishes it? According to Mellor, the difference is in how long it takes for the traveller to get between times in comparison to non-travellers.

> [F]orward time travel, unlike the apparent flow of time, is more than psychological, and is not restricted to the latter's tautological rate of seven days a week. An example of it would be someone taking only an hour to reach the end of the next century, and that in principle can be done.
>
> (Mellor 1998, 123)

Two ways to think of this travel is of the traveller moving from one moment to a much later moment by either:

a)   Occupying every moment in-between the two moments
b)   Skipping large periods of time in-between

Mellor thinks that a) is a good and easy example of future/forward time travel. To time travel like this, one need only "reduce their rates of change and decay so much that they take a century to reach physical and mental states which they would otherwise reach in an hour" (1992, 121).

However, described this way, it continues to include common processes we do not think of as time travel. We freeze vegetables. We reduce their rates of change and decay so that they take months to reach physical states they would otherwise reach in a few days. Say we perfect a freezing process so that the vegetables decay thousands of times more slowly than they normally do. Then, given Mellor's definition under a), we have sent the vegetables travelling forward in time (unless we eat them first).

We can see this in one fictional case of time travel (amongst many, e.g., *3001* by Arthur C. Clarke; films such as *Demolition Man* or *Aliens*). In *Futurama*, one of the protagonists, Fry, travels from the 20th century to the 30th century. He does so by getting stuck in a fridge and being frozen. While the world moves and transforms dramatically around him, he stays the same. He does not change at all. He, in fact, does the least amount of anything.

This kind of time travel is almost the opposite of travel. The "traveller" does it by *not doing* something everyone else does. The traveller does not eat, sleep, or decay. They do not snore. They do not breathe. They do not die. Yet, they do persist through the period in which they are frozen.

This concept of forward time travel does capture some unusual cases of existence in time. As discussed in Chapter 1, there is Shoemaker's world frozen in time. This frozen world qualifies as a world that undergoes this kind of forward time travel; similarly, from the moment the woman freezes time to prevent a missile impact, the missile and everything else undergo forward time travel.[3] In both cases, a part of the world stops doing anything.

Such a view of forward time travel is too broad. We need to constrain it in some way, distinguishing it from both ordinary temporal existence and these frozen cases.

Skipping

One thing that ordinary temporal existence and freezing share is that they exist in the times between the moments in which they exist. They do not *skip* times.

Of course, both can exist in all those times in such a way that they are not conscious of having existed in them. In that case, the "travellers" just fail to be aware of some periods—the apparently skipped parts. If that was enough for forward time travel, then we all forward time travel. We typically do so at least once a day and, perhaps, more often than that. We forward time travel whenever we sleep. We lose consciousness, then several hours later gain it again, apparently "skipping" the slept time.

However, actually skipping time is challenging. Here is one issue: if we skip time, this seems to block physically possible travel. The principle of the conservation of energy requires that the energy at one time, such as traveller's originating time, is the same as the energy at other times, such as the time just after the originating time. Yet, if I disappear so that I am not at the next time, the energy that constitutes me disappears as well. Given only this account, this is a difference between the energy before I travel and after I travel. This raises a question: what happens to that energy? What allows the decrease in energy after I leave and allows the increase after I arrive?

For the question of what forward time travel means, this need not concern us. What matters is that *something* allows it. For example, perhaps our travel causes something else to come into existence, and then to disappear when we arrive. This does not mean that we occupy the time in between the moments of travel. And that we do not occupy those times is enough to hold that we skip them.

In any case, even if a genuine forward time travel is physically impossible, there may still be time travel. There may be *backwards* time travel.

Backward Time Travel

Past or backward time travel is travelling into a past or earlier moment than the originating time. To seem to do this while ordinarily existing in time is much harder to achieve than with forward time travel. Even in the broadest concept of this travel, we cannot do it by doing nothing, for example, falling in a fridge like Fry did. To travel backwards in time, we must reverse the order in which we occupy time. We must go from one time to an earlier time.

Still, like forward time travel, backwards travel has metaphysical and epistemological issues. Some of the metaphysical issues are based on problems raised in Chapter 4. For example, according to Mellor, causation defines the direction of time. The arrows of time and causation cannot run opposite to each other. However, in most cases, backwards time travel involves backwards causation, e.g., if I go to an earlier time, I at the very least affect or am affected by what happens there.

However, as also discussed in Chapter 4, there are physical reasons to hold that there is no absolute direction to time. There is a direction of time of a kind, but it is merely local, relativized to frames of reference. If that is right, then there is no absolute backwards time travel. There is only relative backwards travel. So, if we follow Price, and not Mellor, we can have at least *local* ordinary existence and forward time travel. Price's metaphysical view of time allows a local direction to time. All that we need for backwards time travel is that the travel is in the *other* direction.

The second, epistemological issue concerns how to distinguish backwards time travel from ordinary existence in time. As we saw with forward travel, some cases of ordinary existence—albeit unusual cases—resemble it in ways such that it is tempting to call them forward time travel. However, because they only involve ordinary temporal existence, they are not.

For example, in Pohl's *The Tunnel Under the World*, the main character wakes every day in his hometown to a situation that is identical to the day before. It is as if everything that happened the day before was undone, rolled back, or had never happened. It turns out that this is indeed the case: every-thing in the town during the night is restored by outside actors to the way it was the day before.

This character is not travelling backwards in time. The changes in the world, including his own, are being wiped out while he sleeps. It is as much time travel as tidying your room (albeit for more sinister reasons, and by more underhanded means).

Personal Time

One possibility is that ordinary existence involves one kind of time whereas time travel, including backwards time travel, involves another kind of time. Lewis distinguishes between *personal time* and *non-personal time*:

> I [distinguish] time itself, external time as I shall also call it, from the personal time of a particular time traveller: roughly, that which is measured by his wristwatch. His journey takes an hour of his personal time, let us say; his wristwatch reads an hour later at arrival than at departure. But the arrival is more than an hour after the departure in external time, if he travels toward the future; or the arrival is before the departure in external time (or less than an hour after), if he travels toward the past.
>
> (Lewis 1976/1991, 136)

Presumably, for Lewis, "time itself" is time that we all ordinarily exist in. Thus, we have:

- *Personal time:* the temporal order and durations of events according to an individual.
- *External time*: the temporal order and durations of events according to everything else. As the opposite of *personal* time, call this *public time*.[4]

For example, if I time travel to Ancient Greece, there is a moment when I stand in my room in 2020 CE and a *later* moment when I stand in 300 BCE. In this description, 2020 CE is *earlier* than 300 BCE. The "later" and "earlier" are terms for events in my personal time. Yet, for everyone else, 2020 is *later* than 300 BCE. This "later" is a term for events in *public* time. Furthermore, I travel backwards in time because my personal time is the reverse of public time.

One difficulty with this distinction as a means of determining backwards time travel is that it depends on a prior understanding of public time. We can assume everyone has personal time: it is just what the temporal properties and relations are according to each person. These include the duration and temporal order of events according to each person. When a person occupies time, as far as I know, as anyone reading this occupies time, their personal time is the same as public time. We all agree on the order and duration of events.

272 Philosophy of Time Travel

It is the difference to public time that makes one a time traveller. Yet, what makes *public* time not merely another personal time, for example, a group personal time?

Perhaps there is nothing to distinguish them. Public time is only the order and duration of events which most people agree with, and which the least people disagree with. In that case, it is possible for a few people to agree on events while disagreeing with public time. You and I might both travel backwards in time, such that the order of events for both of us is the reverse of public time. But, say, if enough of us travelled in the same direction as us, we would be in public time, as would anyone else sharing our personal time. The difference is a matter of numbers.

We need not worry about this distinction, however. As time travel is typically conceived, this is not how time travel works. The order of public time is overwhelmingly shared by the greater number of individuals. In it, the dinosaurs existed earlier than humans, and the sun's death happens later than humans. That something's temporal order differs from that order is enough for it to be travelling backwards in time.

Causation in Time Travel

Time travellers are time travellers because they travel to earlier, or past, times or travel into later, or future, times. Yet, this is not all that happens to them. There is also what happens in the time when they arrive.

Call the moment from which the traveller travels the *origin time* of the traveller. Call the other time to which they travel the *arrival time*. For example, if I travel from 1 September 2020 to 31 October 2020, then the *origin time* is 1 September and the *arrival time* is 31 October.

In fiction, time travellers are described as being capable of different kinds of activity through time travel.[5] Here are some examples:

- *Epiphenomenal time travel:* The traveller cannot cause anything to happen at the other time.
- *Causal time travel:* the traveller can cause things to happen at the other time.
- *Causal loops*: The traveller can cause things to happen at the other time, things which at least partly cause the traveller to do things at the origin time.
- *Changing the past*: The traveller can change what happens before the origin time.
- *Change the time series:* The traveller can travel to a series of moments that are not part of the time series containing their origin time.
- *Time series creation:* The traveller creates a time series.

Epiphenomenal Travel

The traveller can do nothing in the arrival time. They do not interact, cause, or change anything in the other time. At best, they can observe events. An example of this is Scrooge in Dickens's *A Christmas Carol*. If taken as actual events in the fictional universe (and not, for example, a prophetic or guilt-ridden dream), Ebenezer Scrooge visits the past and future. However, he can do nothing in those events except witness them.

This does not mean there is no causal interaction between the time traveller and the time they visit. What happens at the time can cause things to happen to the traveller. For example, Scrooge can relive his happy past, see his gravestone, and feel fear and longing strike him from what he observes. What happens at that time can still cause things in him.

Causal Travel

The traveller contributes to events at the time they visit. In Wells's *The Time Machine*, many thousands of years of public time after a dinner party, the time traveller kills a Morlock. In the traveller's own personal time, the Morlock attacks the traveller *earlier* than the dinner party. Indeed, the Morlock's attack on the traveller is part of what *causes* the traveller to tell the story to his friends (at his origin time). However, to the listeners, in public time, the Morlock attacks *later* than the party.

There are many different kinds of causation proposed in time travel stories. The most significant are (a) causal loops and (b) changing the past.

Causal Loops

The time traveller causes situations to exist or occur at the origin time. Examples of this are the films *Bill & Ted's Excellent Adventure* (1989) and *Twelve Monkeys* (1999). Bill and Ted pass their history exam, which causes a future world of peace and prosperity. That future world sends Lucius back in time to help Bill and Ted, causing them to pass their exam. Thus, we have at least two ways of describing this causal loop:

1. Through helping Bill and Ted, the future world causes the future world.
2. Through accepting the future world's help, Bill and Ted's exam success causes the exam success.

We might wonder what starts the loop. Is it the future world sending back Lucius, revealing to the two that they are set to cause a world of peace and prosperity, or is it Bill and Ted's exam success? One possibility is that the loop starts with the earliest cause. Yet, this raises a further question: what is the earliest cause? Is it the earliest cause in public time or personal time?

In personal time, there seems to be no earliest cause. The younger Bill and Ted may hold their decision to climb into the machine is the earliest cause. For them, nothing happened earlier than that. However, this action is driven by Lucius time-travelling to meet them. For Lucius's personal time, this is not the earliest cause. Instead, it is the moment when he accepted the mission. Again, in public time, Bill and Ted's decision is earlier than Lucius's acceptance, but that is not personal time.

Here is a sample of some stages in the causal chain leading to Bill and Ted passing their history exam:

1. Lucius travels to meet them: in Lucius's personal time, this is earlier than Bill and Ted getting into the machine.
2. Still in Lucius's personal time, Lucius is sent by his peers into the past.
3. His peers, knowing that Bill and Ted need help, decide to send Lucius into the past.
4. They acquire that knowledge from records of the past.
5. Bill and Ted climb into the machine.

All of these are part of Lucius's personal chain of cause and effect. They are all causes and all effects. They are also exaggerated forms of any causal loop that causes one to participate in events about which one knows something, while at the origin time, before participation.

Self-Creating and Uncreated Objects

A counter-intuitive possibility of causal loops concerns how some events or objects in such loops are created. The internet's invention is often accredited to Tim Berners-Lee. However, if someone else thought of the idea and simply told Berners-Lee about it, Berners-Lee did not invent it. Instead, he merely implemented the ideas in it. He is like someone who is given instructions on how to make the internet; he did not write the instructions himself or invent the thing. Someone else invented it.

Say Berners-Lee was told about the internet. Then he did not invent it. But now, say that the person who told him came from the future—and visited him precisely because they believed Berners-Lee invented the internet.

For this example of the internet, at least the internet was built at some time. There is a moment in which the internet originates. But, in other possible scenarios, just as causal loops do not obviously have an originating cause, causal loops can occur in which objects in the loops lack an origin.

The Time Machine Instruction Manual

A common example is a time machine instruction manual (e.g., Lowe 2003). In 2020, in his workshop, Mike receives a visit from an old man named Kim. Kim tells Mike he is a time traveller, and he wants to help Mike invent a time machine. He gives Mike an instruction manual for building and operating time machines. Mike uses the manual to design, test, build, and finally operate an actual time machine. It takes thirty years, but he eventually succeeds.

Finally, in 2050, as an old man, Mike gets in the time machine and travels back to his 2020 workshop and meets himself as a young man. He tells his younger self that his name is Kim, and he wants to help him invent a time machine. Old Mike (now Kim) hands young Mike the time machine instruction manual.

Where did the instruction manual come from? Mike did not write it—not when he was young, and not as old Kim. Old Kim did not get it from somewhere else that is left out of the story. The book is by his side throughout his development of the machine. He got it when he was young, used it throughout the years, and finally returned it to himself.

Lowe considers this not just a strange-sounding situation, but one that is problematic in terms of explanation and causation:

> The problem is that the plans appear to come from nowhere; even though every event in their circular history may seem to be causally explicable in terms of other events, the "explanations" involved are ultimately circular and hence not genuinely explanations at all (assuming, as we seem entitled to do, that explanation is an asymmetrical relation).
>
> (Lowe 2002, 340)

One way to avoid this problem is to hold it that time travel cannot violate rules about objects coming into existence. An object must have an origin. No object can simply exist in a loop.

This seems intuitive enough. Yet, if anywhere is a place to ignore intuition, it is in time travel. (If intuition is sufficient reason to deny time travel, then for this author there is no time travel.) Is there no better reason than intuition to deny such a loop?

Wear and Tear Paradox

One possibility is that, for any kind of normal everyday object, it is impossible that they lack an origin. This is because they are subject to entropy.

Let us describe the time machine instruction manual story from the "personal" time of the book. To indicate such personal time (since books are not persons), adapting Lewis's example, we might attach a clock to the book and let it tick along as the book travels about in time. (This also indicates that "personal" is perhaps not the best general term for this kind of time.)

The book is travelling through time. The book is a physical object, one susceptible to wear and tear. Once Mike gets his hands on it, he thumbs through the pages, causing them to crease a little and the ink to rub off on his hands. Furthermore, he turns the pages, weakening the spine a little. The sunlight in his workshop causes the paper to ever-so-slightly dry and the ink to fade.

By the time Mike is Kim in 2050, and as Kim takes the book back to Mike in 2020, the book has worn out a little. It is a little more fragile, a bit more decomposed, a little closer to disintegration than when Mike first received it.

Let us attach a figure to the wear the book goes through Mike's use. Say he received it in 100% condition, and it wears out by 10%. As a result, it is in 90% condition by the time Mike is done with it.

However, the book cannot be worn out to any amount through the years it is in Mike's workshop. This is an uncreated book—a demon of its loop. The book that Mike receives in 2020 is the same book that is there some years after he received it.

If it is worn out by his use, then there is the following paradoxical scenario:

1. Kim travels back from 2050 to 2020 with the time travel manual in 100% condition and delivers it to Mike.
2. In 2020, Mike receives the book.
3. Mike uses the book from 2020 to 2050, wearing it out so that, by 2050, it is only in 90% condition.
4. Mike (now Kim) travels back from 2050 to 2020 with the time travel manual in 90% condition and delivers it to Mike.
5. (From 1 and 2) In 2020, Mike receives the book in 100% mint condition.
6. (From 2 and 4) In 2020, Mike receives the book in 90% mint condition.
7. (From 5 and 6) In 2020, Mike receives the book in 100% and 90% book condition.
8. Nothing can be both 100% and 90% condition at the same time. 7 is a contradiction.

We have a contradiction. To avoid it, which premises can we reject? We cannot reject 7 or 8 without rejecting earlier premises. Similarly, 5 and 6 follow from previous premises, so we can only deny those by denying at least one of the previous premises—1, 2, 3, or 4.

If we deny 2, then Mike does not receive the book. In that case, there is no uncreated object or even time travel in this story: Mike never receives a book at all—and so never travels through time to deliver it to himself. Similarly, if we deny 1 and 4 outright, then there is no time travel. 4 involves the book in 90% condition, because of what is stated in 3.

So, we deny 3: the book is not worn out by its use. This is the only option if we want Mike to time travel and to receive the book.

Yet, if we deny 3, then it seems we have an *immutable* book. The book cannot change travelling through time. So, when we turn the page, no ink can rub off our fingers. No matter how we try, we cannot crease the spine. It cannot get wet unless it dries perfectly. The sun cannot fade its cover. Air cannot react with elements in it. It will not burn, even a tiny bit. If it is an electronic tablet, the battery cannot wear out; its surface cannot be scuffed. If it is an electronic book, we cannot change the software that is on it: we cannot update it to the latest version or, given it comes from 2050 to 2020, downgrade it to an earlier version. The screen cannot become a little less responsive. The processor cannot slow. A cup of coffee spilled on it cannot damage it. To ensure it is the same in 2050 as it is in 2020, nothing about its composition will change between those times.

Furthermore, even the unobserved condition of the book in 2050 must be perfectly identical to how it is when Mike receives it in 2020. It must have the same fundamental constituents, such as particles, even though no one working with it observes them. There can be no actual difference—for otherwise, that difference generates a contradiction similar to 7 above.

For something such as a book, this seems to block any possibility of it being created.

However, there is a case where such a scenario is possible. But it does not concern books, or any other known macroscopic object.

Feynman's Time-Travelling Particle

The standard model of electrons and positrons is this:

- Electrons are point particles with a mass and a single electron-volt (eV) negative charge.
- Positrons or anti-electrons are identical to electrons except that they have a positive charge.
- When electrons and positrons collide, they both disappear, emitting massless photons of light.

The physicist Feynman suggested a different interpretation of such fundamental particles, photons, and their interactions. He suggested that the electrons and positrons in such interactions are not, in fact, different kinds of particle. They are not even different particular particles. They are both the one numerically identical particle, a single electron. "They" is misleading; there is no plural, only a singular "it".

How is this possible? Feynman suggests that this single particle travels in different directions in time. An electron and a different positron do not "collide", emitting photons. Instead, an electron abruptly emits a photon and then the electron reverses its direction in time. Feynman suggests the following metaphor:

> It is as though a bombardier flying low over a road suddenly sees three roads and it is only when two of them come together and disappear again that he realises that he has simply passed over a long switchback in a single road.
> (Feynman 1949, 749)

The diagrams (a) and (b) in Figure 10.1 depict the different interpretations of the same observable physical activity.

- (a) is an interpretation of the activity of several particles. A photon travels from the left until, at t_1, it ceases to exist, and a positron and electron are emitted at the place of the photon. The positron travels from the left until, at t_1, it meets and collides with an electron travelling from the right. In this collision, both electron and positron vanish, emitting a photon.

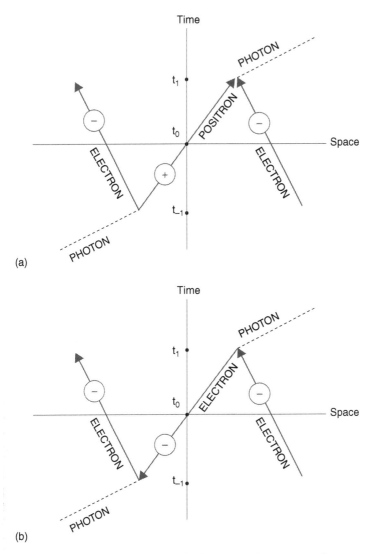

Figure 10.1 Two Interpretations of Electron-Positron Interaction

- (b) is an interpretation of the activity as one particle (call it an electron) travelling forwards and backwards in time. The electron travels from the right,
  emits a photon at t_1, and changes direction in time. It travels backwards in
  time until, at t_{-1}, it emits a photon and changes direction again in time—this
  time, to go forward once more in time.

(b) serves as the basis for a single particle that travels in a loop, similar to the
uncreated book. This is depicted in Figure 10.2.

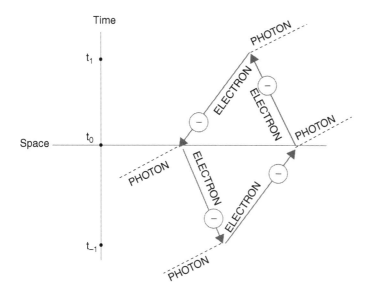

Figure 10.2 An Electron Looping through Time

Instead of just an electron reversing in time (appearing at that moment to be the collision of an electron and positron), we have the following complete loop of an electron's life-cycle:

1. An electron travels from one moment t_0 to another t_1, emits a photon, and then reverses direction in time. It continues backwards in time from t_1 to t_0.
2. At t_0, it emits a photon, changes direction in space, until it arrives at t_{-1}.
3. Again, it emits a photon, changes direction in time, and continues to t_0.
4. At t_0, it emits a photon—arriving at the same point and time where it began.

If we interpret each of these events as causing the next, this is a causal loop. Nothing causes the electron to come into existence, other than its own interactions with photons and travels through space and time. It exists as a loop, like the uncreated book.

Most current physicists do not take this idea of time-travelling electrons seriously. The current view is there is matter and antimatter, not forward travelling and backward traveling matter. However, for philosophical thinking about time travel, we can say this: if a particle did travel like this, it would not be subject to the problems for the uncreated time-travelling book. The properties that the electron (or positron) possesses throughout its journey remain the same. None of the changes in the particle—such as its location, its direction in time—survive its changes in direction in time (especially and obviously not its direction).

For example, an electron travels from Tuesday to Wednesday, then emits a photon and, on Wednesday, travels backwards in time to Tuesday (seeming to be a positron). As it travels, it may increase speed (seeming to those existing in forward time to be decreasing speed—this can get confusing) until finally it emits another photon and begins travelling forward in time (seeming to be an electron again). This may begin the looping journey of this one electron (or the end of the journey of the positron). However, there is no wear on the electron at any point. It simply has the properties that electrons have throughout its life.

Could an uncreated book do this? It would be an additional strange feature to it. For a book to be uncreated, and to exist only in the loop, it needs to somehow become unworn as it travels back in time. When Kim takes the 90% condition book back in time, the act of travelling in time undoes what wears it out. Travelling back in time restores it to a more pristine condition.

However, if anyone in public time, such as Mike's friends, manages to observe this undoing of the wear, it seems to them to just be the book aging normally. In 2020, it is less worn than it is at some intermediate date, say, 2035. And, in 2035, it is less worn than it is in 2050.

The most importance difference, however, is that the aging of the backwards-travelling book has a strange feature. Unlike the book in Mike's hands, the time-travelling book's apparent "ordinary" aging is inexplicable. There is no explanation for it being more worn in 2050 than it is in 2020, when it arrives—and there is especially no explanation for why the book wears away exactly the same way it does by Mike using it when it is part of public time. Mike did not thumb through it, not even as Kim; for Kim, in his backwards-travelling aged hands, the book inexplicably restores itself to 100% condition. From public time, it wears out as one might expect, except it does so for no reason at all.

These two appearances of the same miracle—restoration in personal time, apparently uncaused decay in public time—are not obviously incoherent. However, they require extra conditions on time travel objects omitted by a typical description of causal loops. The causal loop, as Lowe saw, is indeed very strange.

Changing the Past

The radio show *This American Life* asked members of the public: why would you like there to be time machines? Most people answered that they would like to change the past. For example, many said they would go back and kill Hitler before he rose to power. Others were motivated by personal regret. They would prefer if they had not done some things. And surely this is an understandable impulse? If you regret doing something, and you could travel back in time and ensure it never happened, then would you not do it, rather than let it be?

It is a common trope of time travel stories that, if one can travel in time, one can change the past. It is a significant part of the drama in such varied time travel stories as *Back to the Future, Looper, Primer*, and *About Time*. (It is not part of the drama in other stories, such as *La Jetée, The Time Traveller's Wife, Interstellar*, or *Bill & Ted's Excellent Adventure*.)

Yet, changing the past may be the most controversial possibility of time travel. It gives rises to the *grandfather paradox*.

The Grandfather Paradox

Lewis succinctly describes the grandfather paradox (1976/1991). In summary:

1. Tom hates his grandfather. He has a time machine and a laser gun. He is the world's best sharpshooter with laser guns.
2. Tom travels back in time to before his grandfather meets his grandmother.
3. Tom kills his grandfather with his laser gun.

As a consequence, there is the following series of events:

4. Tom's grandfather does not meet Tom's grandmother.
5. Tom is not born.
6. Tom does not hate his grandfather, does not have a time machine, and does not have a laser gun.
7. Tom does not travel back in time and kill his grandfather with his laser gun.
8. Tom's grandfather meets his grandmother.

As a consequence, there is the following series of events:

9. Tom is born.
10. Tom hates his grandfather, has a time machine, has a laser gun, travels back in time, and kills his grandfather.
11. Tom is not born ... and so never kills his grandfather—

... and, like a causal loop, seemingly for infinity.

However, it is not for infinity at all. It is an impossible loop. It is a collection of two sets of statements, from which a statement in one set contradicts a statement from the other set:

Set 1: Tom kills his grandfather before Tom is born		Set 2: Tom does not kill his grandfather before Tom is born
1. Tom kills his grandfather.		1. Tom does not kill his grandfather.
2. Tom's grandfather does not meet Tom's grandmother.		2. Tom's grandfather does meet Tom's grandmother.
3. Tom is not born.	Contradicts	3. Tom is born.
4. Tom does not get to hate his Grandfather, get a time machine, or have a laser gun.		4. Tom does get to hate his Grandfather, get a time machine, and has a laser gun.
5. Tom does not travel back in time and kill his grandfather.		5. Tom does travel back in time and kill his grandfather.

The paradox is not that Tom can kill his grandfather. It is that, in doing so, he also ensures *his grandfather lives*. The contradiction is that, in being able to travel back and successfully act on his murderous intentions, Tom both kills and does not kill his grandfather, is born and isn't born, travels in time and doesn't travel in time.

If the sequence of events—infinite and repeating—is of contradictory events, then this not a possible sequence of events. It is like the wear and tear paradox: what is done results in two contradictory situations for one and the same thing. For wear and tear, it is a contradiction in the condition of the book. For the grandfather paradox, it is a contradiction in the state of Tom's grandfather after Tom meets him, Tom's existence, and Tom's actions—that is, in everything relevant that happens.

According to Lewis, we can still have time travel. To do so, we deny some premise from either only set 1 or set 2. For example, we deny 1, that Tom shoots his grandfather dead. If we deny that, then all the other events in that sequence do not happen.

However, in denying one of these sets, we also deny that the past can be changed. In all cases where the past is changed, there are such sets of statements that conflict with one another: the statements that, according to the time travel story, describe events *before* the past change and the statements that describe events *after* the past change.

Yet, what exactly prevents Tom killing his grandfather? According to Lewis, any reason will do. People do fail in these situations. Tom is distracted by a bee; the grandfather bends down to tie his shoelace. Tom is pecked to death by a maddened pigeon; Tom himself can die without causing a paradox (perhaps giving a more rational would-be assassin pause).

It does not matter. As Lowe puts it:

> What we should evidently say is that, for some reason or another, the time traveller must fail to kill his grandfather, despite his best efforts to succeed in doing so. His failure to do so will not simply be a miracle. It will have a perfectly ordinary causal explanation of some kind, even if we cannot specify, in advance of knowing the details of the specific case, what this explanation might be.
>
> (Lowe 2003, 338)

Yet, if we are to undo the wrongs of our past through time travel, we need to be able to change the past. So, is this impossible? Or can we avoid this paradox and change the past?

Multiple Timelines

One possible solution is that the traveller does not alter the time series that she belongs to. Instead, her actions cause events in *other time series* or *timelines*. By travelling into the past, and causing something that happens, she does not cause it to happen in her own timeline. She causes it to happen in another timeline.

For example, Oona time travels from 2050 in a particular timeline—call it *timeline 1*—to 2000. She causes something to happen in 2000 that does not happen in 2000 in timeline 1. For example, she kills her grandfather, ensuring neither her mother nor herself is born. Or she destroys the time machine manual that she herself used to build the time machine.

However, there is no contradiction in her doing all this. Instead, she causes a different set of events than those in timeline 1. These events belong to a different timeline—call it *timeline 2*.

Usually, in time travel stories, the time traveller then returns back to a time in the new timeline. There is no obvious reason this must be the case—Oona could cause things in timeline 2 but return to timeline 1. But there is also no contradiction in her doing so. Oona may very well return to a time where she does not exist, or she never travelled through time. Still, the original timeline also exists in which she did do these things.

Objection 1: The Past Is Not Changed

However, this is not a case of changing what happened in her past. In Oona's original timeline, her grandfather is going to be born, and she as well. If she hates her own circumstances, she has done nothing to change them. She has only caused an alternative way the world turns out to be. If she ends up in timeline 2 as a result, and thus a world with happier circumstances, she has escaped her less happy world. However, the less happy world of timeline 1 is still there. If she regrets actions she wanted to undo, she does not undo them.

Response: The New Timeline Is Created

Perhaps one way around this is that Oona does not just cause events in the new timeline; she *creates* the new timeline. In 2050, before she travels back to 2020 where she causes things to happen, there is no timeline 2 after 2020. There is only timeline 1. Timeline 2 comes into existence at that time only *after* she travels back to 2020 and *when* she causes it to happen.

As such, one might hold that Oona does makes a difference. Oona creates a timeline which is happier. The old timeline 1 might continue to exist (or be destroyed by her actions—but this only exacerbates the problem to be discussed). However, there is also this new, better timeline 2. If she did not travel back in time and create it, there would be no timeline 2. There would only be the bad circumstances of timeline 1. So, she has made things better by creating a better timeline.

Objection 2: A Created Timeline Has the Same Problems as the Grandfather Paradox

However, a created timeline 2 does not avoid paradoxes such as the wear and tear or grandfather paradox. We just get a similar problem to the grandfather paradox.

In this case, the contradictory set of facts is that, in 2020, there is no timeline 2 (before Oona travels) and there is a timeline 2 (after Oona travels, and creates it). The specifics of this paradox are more metaphysical than murdered relatives or worn books. However, it is still a paradox. The time traveller goes to a time and changes what happens at it: in this case, from there being no second timeline to there being a second timeline.

Yet, if changing the past is not possible, not even by creating new timelines, then what are we to make of stories that seem to be of time travel where such changes occur? We may simply say that they are incoherent stories and dismiss them; they do not describe anything possible, no matter how compelling.

Here are two other possibilities. In these stories:

- The travel is not time travel. It is *pseudo-time* travel.
- These travels are time travel and travel between parallel worlds.

Pseudo-Time Travel

There are many cases in which there seems to be time travel, yet there is not actual time travel. These cases are where the ordinary existence in time is enough to explain what happens. We have already encountered some examples.

These cases can still be strange or even fantastical; indeed, to even seem to be time travel, they must be odd in some way. However, the strange and fascinating aspects do not involve fascinating and strange time. Events occur in a linear and shared fashion for all participants; there is just public time; there is no backwards travel, skipped time, no discrepancies in simultaneity or order.

Accounts of ordinary existence in time can be *presented as* accounts of time travel. However, if we are to treat them as philosophically serious accounts of time travel, then *presentation as* is not enough. Being said to be a kind of account does not make it such an account, even if its author is otherwise convinced. A so-called love story can be an oppressive tale of gender politics. Propaganda tales can often be presented as innocent accounts of everyday life and beliefs. Similarly, though less seriously, so-called time travel stories can be something else.

The consequence of some activity X presented as a kind of time travel *not being* time travel is that what is allowed or constrained by X tells us nothing about what is allowed or constrained by time travel. Notably, it does not mean that such things as changing the past are possible.

Parallel Universe Travel

In William Gibson's *The Peripheral*, people hundreds of years from now seem to discover, through quantum computers, a visual and auditory link to their past.[6] These people can alter the events in this world they link to. They use hindsight of their past to manipulate events, reaping benefits in their own time and altering those events. However, changes in this apparent past do not alter these future people's own past. When a protagonist kills their ancestor, no grandfather paradoxes arise. They do not cease to exist or fade away. Despite significantly manipulating events, only the knowledge someone gains from interacting with this other world leads to changing events in their own time.

How is this possible? Is there some sort of complex metaphysics of time involved? No, *these are parallel universes*.[7] Each universe resembles other universes, but the way those other universes are at different times. When they interact with the other world, the people hundreds of years from now do not interact with their past. They interact with a parallel universe that resembles their past.

This is a story about interaction between different parallel worlds. It is not time travel. However, it resembles time travel. It also offers many of the benefits of time travel, allowing one to learn about the past and, indirectly, to prevent bad things happening that happened in one's own past. For example, as future people, we might intercede in a genocide we know occurs in our own past or intro- duce modern solutions to prevent global warming in this other universe's 1960s. However, these bad things are not our own past bad things. They are bad things that resemble our own past bad things. Our own past bad things still happened.

As Abbruzzese states, a traveller to a parallel universe in which events are identical to events in the traveller's universe in 1001 "is not traveling *back* to 1001 at all, as the traditional conception of time travel would seem to require":

> [H]e is traveling to a similar year in another universe, a year that the defender of the multiverse presumes to be exactly like our own. But exact similarity, as the metaphysicians tell us, falls short of identity.
>
> (Abbruzzese 2001, 38)

Abbruzzese refers here to the commonly rejected part of Leibniz' law known as the identity of indiscernibility, the view that there cannot be two entities iden- tical in all their properties.[8] However, as Abbruzzese notes, even if the identity of indiscernibles were true, it would not help. By definition, this other universe's time belongs to another universe. By definition, that time is numerically different to our own time. It is not the identical time.

Causation between Parallel Worlds

Pseudo-travel can explain how travel into the past gives rise to multiple timelines. We can mix parallel universe travel with time travel that involves no changing of the past. We travel through time in our own universe and travel through time in the other universe.

Let a time T in our universe be T_a and let time T in the other universe be T_b. Then, we have the following account:

1. We time travel from 2020_a back to a time in our world, e.g., to 1020_a.
2. From 1020_a, we travel across to a similar time in the other universe, e.g., 1020_b.

In this way, we do travel into our own past—to 1020_a. Furthermore, we can also seem to change that past:

3. In 1020_b, we cause an event B that does not happen in 1020_a.

Then, we time travel again—but we do so in the *other* universe.

4. We time travel from 1020_b forward to a time in the other universe, e.g., to 2020_b.

In this other universe, we can seem to live in a world where our past is changed:

5. In 2020_b, we have a history that includes an event B that does not happen in our universe's 1020_a.

We can use this to make sense of time travel in which "the past" is changed, but there is no paradox. Take Bradbury's "The Sound of Thunder". In this short story, a time-travelling character lives in a time with a democracy. He travels to the prehistoric past to hunt dinosaurs, and steps on a past butterfly. The story then implies that this simple action changes the original time in significant ways: the world the characters return to is no longer a democracy but a fascist state.

Adapting 1–5 above, we explain this as follows. Call the original universe U_D (for democracy) and the parallel universe U_F (for fascism). Keep the original date as 2020 and the travelling date P (for *prehistory*). For both 2020 and P, add the subscript $_D$ or $_F$ depending on which universe it is in:

1. In U_D, we time travel from 2020_D back to prehistory, P_D.
2. From U_D, we travel between universes to a counterpart prehistoric time in the other universe U_F, P_F.
3. At P_F, we cause an event B—stepping on a butterfly. B does not happen at P_D.
4. From U_F, we time travel from P_F forward to U_F's counterpart of our original time, e.g., 2020_F.

Furthermore, in this other universe, we even seem to live in a world where our past is changed:

5. In 2020_F, the history includes an event B—stepping on a butterfly—at P_F that does not happen at P_D.

Having "changed the past", the travellers end up in the other universe. But they do not change the past. They move between pasts of different universes.

Back to the Future Time Travel

Yet, what of those stories where characters in the original time are aware of the changes? For example, in Bradbury's short story, some characters in the present time are aware that "the past" has changed—with one murderously angry at the one who made the change (Bradbury 1953).

A more complicated example is Marty's experience in *Back to The Future*. Marty, while in "the past" (1955), watches a photo of his family and even his own hand disappear. These disappearances are caused by his changes of the past, changes that mean he and his family never existed. How can this be?

Here is one way to explain this; this does not raise a paradox, but more than time travel is involved. We use parallel universes, U_a and U_b. Update it for the 2020s. The origin time is 2020, with that time in our universe referred to as 2020_a and the time in the other universe as 2020_b. The time we travel back to in our original universe is 1980_a and the counterpart time in the other universe is 1980_b:

1. In U_a, we time travel from 2020_a back to 1980_a.
2. From U_a, we then travel across to the same time in U_b, the other universe, i.e., 1980_b.
3. In U_b, in 1980_b, we cause an event B—ensuring our parents never meet—that does not happen in 1980_a.
4. In U_b, we time travel from 1980_b forward to 2020_b.
5. 2020_b has a history that includes an event B—ensuring our parents never meet—at 1980_b that does not happen in 1980_a.

For the *Back to the Future* scenario, one more thing is required:

6. Events in one universe, e.g., U_b, can cause events in the other universe, e.g., U_a.

For example, in the original 2020_a, people and things are altered by events in the other universe, e.g., events in 2020_b. They are altered in such a way that they end up resembling the events of the other universe at that time. Our parents in 2020_a, who until we travelled remember us, and remember years with each other, are altered by events in U_b, a place where they never met or had children. Their memories fade, their clothes, jobs, diets, locations—all these change for them, so that they come to resemble their counterparts in U_b.

What becomes of the original universe U_a, and its set of events? Everything until the moment we travelled is the same; there is no paradox. But people who live in the U_a do change after we travel. They remember—quickly or gradually—what appear to be consequences of events from the other universe U_b.

Unlike the grandfather paradox, there is no obvious metaphysical problem with U_a in 2020_a being altered by events in 1980_b. It must only be that the change happens after the traveller leaves. Yet, nothing in this account demands otherwise.

Until the traveller leaves, U_a is a universe unaltered by the time traveller's actions. The traveller does not change things in 1980_a (or 1980_b, for that matter). Nor do they change things in the time between 1980_a and 2020_a (or, indeed, the time between 1980_b and 2020_b). The changes to times later than the traveller's original time do not come through the years of the original universe (U_a). They come *from* the other universe (U_b).

One may wonder how such changes transmit between the different universes. Yet, how that happens is not a matter of time travel, nor is it a matter of its effects. It is a matter of travel between universes and its effects. If it has its own contradictions, they are contradictions in travel between parallel universes, not in time travel. And this combination of travel between parallel universes and times allows something resembling the act of changing the past.

Satisfying Regret

But does this time and universe travel satisfy the desire to change the past? For example, if I regret my past actions, can I redo them by time travelling through multiple parallel universes? Even in these cases, strictly speaking, this is not a case in which what we did was never done. The impulse from regret is not satisfied by this. Even if people change in 2020_a after we left and changed things in 1980_b, what happened in 1980_a remains unchanged. People are just aware of, or only believe in, or are additionally affected by events in 1980_b.

Yet, there is a way to satisfy the desire in regret. We can undo some consequences of what we did. Say that Oona seriously injures her friend Joe in 1980_a. From then up to 2020_a, Joe has a severely restricted life, his hopes and dreams altered beyond repair. Oona travels back to 1980_b. She prevents the injury to Joe in 1980_b. As a result, events in U_b change U_a. In U_a, Joe's injuries are removed, replaced by an uninjured Joe with no memory of Oona's injury.

The ethics of this are, perhaps, awkward. Joe in U_a falsely remembers having the same life as his counterpart in U_b. However, he is also in a better situation than he was previously. This may be enough to justify the time travel. Even if he discovers his life is changed by Oona's travel, and why, he is in a better situation. If that is morally justified, then time travel can undo some wrongs—at least, so long as there are parallel worlds.

Study Questions

1. Like Fry from *Futurama*, or Rip Van Winkle, you fall asleep and wake up many years later. Have you travelled through time? What if you just woke up the next day?
2. You forgot your keys when you left the house this morning. Now, you are locked out. There is no one else to call who has keys or to let you in. Luckily, you have a time machine. Can you travel back in time and remind yourself to bring your keys?

3. If neither the past nor the future exists, how can you travel there? Does that mean time travel is impossible in a world in which presentism is true?
4. Is there a world out there where Marty's actual girlfriend, actual parents, and actual bully will never know what happened to him, always thinking he disappeared when his scientist friend died in an experiment?
5. You have a job that involves a time machine. You have been instructed to travel back in time and deliver Shakespeare the entirety of his plays before he has written them. You succeed. Is Shakespeare the author of those plays?
6. How would you convince someone you had time-travelled? Try this exercise with someone else. The other person's job is to be as suspicious as possible about your claim. You have two different scenarios:
    a) You *cannot* bring them on the machine you believe to be a time machine.
    b) You can bring them in the machine you believe to be a time machine.

Notes

1 See Chapters 2 and 5.
2 I can only think of one exception: Stephen King's 1990 novella, *The Langoliers*. In it, people travel back to yesterday and discover a world empty of people (it does not make much sense; it is not King's best).
3 See Chapter 1.
4 As can be seen in the quote, Lewis calls it external time. However, he does not explain why he does so nor is it obvious why one would. The opposite of "personal" is "public" so I use that phrase here.
5 One kind of time travel story is where guardians of time prevent travellers from doing things such as changing the future or stealing technology. Examples include the film *Timecop*, and the shows *Star Trek*, *Continuum*, *The Ministry of Time*, and *Timeless*. I am interested in what one can do, and what this means for the possibility of time travel. If people must intervene to stop others doing something, then I assume it is because it can otherwise be done. Unless, perhaps, the time police are fools, believing what is not true.
6 In fact, it is past to them, but future to my writing this.
7 Bourne and Caddick Bourne propose an analysis of time travel *stories* in fiction using possible worlds. I propose parallel worlds. How do these parallel universes relate to possible worlds in metaphysics?

    If such parallel worlds exist, then they are not merely possible worlds. It is assumed that possible worlds are causally closed with respect to one another. It is not possible to causally interact with merely possible worlds, that is, non-actual possible worlds.

    But there is no reason for parallel worlds to be similarly closed causally. As evident in Gibson 2015, denizens of different parallel worlds can communicate. In examples later in this chapter, we can travel back and forth between such worlds.

As such, I assume that, if the actual world can interact with these worlds, then these parallel worlds are part of that actual world. But, what, then of Bourne and Caddick Bourne's use of possible worlds? These authors are talking only about time travel in fiction, rather than something coherent or possible. Such stories, like Escher's staircases, need not make sense (see the Philosophy of Art chapter).

8 See Chapter 3.

Suggested Readings

For a recent monograph dedicated to the philosophy of time travel, see Effingham 2020. Otherwise, there are not many purely philosophical monographs dedicated to the subject (surprisingly, given its popularity). There are many *parts* of books, however: Le Poidevein 2003 is good on time travel generally. Dainton 2001 (and 2010) and Lockwood 2005 are excellent on the metaphysics and physics. Lowe 2003's section on time travel is good about the strangeness of causal loops.

Mellor 1998 contains an argument *against* time travel from a tenseless theorists—because, he argues, all time travel results in the grandfather paradox; his 1981 has a similar argument, although it is not as clear. Sider 2001 is useful for time travel and the identity of ordinary objects in time. Price 1997 argues that time travel is not mere fiction; there is actual time travel because there is backwards causation; Price argues such causation best explains various physical phenomena.

Finally, it is worth noting some texts beyond philosophy (but relevant to philosophy). Time travel is such a familiar trope that it can be difficult to examine one's intuitions about it (if there are any at all). As such, Gleick 2016 is interesting, despite not being about the philosophy of time. A popular history of time travel, it includes overviews of early debates about the concept; why and how some early commentators objected to it. Similarly, there are countless stories about time travel. Wells's original *The Time Machine* is a classic (and disturbing). There are many more stories. For a recent anthology of time travel stories, under different themes, see Van Der Meer and Van Der Meer 2013. Finally, for a discussion of time travel and fiction, see Bourne and Caddick 2012, and Bourne and Caddick Bourne 2016.

Bibliography

Abbruzzese, J. 2001. "On Using the Multiverse to Avoid the Paradoxes of Time Travel", *Analysis*, 61(1): 36–38.

Abell, C. 2010. "Cinema as a Representational Art", *British Journal of Aesthetics*, 50(3): 273–286. https://doi.org/10.1093/aesthj/ayq020

Adams, D. 1980. *The Restaurant at the End of the Universe*. London: Pan Books.

Allen, S. 2006. "A Space Oddity: Colin McGinn on Consciousness and Space", *Journal of Consciousness Studies*, 13(4): 61–82.

Alperson, P. 1980. "'Musical Time' and Music as an 'Art of Time'", *Journal of Aesthetics and Art Criticism*, 38(4): 407–417.

Anders, C.J. 2012. "Why Time Travel Stories Should Be Messy", https://io9.gizmodo.com/why-time-travel-stories-should-be-messy-5945991. Retrieved 1 October 2020.

Arstila, V. 2005. *The Paradox of Colors*. Turku: University of Turku.

Arstila, V. 2019. "Time Markers and Temporal Illusions", in Arstila, V., Bardon, A., Power, S. and Vatakis, A. (eds) *The Illusions of Time: Philosophical and Psychological Essays on Timing and Time Perception*. Basingstoke: Palgrave.

Augustine. 1961. *Confessions*, trans. Pinecoffin, R.S. St Ives: Penguin.

Austin, J.L. 1979. *Philosophical Papers*, ed. Ormson, J.O. and Warnock, G.J. Oxford: Oxford University Press.

Aveni, A. 1989. *Empires of Time: Clocks, Calendars, and Cultures*. New York: Basic Books.

Baker, K. 1997. *In the Garden of Iden*. New York: Tor Books.

Balashov, Y. 2005. "Special Relativity, Coexistence and Temporal Parts: A Reply to Gilmore", *Philosophical Studies*, 124(1): 1–40.

Balashov, Y. 2007. "Defining 'exdurance'", *Philosophical Studies*, 133: 143–149.

Barbour, J. 1999. *The End of Time: The Next Revolution in Our Understanding of the Universe*. Oxford: Oxford University Press.

Bardon, A. (ed.) 2012. *A Future for the Philosophy of Time*. Oxford: Routledge.

Bardon, A. 2013. *A Brief History of the Philosophy of Time*. Oxford: Oxford University Press.

Berger, J. 2019. *What is Time?* Kendal: Notting Hill Editions.

Bergson, H. 1889. *Time and Free Will: An Essay on The Immediate Data of Consciousness*. London: George Allen & Unwin, trans. Podgson, F.L.

Bergson, H. 1999. *Duration and Simultaneity*. Manchester: Clinamen Press.

Bigelow, J. 1996. "Presentism and Properties", Noûs, 30(10): 35–52.

Blackmore, S. 2003. *Consciousness: An Introduction*. Abingdon: Hodder & Stoughton.

Blumson, B. 2014. *Resemblance and Representation*. Cambridge: Open Book Publishers.

Boroditsky, L. 2000. "Metaphoric Structuring: Understanding Time through Spatial Metaphors", *Cognition,* 75: 1–28.

Bortolloti, L. 2014. *Irrationality.* Cambridge: Polity Press.

Bortolotti, L. and Mameli, M. 2012. "Self-Deception, Delusion and the Boundaries of Folk Psychology", *Humanamente,* 20: 203–221.

Bosch, R. 1999. "Integer Programming and Conway's Game of Life", *SIAM Review,* 41(3): 594–604.

Bourne, C. and Caddick Bourne, E. 2016. *Time in Fiction.* Oxford: Oxford University Press.

Bourne, C. and Caddick, E. 2012. "On What We May Infer from Scientific and Artistic Representations of Time", *Writing Visual Culture,* 5. https://uhra.herts.ac.uk/handle/2299/9506. Retrieved 1 October 2020.

Bourne, C. 2006. *A Future for Presentism.* Oxford: Oxford University Press.

Bowen, A.J. 2013. "Dissolving an Epistemological Puzzle of Time Perception", *Synthese,* 190(17): 3797–3817.

Bradbury, R. 1953. "The Sound of Thunder", in *The Golden Apples of the Sun.* London: Harper Collins.

Briggs, R. and Forbes, G.A. 2017. "The Growing-Block: Just One Thing After Another?", *Philosophical Studies,* 174(3): 927–943.

Broad, C.D. 1923. *Scientific Thought.* London: Trubner.

Broad, C.D. 1938. *An Examination of McTaggart's Philosophy,* Vol. 2. Cambridge: Cambridge University Press.

Brooks, D.H.M. 1994. *The Unity of the Mind.* Basingstoke: Macmillan.

Buss, D. 2011. *The Dangerous Passion.* New York: Free Press.

Calabi, C. 2012. "Introduction", *Perceptual Illusions.* Basingstoke: Palgrave.

Callender, C. 1998. "The View from No-when: Review Article", *British Journal Philosophy of Science,* 49: 135–159.

Callender, C. (ed.) 2011. *The Oxford Handbook of the Philosophy of Time.* Oxford: Oxford University Press.

Cameron, R.P. 2015. *The Moving Spotlight: An Essay on Time and Ontology.* Oxford: Oxford University Press.

Canales, J. 2016. *The Physicist and the Philosopher: Einstein, Bergson, and the Debate that Changed Our Understanding of Time.* Princeton, NJ: Princeton University Press.

Capek, M. 1991. *The New Aspects of Time: Its Continuity and Novelties.* Dordrecht: Kluwer.

Carnap, R. 1932. "The Elimination of Metaphysics through Logical Analysis of Language", *Erkenntnis,* 2 (trans, Pap, A.).

Carroll, N. 2012. *Philosophy of Art: A Contemporary Introduction.* Oxford: Routledge.

Christensen, F. 1974. "McTaggart's Paradox and the Nature of Time", *Philosophical Quarterly,* 24(97): 289–299.

Churchland, P. 1987. "Epistemology in the Age of Neuroscience." *Journal of Philosophy,* 84(10): 544–553

Craig, E. 1998. "Metaphysics", *Routledge Encyclopedia of Philosophy.* www.rep.routledge.com/articles/overview/metaphysics/v-1/bibliography/metaphysics-bib. Retrieved 1 October 2020.

Craig, W.L. 2001. "Wishing It Were Now Some Other Time", *Philosophy and Phenomenological Research,* 62(1): 159–166.

Crane, T. 2011. "The Problem of Perception", *The Stanford Encyclopedia of Philosophy (Spring 2011 Edition),* ed. Zalta, E.N., http://plato.stanford.edu/archives/spr2011/entries/perception-problem/.

Craven, W. (director) 1985. "A Little Peace and Quiet", *The Twilight Zone.*

Crisp, T. 2005. "Presentism and 'Cross-Time' Relations", American Philosophical Quarterly, 42(1): 5–14.

Currie, G. 1995. *Image and Mind.* Cambridge: Cambridge University Press

Dainton, B. 2000. *The Stream of Consciousness: Unity and Continuity in Conscious Experience.* Oxford: Routledge

Dainton, B. 2001. *Time and Space.* Chesham: Acumen.

Dainton, B. 2010. *Time and Space*, 2nd edition. Chesham: Acumen.

Davidson, D. 2001. "The Logical Form of Action Sentences", in *Essays on Actions and Events.* Oxford: Oxford University Press.

De Warren, N. 2009. *Husserl and the Problem of Time: Subjectivity in Transcendental Phenomenology.* Cambridge: Cambridge University Press.

Deleuze, G. 1989. *Cinema II: The Time-Image.* London: Bloomsbury Academic.

Deng, N. 2013. "Our Experience of Passage on the B-Theory", *Erkenntnis*, 78(4): 715–725.

Deng, N. 2016. "Response to Fear of Death and the Symmetry Argument", *Manuscrito*, 39(4). http://dx.doi.org/10.1590/0100–6045.2016.v39n4.gy. Retrieved 10 May 2020.

Dennett, D. 1991. *Consciousness Explained.* St. Ives: Penguin.

Dennett, D. 2009. "The Part of Cognitive Science that Is Philosophy", *Topics in Cognitive Science*, 1: 231–236.

Dennett, D. and Kinsbourne, M. 1992. "Time and the Observer: The Where and When of Consciousness in the Brain", *EBehavioral and Brain Sciences*, 15: 183–247

Diekemper, J. 2014. "The Existence of the Past", *Synthese*, 191(6): 1085–1104.

Dolev, Y. 2007. *Time and Realism: Metaphysical and Antimetaphysical Perspectives.* London: MIT Press.

Dorato, M. 2006. "The Irrelevance of the Presentist/Eternalist Debate for the Ontology of Minkowski Spacetime", in Dieks, D. (ed.) *The Ontology of Spacetime.* Dordrecht: Elsevier.

Dyke, H. and Bardon, A. (eds) *A Companion to the Philosophy of Time.* Oxford: Wiley & Sons.

Earman, J. 1967. "On Going Backward in Time", *Philosophy of Science*, 34(3): 211–222.

Earman, J. 1974. "An Attempt to Add a Little Direction to the Problem of the Direction of Time", *Philosophy of Science*, 41(1): 15–47.

Effingham, N. 2020. *Time Travel: Probability and Impossibility.* Oxford: Oxford University Press.

Einstein, A. 1905. "On the Electrodynamics of Moving Bodies", *Annalen der Physik*, 322(10): 891–921.

Elliott, M., Zhuanghua, S., and Kelly, S.D. 2006. "A Moment to Reflect upon Perceptual Synchrony", *Journal of Cognitive Science*, 18(10): 1663–1665.

Emmett, D. 1992. *The Passage of Nature.* London: Macmillan.

Escher, M.C. 1953. *Relativity.* Lithograph.

Falk, A. 2003. "Time Plus the Whoosh and Whiz", in Jokic, A. and Smith, Q. (eds) *Time, Tense, and Reference.* Cambridge, MA: MIT Press.

Falk, D. 2016. "A Debate over the Physics of Time". *Quanta Magazine.* www.quantamagazine.org/a-debate-over-the-physics-of-time-20160719/. Retrieved 31 October 2020.

Fernandez, M.P. and Fernandez, P.C. 1996. "Precision Timekeepers of Tokugawa Japan and the Evolution of the Japanese Domestic Clock", *Technology and Culture*, 37(2): 221–248.

Feynman, R. 1949. "The Theory of Positrons", *Physical Review*, 76(6): 49–59.

Forbes, G. 1991. "Time, Events, Modality", in Le Poidevin, R. and MacBeath, M. (eds) *The Philosophy of Time*. Oxford: Oxford University Press,.

Forbes, G.A. 2016. "The Growing Block's Past Problems", *Philosophical Studies*, 173(3): 699–709.

Forbes, G.A. 2020. Personal correspondence.

Freeman, A (ed.) 2006. *Consciousness and its Place in Nature: Does Physicalism Entail Panpsychism?* Exeter: Imprint Academic.

Frisch, M. 2013. "Time and Causation", in Dyke, H. and Bardon, A. (eds) *A Companion to the Philosophy of Time*. Oxford: Wiley & Sons.

Galison, P. 2000. "Einstein's Clocks: The Place of Time", *Chicago Inquiry*, 26(2): 355–389.

Galison, P. 2003. *Einstein's Clocks, Poincare's Maps: Empires of Time*. London: Norton.

Gallagher, S. 2003. "Sync-Ing in the Stream of Experience: Time-Consciousness in Broad, Husserl, and Dainton", *Psyche*, 9(10), http://journalpsyche.org/files/0xaabb.pdf.

Gallagher, S. 2012. *Phenomenology*. Houndmills: Palgrave.

Geach, P. 1966/1998. "Some Problems of Time", in Van Inwagen, P. and Zimmerman, D. (eds) *Metaphysics: The Big Questions*. Oxford: Blackwell, .192–203.

Geach, P.T. 1979. *Truth, Love and Immortality*. London: Hutchinson.

Gendler, T.S. 2008. "Alief and Belief", *Journal of Philosophy*, 105(10): 634–663.

Gibson, W. 2015. *The Peripheral*. London: Penguin.

Gleick, J. 2016. *Time Travel*. London: Harper Collins.

Goldsworthy, A. 2008. *Time*. London: Thames & Hudson.

Goldsworthy, A. 2014. "Interview with Jessica Harris". *From Scratch,* podcast, www.fromscratchradio.org/show/andy-goldsworthy. Retrieved 10 October 2020.

Goldsworthy, A. 2015. *Ephemeral Works: 2004–2014*. New York: Harry N. Abrams.

Golosz, J. 2018. "Presentism and the Notion of Existence", *Axiomathes*, 28: 395–417.

Gombrich, E.R. 1964. "Moment and Movement in Art", *Journal of the Warburg and Courtauld Institute*, 27: 293–306.

Graham, J.W. 1956. "A Negative Note on Bergson and Virginia Woolf", *Essays in Criticism*, 7(1): 70–74.

Green, P. and Sullivan, M. 2015. "Time Bias", *Ethics*, 125(4): 947–970.

Gribbin, J. 1999. *In Search of the Edge of Time: Black Holes, White Holes, Wormholes*. London: Penguin.

Grush, R. 2005. "Brain Time and Phenomenological Time", in Brook, A and Akins, K. (eds) *Cognition and the Brain: The Philosophy and Neuroscience Movement*. Cambridge: Cambridge University Press. , 160–207.

Hare, C. 2007. "Self-Bias, Time-Bias, and the Metaphysics of Self and Time", *Journal of Philosophy*, 104(7): 350–373.

Hare, C. 2013. "Time: The Emotional Asymmetry", in Dyke, H. and Bardon, A. (eds) *A Companion to the Philosophy of Time*. Oxford: Blackwell, 507–520.

Haslanger, S. 2003. "Persistence through Time", in Loux, M. and Zimmerman, D.W. (eds) *The Oxford Handbook of Metaphysics*. Oxford: Oxford University Press, 315–354.

Hasle, P., Blackburn, R., and Øhrstrøm, P. 2019. *Logic and Philosophy of Time: Further Themes from Prior*, Vol. 2. Aalborg: University of Aalborg Press.

Hasle, P., Blackburn, R., and Øhrstrøm, P. 2017. *Logic and Philosophy of Time: Themes from Prior,* Vol. 1. Aalborg: University of Aalborg Press.

Hawley, K. 2004. *How Things Persist*. Oxford: Oxford University Press.

Hawley, K. 2006. "Science as a Guide to Metaphysics?", *Synthese*, 149(3): 451–470. www.jstor.org/stable/20118745

Hawley, K. 2015. "David Lewis on Persistence", in Loewer, B. and Schaffer, J. (eds) *A Companion to David Lewis*. Chichester: Wiley, 237–249.

Healey, R. 2002. "Can Physics Coherently Deny the Reality of Time?", in Callender, C. (ed.) *Time, Reality, and Experience*. Cambridge: Cambridge University Press.

Heil, J. 2004. *Philosophy of Mind: A Contemporary Introduction*. Oxford: Routledge.

Herek, S. (director) 1989. Bill & Ted's Excellent Adventure.

Hinchliff, M. 1996. "The Puzzle of Change", *Philosophical Perspectives*, 10, *Metaphysics*, 119–136.

Hoffman, D. 2013. "Public Objects and Private Qualia: The Scope and Limits of Psychophysics", in Albertazzi, L. (ed.) *Handbook of Experimental Phenomenology: Visual Perception of Shape, Space and Appearance*. Oxford: Wiley-Blackwell, 71–91.

Holland, T. (director) 1994. *The Langoliers*.

Holmes, E.C. 1955. "Kantian Space and Time Reevaluated", *Philosophy and Phenomenological Research*, 16(2): 240–244.

Houts, R. 1980. "Some Implications of the Time-Lag Argument", *Philosophy and Phenomenological Research*, 41: 150–157.

Hume, D. 1776/1993. *An Enquiry into Human Understanding*. Indianapolis: Hackett Publishing Co.

Husserl, E. 1919/1991. *The Phenomenology of Internal Time-Consciousness*, trans. Brough, J.B. Dordrecht: Kluwer.

Ingthorsson, R.D. 2016. *McTaggart's Paradox* (Routledge Studies in Contemporary Philosophy Book 84). Oxford: Routledge.

James, W. 1918. *The Principles of Psychology*. New York: Dover.

Jammer, M. 2006. *Concepts of Simultaneity: From Antiquity to Einstein and Beyond*. Baltimore, MD: Johns Hopkins University Press.

Jokic, A. and Smith, Q. (eds) 2003. *Time, Tense, and Reference*. London: Bradford Books.

July, M. (director) 2005. *Me and You and Everyone We Know*.

Kant, I. 1787/1996. *Critique of Pure Reason*, trans. Pluhar, W.S. Indianapolis: Hackett Publishing Co.

Kant, I. 1787/1987. *Critique of Judgment*, trans. Pluhar, W.S. Indianapolis: Hackett Publishing Co.

Kelly, S. D. 2005. "The Puzzle of Temporal Experience", in Brook, A and Akins, K. (eds) *Cognition and the Brain: The Philosophy and Neuroscience Movement*. Cambridge: Cambridge University Press, 208–238.

Kim, J. 2000. *Mind in a Physical World*. Cambridge, MA: MIT Press.

Koffka, K. 1935. *Principles of Gestalt Psychology*. London: Lund Humphries.

Köhler, W. 1929/1971. "An Old Pseudoproblem", trans. Goldmeyer, E. www.gestalttheory.net/archive/kohl1.html. Retrieved 26 May 2020.

Kölers P.A. 1972. *Aspects of Motion Perception*. Oxford: Pergamon.

Korman, D.Z. 2020. "Ordinary Objects". The Stanford Encyclopedia of Philosophy (Fall 2020 Edition), ed. Zalta, E.N. https://plato.stanford.edu/archives/fall2020/entries/ordinary-objects/.

Kragh, H. 2007. *Conceptions of Cosmos from Myths to the Accelerating Universe: A History of Cosmology*. Oxford: Oxford University Press.

Kroes, P. 1984. "Objective versus Minddependent Theories of Time Flow", *Synthese*, 61(3): 423–446.

Lakoff, G. and Johnson, M. 1980. *Metaphors We Live By*. Chicago, IL: University of Chicago

Lange, M. 2002. *An Introduction to the Philosophy of Physics*. Oxford: Blackwell Publishing.

Langton, R. and Lewis, D. 1998. "Defining Intrinsic", *Philosophy and Phenomenological Research*, 58(2): 333–345.

Lazarovici, D. and Reichert, P. 2015. 'Typicality, Irreversibility and the Status of Macroscopic Laws', *Erkenntnis*, 80: 689–716.

Le Poidevin, R. 1998. "Continuants", in *The Routledge Encyclopedia of Philosophy*. Abingdon: Routledge. 10.4324/9780415249126-N009–1. Retrieved 5 May 2019.

Le Poidevin, R. 2003. *Travels in Four Dimensions*. London: Oxford University Press.

Le Poidevin, R. 2004. 'A Puzzle Concerning Time Perception', *Synthese*, 142(1): 109–142.

Le Poidevin, R. 2007. *Images of Time: An Essay on Temporal Representation*. Oxford: Oxford University Press.

Le Poidevin, R. and MacBeath, M. (eds) 1991. *The Philosophy of Time*. Oxford: Oxford University Press,

Leininger, L. 2015. "Presentism and the Myth of Passage", *Australasian Journal of Philosophy*, 93(4): 724–739.

Lessing, G.F. 1898/2005. Laocoon: An Essay *u*pon the Limits of Painting and Poetry, trans. Frothingham, E. (1898). New York: Dover.

Lewis, C.S. 2009. *The Lion, the Witch, and the Wardrobe*. London: Harper Collins.

Lewis, D. 1986. *On the Plurality of Worlds*. Oxford: Blackwell.

Lewis, D. 1991. "The Paradoxes of Time Travel", in Le Poidevin, R. and MacBeath, M. (eds) *The Philosophy of Time*. Oxford: Oxford University Press, 134–146.

Lewis, D. 1998. "The Problem of Temporary Intrinsics: An Excerpt from On the Plurality of Worlds", in Van Inwagen, P. and Zimmerman, D. (eds) *Metaphysics: The Big Questions*. Oxford: Routledge, 204–206.

Libet, B. 2004. *Mind Time*. Cambridge, MA: Harvard University Press.

Libet, B., Freeman, A. and Sutherland, K. 1999. *The Volitional Brain: Towards a Neuroscience of Free Will*. Thorverton: Imprint Academic.

Lloyd, G. 1993. *Being in Time*. Oxford: Routledge.

Lockwood, M. 2005. *The Labyrinth of Time: Introducing the Universe*. Oxford: Oxford University Press.

Loizou, A. 1986. *The Reality of Time*. Aldershot: Gower.

Loux, M. 2002. *Metaphysics: A Contemporary Introduction*. Oxford: Routledge.

Lowe, E.J. 2003. *A Survey of Metaphysics*. Oxford: Oxford University Press.

Lucretius. 1910. *On the Nature of Things*, trans. Bailey, C. Oxford: Clarendon Press.

Macdonald, C. 2005. *Varieties of Things: Foundations of Contemporary Metaphysics*. Oxford: Wiley-Blackwell.

Maher, A. 1995. Artwork: "Nettle coat". http://alicemaher.com/works/nettle-coat. Retrieved 10 March 2020.

Maher, A. 2020. Personal correspondence (email).

Major, J. 2012. "Faster than Light Neutrinos? More Like Faulty Wiring". https://phys.org/news/2012-02-faster-neutrinos-faulty-wiring.html. Retrieved 10 January 2018.

Markosian, N. 2000. "What are Physical Objects?", *Philosophy and Phenomenological Research*, 61(2): 375–395.

Markosian, N. 2020. "Sideways Music", *Analysis*, 80(81): 51–59.

Maudlin, T. 2002. "Remarks on the Passing of Time", *Proceedings of the Aristotelian Society*, 102: 237–252.

McClain, J. 1985. "Time in the Visual Arts: Lessing and Modern Criticism", *Journal of Aesthetics and Art Criticism*, 44(1): 41–58.

McCloud, S. 2001. *Understanding Comics*. New York: William Morrow Paperbacks.

McTaggart, J.M.E. 1927. "The Unreality of Time", in Le Poidevin, R. and McBeath, M. (eds) *The Philosophy of Time*. Oxford: Oxford University Press, 23–34.

Mellor, D.H. 1981. *Real Time*. Oxford: Oxford University Press.

Mellor, D.H. 1991. 'Causation and the Direction of Time', *Erkenntnis*, 35(1): 191–203.

Mellor, D.H. 1998. *Real Time II*. Oxford: Oxford University Press.

Merleau-Ponty, M. 1962. *Phenomenology of Perception*. Oxford: Routledge.

Merricks, T. 1994. "Endurance and Indiscernibility", *Journal of Philosophy*, 91: 165–184.

Midgley, M. 2014. *Are You an Illusion?* Oxford: Routledge.

Miller, K. 2019. "Does it Really Seem as though Time Passes?", in Arstila, V., Bardon, A., Power, S.E. and Vatakis, A. (eds) *The Illusions of Time: Philosophical and Psychological Essays on Timing and Time Perception*. Basingstoke: Palgrave Macmillan, 17–33.

Mitchell, W.J.T. 1985. "The Politics of Genre: Space and Time in Lessing's Laocoon", *Representations*, 6: 98–115.

Montero, B. 1999. "The Body Problem", *Noûs*, 33(2): 183–200.

Moore, G.E. 1953. *Some Main Problems of Philosophy*. London: Allen & Unwin.

Mork and Mindy. 1981. (TV series.)

Mormann, F. and Koch, C. 2007. "Neural Correlates of Consciousness", *Scholarpedia*, 2: 1740. 10.4249/scholarpedia.174.

Morrison, G. and Yeowell, S. 1992. *Zenith: Phase IV*. London: Titan Books.

Morrison, R.D. 1987. "Einstein on Kant, Religion, Science, and Methodological Unity", in Ryan, D.P. (ed.) *Einstein and the Humanities*. New York: Greenwood Press, 47–58..

Neurath, O. 1931. "Physicalism: The Philosophy of the Viennese Circle", *The Monist*, 41: 618–623.

Newton, I. 1726/1972. *Philosophiae Naturalis Principia Mathematica*, ed. Koyré, A., Bernard Cohen, I., and Whitman, A. Cambridge, MA: Harvard University Press.

Newton-Smith W.H. 1980. *The Structure of Time*. Oxford: Routledge and Kegan Paul.

Noë, A. 2006. "Experience of the World in Time", *Analysis*, 66(1): 26–31.

Nolan, C. (director) 2014. *Interstellar.*

North, J. 2002. "What Is the Problem about the Time-Asymmetry of Thermodynamics? A Reply to Price", *British Journal of the Philosophy of Science*, 53(1): 121–136.

Oaklander, L.N. 2012. "A-, B and R-Theories of Time: A Debate", in Bardon, A. (ed.) *The Future of the Philosophy of Time*. Oxford: Routledge.

Oaklander, L.N. 2015. "Temporal Phenomena, Ontology and the R-Theory", *Metaphysica*, 16(2): 253–269.

Oaklander, L.N. 2020. *C.D. Broad's Philosophy of Time*. Oxford: Routledge.

Øhrstrøm, P. and Hasle, P. 1995. *Temporal Logic: From Ancient Ideas to Artificial Intelligence* (Studies in Linguistics and Philosophy 57). Dordrecht: Springer.

Parfit, D. 1984. *Reasons and Persons*. Oxford: Oxford University Press.

Paton, H.J. 1936. *Kant's Metaphysics of Experience*, Vol. 1. London: Allen & Unwin.

Paul, L. 2010. "Temporal Experience", *Journal of Philosophy*, 107(7): 333–359.

Penrose, L.S. and Penrose, R. 1958. "Impossible Objects: A Special Type of Visual Illusion", *British Journal of Psychology*, 49(1): 31–33. doi:10.1111/j.2044–8295.1958. tb00634.x

Persson, I. 2005. *The Retreat from Reason*. Oxford: Oxford University Press.

Peterson, 2016. "The Grounding Problem of Eternalism", *Philosophical Studies*, 173(7): 1819–1852.

Pohl, F. 1981. "The Tunnel Under the World", in Amis, K. (ed.) *The Golden Age of Science Fiction*. London: Hutchinson.

Polák, M. and Marvan, T. 2018. "Neural Correlates of Consciousness Meet the Theory of Identity", *Frontiers in Psychology*, 9: 12–69.

Portas, C., Maquet, P., Rees, G., Blakemore, S., and Frith, C. 2004. "The Neural Correlates of Consciousness", in Frackowiak, R.S.J., Friston, K.J., Frith, C.D., Dolan, R.J., Price, C.J., Zeki, S., Ashburner, J.T., and Penny, W.D. (eds) *Human Brain Function*. Amsterdam: Elsevier, 269–301.

Poussin, N. (artist). 1636. A Dance to the Music of Time. The Wallace Collection.

Power, S.E. 2010. "Complex Experience, Relativity and Abandoning Simultaneity", *Journal of Consciousness Studies*, 17(3–4): 231–256.

Power, S.E. 2012. "The Metaphysics of the 'Specious' Present", *Erkenntnis*, 77: 121–132. https://doi.org/10.1007/s10670-011-9287-x.

Power, S.E. 2013. "Perceiving External Things and the Time-Lag Argument", *European Journal of Philosophy,* 21(1): 94–117.

Power, S.E. 2015. "Perceiving Multiple Locations in Time: A Phenomenological Defence of Tenseless Theory", *Topoi*, 34: 249–265.

Power, S.E. 2016. "Relative and Absolute Temporal Presence", in Mölder, B., Arstila, V., and Øhrstrøm, P. (eds) *Philosophy and Psychology of Time* (Studies in Brain and Mind 9). London: Springer.

Power, S.E. 2018. *Philosophy of Time and Perceptual Experience*. Oxford: Routledge.

Price, H. 1997. *Time's Arrow and Archimedes Point: New Directions for the Physics of Time*. Oxford: Oxford University Press.

Price, H. 2002. "Boltzmann's Time Bomb", *British Journal for the Philosophy of Science*, 53(1): 83–119.

Price, H. 2011. "The Flow of Time", in Callender, C. (ed.) *The Oxford Handbook of the Philosophy of Time*. Oxford: Oxford University Press, 276–311.

Prior, A.N. 1959. "Thank Goodness that's over", *Philosophy*, 34(128): 12–17.

Prior, A.N. 1967. *Past, Present, and Future*. Oxford: Clarendon Press.

Prior, A.N. 1991. "Changes in Events and Changes in Things", in Le Poidevin, R. and McBeath, M. (eds) *Philosophy of Time*. Oxford: Oxford University Press.

Prior, A.N. 1998a. "Some Free Thinking about Time", in Van Inwagen, P. and Zimmerman, D. (eds) *Metaphysics: The Big Questions*. Oxford: Blackwell, 104–107.

Prior, A.N. 1998b. "The Notion of the Present", in Van Inwagen, P. and Zimmerman, D. (eds) *Metaphysics: The Big Questions*. Oxford: Blackwell, 80–81.

Pritchard, D. 2017. *Epistemology*. London: Palgrave.

Prosser, S. 2012. "Why Does Time Seem to Pass?", *Philosophy and Phenomenological Research*, 85(1): 92–116.

Prosser, S. 2013. "Passage and Perception", *Noûs*, 47(1): 69–84.

Prosser, S. 2016. *Experiencing Time*. Oxford: Oxford University Press.

Putnam, H. 1967. "Time and Physical Geometry", Journal of Philosophy, 64: 240–247.

Ray, C. 1991. *Time, Space, and Philosophy*. Oxford: Routledge.

Reichenbach, H. 1928/1958. *The Philosophy of Space and Time*. New York: Dover, English translation.

Reichenbach, H. 1956. *The Direction of Time*. Los Angeles: University of California Press.

Reynolds, R.I. 1988. "A Psychological Definition of Illusion", *Philosophical Psychology*, 1(2): 217–223.

Roache, R. 1999. "Mellor and Dennett on the Perception of Temporal Order", *Philosophical Quarterly*, 49(195): 238–251.

Robinson, H. 2017. "Dualism", in *The Stanford Encyclopedia of Philosophy (Fall 2017 Edition)*, ed. Edward N. Zalta, <https://plato.stanford.edu/archives/fall2017/entries/dualism/>.

Rosen, G. and Dorr, C. 2002. "Composition as a Fiction", in Hawthorne, J. (ed.) *The Blackwell Guide to Metaphysics*. Chichester: Wiley, 151–174..

Sagan, C. 1985. *Contact*. New York: Simon & Schuster.

Sartre, J.-P. 1947. *Situations I*. Paris: Gallimard.

Sauvage, M. 1958. "Notes on the Superposition of Temporal Modes in Works of Art", in *Reflections on Art*. Baltimore, MD: Johns Hopkins University Press, 161–173.

Savitt, S. 1996. "The Direction of Time", *British Journal of Philosophy of Science*, 47: 347–370.

Schaffer, J. 2009. "Spacetime the One Substance", *Philosophical Studies*, 145: 131–148.

Schlesinger, R. 1980. *Aspects of Time*. Indianapolis: Hackett.

Schurger, A., Sitt, J.D., and Dehaene, S. 2012. "An Accumulator Model for Spontaneous Neural Activity Prior to Self-Initiated Movement", *PNAS*, 109(42): E2904–E2913.

Scott, C. and Tucci, S. (director) 1999. *Big Night*.

Sextus Empiricus. 2000. *Outlines of Scepticism*, ed. Annas, J. and Barnes, J. Cambridge: Cambridge University Press.

Shoemaker, S. 1969. "Time without Change", *Journal of Philosophy*, 66: 363–381.

Sider, T. 1999. 'Presentism and Ontological Commitment', *Journal of Philosophy*, 96(7): 325–347.

Sider, T. 2001. *Four-Dimensionalism: An Ontology of Persistence and Time*. Oxford: Oxford University Press.

Singer, W. 2016. "The Ongoing Search for the Neuronal Correlate of Consciousness", in *Open Mind*, ed. Metzinger, T., and Windt, J.M. Cambridge, MA: MIT Press.

Skow, B. 2011. "Experience and the Passage of Time"", *Philosophical Perspectives*, 25, *Metaphysics*, 359–387.

Smart, J.J.C. 1963. *Philosophy and Scientific Realism*. Oxford: Routledge.

Smolin, L. 2014. *Time Reborn: From the Crisis in Physics to the Future of the Universe*. Boston: Houghton Mifflin.

Souriau, E. 1949. "Time in the Plastic Arts", Journal of Aesthetics and Art Criticism, 7(4): 294–307

Sparshott, F.E. 1971. "Basic Film Aesthetics", *Journal of Aesthetics*, 5(2): 11–34.

Squires, E. 1990. *Conscious Mind in the Physical World*. Bristol: Adam Hilger.

Steward, H. 2009. "Fairness, Agency, and the Flicker of Freedom", *Noûs*, 43(1): 64–93.

Sullivan, M. 2018. *Time Biases: A Theory of Rational Planning and Personal Persistence*. Oxford: Oxford University Press.

Tallant, J. and Ingram, D. 2015. "Nefarious Presentism", *Philosophical Quarterly*, 65(260): 355–371.

Tallant, J. 2020. Personal correspondence.

Tarantino, Q. (director) 1994. *Pulp Fiction*.

Tarkovsky, A. 1989. *Sculpting in Time*. Austin, TX: University of Texas Press.

Tate Gallery. "Found objects". www.tate.org.uk/art/art-terms/f/found-object. Retrieved 15 May 2020.

Taunton, M. 2016. "Modernism, Time and Consciousness: The Influence of Henri Bergson and Marcel Proust". www.bl.uk/20th-century-literature/articles/modernism-time-and-consciousness-the-influence-of-henri-bergson-and-marcel-proust. Retrieved 21 April 2020.

Taylor, R. 1955/1964. "Spatial and Temporal Analogies and the Concept of Identity", in Smart, J.J.C. (ed.) *Problems of Space and Time*. New York: Macmillan, 381–396.

Taylor, R. 1958. "Determinism and the Theory of Agency", in Hook, S. (ed.) *Determinism and Freedom in the Age of Modern Science*. New York: Collier. , 224–230.

Thagard, P. 2019. "Cognitive Science", in *The Stanford Encyclopedia of Philosophy (Spring 2019 Edition)*, ed. Zalta, E.N. <https://plato.stanford.edu/archives/spr2019/entries/cognitive-science/>.

Thomas, E. 2019. "The Roots of C.D. Broad's Growing Block Theory of Time", *Mind*, 128(510): 527–549.

Tooley, M. 1997. *Time, Tense, and Causation*. Oxford: Oxford University Press.

Totaro, D. 1992. "Time and the Film Aesthetics of Andrei Tarkovsky", *Canadian Journal of Film Studies*, 2(1): 21–30.

Turetzky, P. 1998. *Time*. Oxford: Routledge.

Van Bendegam, J.W. 2011. "The Possibility of Discrete Time", in *The Oxford Handbook of the Philosophy of Time*. Oxford: Oxford University Press.

Van Der Meer, A. and Van Der Meer, J. 2013. *The Time Traveller's Almanac*. London: Head of Zeus.

Van Inwagen, P. 2011. "Relational vs. Constituent Ontologies", *Philosophical Perspectives*, 25, *Metaphysics*, 389–405.

Van Inwagen, P. and Zimmerman, D. (eds) 1998. *Metaphysics: The Big Questions*. Oxford: Blackwell.

Varela, F.J. 1996. "Neurophenomenology: A Methodological Remedy for the Hard Problem", *Journal of Consciousness Studies*, 3: 330–350.

Varela, F.J. 1999. "The Specious Present: A Neurophenomenology of Time Consciousness", in J. Petitot, F. J. Varela, B. Pachoud, and J.-M. Roy (eds) *Naturalizing Phenomenology: Issues in Contemporary Phenomenology and Cognitive Science*. Stanford, CA: Stanford University Press, 266–314.

Varela, F.J. and Shear, J. 1999. "First-Person Methodologies: What, Why, How?", *Journal of Consciousness Studies*, 6(2–3): 1–14.

Warren, J. 2003. "Sextus Empiricus and the Tripartition of Time", *Phronesis*, 48(4): 313–343.

Wegner, D.M. 2002. *The Illusion of Conscious Will*. Cambridge, MA: MIT Press.

Wegner, D.M. 2003. "The Mind's Best Trick: How We Experience Conscious Will", *Trends in Cognitive Science*, 7: 65–69.

Weingard, R. 1977. "Space-Time and the Direction of Time", *Nous*, 11(2): 119–131.

Weir, G. 2016. "Memory of an Earlier Talk'. *IMMA Series of Artist's Talks*. Dublin: Trinity College Dublin (TCD).

Weir, G. 2017. Personal correspondence.

Wells, H.G. 1895. *The Time Machine*. London: William Heinemann.

Wittgenstein, L. 1958. *The Blue and Brown Books: Preliminary Studies for the "Philosophical Investigations"*. London: Blackwell.

Wittman, M. 2016. *Felt Time*. Cambridge, MA: MIT Press.

Yehezkel, G. 2016. "Fear of Death and the Symmetry Argument", *Manuscrito*, 39(4): 279–286.

Yourgrau, P. 2005. *A World without Time: The Forgotten Legacy of Gödel and Einstein*. London: Allen Lane.

Yudkowsky, E. 2015. *Rationality: From AI to Zombies*. Berkeley, CA: Machine Intelligent Research Institute.

Zeelenberg, M. and Pieters, R. 2006. "Looking Backward with an Eye on the Future: Propositions Toward a Theory of Regret Regulation", in Sanna, L.J. and Chang, E.C. (eds) *Judgments over Time: The Interplay of Thoughts, Feelings, and Behaviors*. Oxford University Press, 210–229.

Zemeckis, R. (director) 1985. *Back to the Future.*

Zuradzki, T. 2016. "Time-biases and Rationality: The Philosophical Perspectives on Empirical Research about Time Preferences", in Stelmach, J., Brozek, B. and Kurek, Ł. (eds) *The Emergence of Normative Orders*. Krakow: Copernicus Center Press, 149–187.

Index